MODULAR SCIENCE

for AQA

Year 11

HIGHER

MODULAR SCIENCE
for AQA

Keith Hirst
Mike Hiscock
David Sang
Martin Stirrup

Heinemann

Heinemann Educational Publishers
Halley Court, Jordan Hill, Oxford OX2 8EJ
a division of Reed Educational & Professional Publishing Ltd
Heinemann is a registered trademark of Reed Educational & Professional
Publishing Ltd

OXFORD MELBOURNE AUCKLAND
JOHANNESBURG BLANTYRE GABORONE
IBADAN PORTSMOUTH NH (USA) CHICAGO

First published 2002

ISBN 0 435 57196 6

05
10 9 8 7 6 5

Edited by Teresa Brady, Gina Walker and Tim Jackson

Index compiled by Paul Nash

Designed and typeset by Hardlines, Charlbury

Illustrated by Hardlines, Charlbury

Printed and bound in China

Acknowledgements
The authors and publishers would like to thank the following for permission
to use photographs:

Cover photos: Osprey catching fish courtesy of Oxford Scientific Films/Tom
Ulrich; Diamond courtesy of Science Photo Library/Alfred Pasieka; Biker
courtesy of Image Bank.

T = top *B* = bottom *R* = right *L* = left *M* = middle

1 *TL* Corbis/Richard Hamilton Smith, *B* Science Photo Library/Richard T
Nowitz, *TR* BBC Natural History Unit/Karl Amman; **2** Image Bank/Vikki
Hart; **3** EMPICS/Tony Marshall; **4** Science Photo Library/John Greim; **5**
Science Photo Library/Claude Nuridsany & Marie Perennou; **6** Science Photo
Library/Petit Format/Nestle; **9** *L* Bruce Coleman, *R* CEC/Malcolm Boulton;
12 Science Photo Library/John Giannicchi; **13** *T* Science Photo Library/Saturn
Stills, *M* Corbis/Patrick Bennett; **14** Mary Evans Picture Library; **16** *B* Science
Photo Library/Hattie Young; **20** *T* FoodPix/Burke/Triolo Productions, *ML*
Holt Studios/Bob Gibbons, *MR* Holt Studios/Nigel Cattlin; **21** *TL* Bruce
Coleman/Jane Burton, *TR* Holt Studios, *M* Corbis/Yann Arthus-Bertrand, *B*
Woodfall Wild Images/David Woodfall; **22** Corbis/Jonathan Blair; **23** Science
Photo Library/Chris Knapton; **24** Empics/Neal Simpson; **28** *M* Science Photo
Library/Sinclair Stammers, *B* Science Photo Library/J Koivula; **30** *T* Oxford
Scientific Films/Tony Tilford, *M* Science Photo Library/Philippe Plailly; **34**
Corbis; **35** Oxford Scientific Films/Robin Bush; **37** Science Photo
Library/David Campione; **40** Mary Evans Picture Library; **43** Science Photo
Library; **44** Peter Gould; **47** Peter Gould; **54** Martin Stirrup; **55** Mary Evans
Picture Library; **58** Corbis/Bettmann; **60** Peter Gould; **62** *T* Peter Gould, *M*
Trevor Clifford; **63** *(all)* Peter Gould; **65** *T* MWMPC, *M* Peter Gould; **69**
Ed.Pecheur d'images/Guillaume Plisson; **70** Ed.Pecheur d'images/Philip

Plisson; **73** Getty Images/Peter Sterling/FPG International; **74** Bruce Coleman;
76 *L* David Sang, *T* Aerofilms, *R* Trevor Clifford; **78** *T* CEC/Mark Bolton, *M*
Science Photo Library/David Parker; **80** Science Photo Library; **81** *T* Science
Photo Library/Martin Bond, *M* Science Photo Library/David Ducros, *B*
CEC/Mark Bolton; **82** *T* Panos Pictures/Caroline Penn, *M* Science Photo
Library/Pascal Goetgheluck, *B* Science Photo Library/Dave Roberts; **83**
Mediscan.co.uk; **84** Science Photo Library/Deep light productions; **85** Science
Photo Library; **86** John Birdsall Photography; **87** Science Photo Library; **88**
Trevor Clifford; **92** Trevor Clifford, **94** *T* Science Photo Library/Martyn F
Chillmaid, *B* Science Photo Library, *M* Beaumont Veterinary Practice/Ginny
Stroud-Lewis; **95** Science Photo Library/CNRI; **100** *T* Corbis/James L Amos, *B*
Science Photo Library/Peter Menzel; **102** *M* Bruce Coleman/Kim Taylor, *B*
Science Photo Library/Jesse; **103** Science Photo Library/Rosenfeld Images Ltd;
104 *L* Rex Features/Shigeo Kogure/Time, *M* Science Photo Library/Carlos
Munoz-Yague/Eurelios, *R* Corbis/Vince Streano; **115** *(all)* Photodisc; **116** *T*
Corbis/Bettmann, *M* Oxford Scientific Films/Doug Allan, *B* Oxford Scientific
Films/Doug Allan; **117** *T* BBC Wild/Niall Benvie, *TB* Oxford Scientific
Films/Doug Allan, *B* Oxford Scientific Films/Owen Newman, *TM* Science
Photo Library/ER Degginger; **118** *T* BBC Wild/Mark Payne-Gill, *TML* Oxford
Scientific Films/Kathie Atkinson, *MR* BBC Wild/Graham Hatherley, *B* Bruce
Coleman/Natural Selection, *BML* Oxford Scientific Films/William Gray,
BMR Science Photo Library/Tom McHugh; **119** *L* Oxford Scientific Films/Tim
Jackson, *R* BBC Wild/Mary Ann McDonald; **120** *T* Bruce Coleman/John
Cancalosi, *M* Corbis/Ecoscene; **121** Oxford Scientific Films/Kjell Sandved; **122**
TL Hutchison Library/Lesley McIntyre, *TR* Science Photo Library/Phillip
Wallick/Agstock; **124** Corbis/Papilo; **126** *T* Oxford Scientific Films/Jeff
Foott/OKAPIA, *TB* Bruce Coleman/Kim Taylor, *B* Andy Purcell; **127** Science
Photo Library/William Ervin; **128** *T* CEC/Mark Boulton, *M* Bruce Coleman;
130 *T* Hutchison Library/Nick Haslam, *M* Bruce Coleman/Hans Reinhard,
BM Bruce Coleman/Robert Maier, *B* Bruce Coleman/Hans Reinhard; **132** *TL*
Science Photo Library/Jim Gipe/Agstock, *TR* Still Pictures/Joerg Boethling,
M Science Photo Library/Tony Craddock, *B* Corbis/Natalie Fobes; **133** *T*
Hutchison Library/Jeremy Horner, *M* agripicture.com/Peter Dean, *B* Still
Pictures/Ron Giling, *M* Science Photo Library/Rosenfeld Images Ltd, *B* Science Photo Library/Martin Bond; **134** *T* Corbis/Jonathan Blair, *M* Science Photo
Library/Rosenfeld Images Ltd, *B* Science Photo Library/Martin Bond; **135**
Holt Studios/Nigel Cattlin; **136** *T* Bruce Coleman/Luiz Claudio Marigo, *B*
BBC Wild/Bruce Davidson; **137** Holt Studios/Nigel Cattlin; **138**
EMPICS/Neal Simpson; **140** *T* Woodfall Wild Images/David Woodfall, *M*
Science Photo Library/Martin Bond, *BM* Still Pictures/Jim Wark, *B* Science
Photo Library/David Nunuk; **142** *T* Getty Images/Stone, *B* Science Photo
Library/Simon Fraser; **144** *M* Woodfall Wild Images/John Macpherson, *B* Still
Pictures/Mark Edwards; **146** *T* Panos Pictures/Jeremy Hartley, *M* Science
Photo Library/Peter Menzel, *B* Still Pictures/Mark Edwards; **147** Still
Pictures/Mark Edwards; **148** *T* Science Photo Library/Doug Allan, *B* BBC
Wild/Ron O'Connor; **151** Gareth Boden; **154** Peter Gould; **156** *M* Peter Gould,
B Peter Gould; **160** *T* Corbis/Adam Woolfitt, *M* Hutchison Library/Tony Souter, *B* Peter
Gould; **161** CEC/Mark Boulton; **162** *T* CEC/Mark Boulton, *M* CEC/Mark
Boulton, *B* Science Photo Library/Nigel Cattlin/Holt Studios; **163** CEC/Mark
Boulton; **166** *T* Andrew Lambert, *M* Science Photo Library/Martin Land, *BM*
Andrew Lambert, *B* Corbis; **167** Milepost 92 1/2; **168** *T* Peter Gould, *B* Peter
Gould; **170** *(all)* Peter Gould; **172** *T* Trevor Clifford, *M* Peter Gould, *B* Peter
Gould; **174** *T* Science Photo Library/Oscar Burriel, *M* Peter Gould, *B* Peter
Gould; **176** Science Photo Library; **179** Science Photo Library/David
Campione; **183** Science Photo Library/European Southern Observatory; **187** *L*
Alvey & Towers, *R* Alvey & Towers; **188** *T* Trevor Clifford, *B* Getty
Images/FPG International; **190** *T* Alton Towers, *BL* Trevor Clifford, *BR* Trevor
Clifford; **191** Science Photo Library/Erich Schrempp; **193** Alvey & Towers; **194**
T Frank Spooner Pictures/John Paul, *M* Rex Features; **196** Rex Features; **197**
Science Photo Library/Jim Varney; **198** *T* Genesis Space Photo Library, *M*
Getty Images/FPG International; **199** Alvey & Towers; **200** *T* Alvey & Towers,
B Corbis/George Hall; **201** *R* EMPICS, *L* Corbis; **204** Science Photo
Library/David Nunuk; **205** Science Photo Library/Jerry Schad; **206** Science
Photo Library/M-SAT Ltd; **207** Rex Features/Lucy Kelaart; **208** Science Photo
Library/Joe Tucciarone; **210** *T* Science Photo Library/NASA; **212** *T* Science
Photo Library, *ML* Science Photo Library/NASA, *MR* Science Photo
Library/NASA, *B* Genesis Space Photo Library; **213** Science Photo
Library/John Mead.
Picture research by Liz Savery.

The publishers have made every effort to trace the copyright holders, but if
they have inadvertently overlooked any, they will be pleased to make the
necessary arrangements at the first opportunity.

About this book

This is the second book in the AQA Modular Science series and is designed to guide you through the second year of GCSE study. It has been written to help you find everything you need to prepare for your exams.

For ease-of-use the book has been separated into sections by exam. Modules from Year 10 that are in the exams have recap material to aid revision.

The introductory page to each module will help you get a feel of the module. It explains the topics covered and gets you thinking about the science that you already know.

To help you study we have included some useful features in the book. Here are a few:

Double-page spreads

Everything you need to know for each module is covered in double-page spreads. These pages will cover all the topics you need to understand for your exams. To help you find all of the important points we have included questions to test yourself as you learn.

End of module questions

At the end of each module you will find three pages of test questions. Answering lots of questions will help you check what you have learnt and prepare for exams.

Digging Deeper

These boxes contain extra information about the topic that you are studying. The information in these boxes will not be tested in module tests or exams.

Summary

The information in these boxes summarises the most important points on the page. In your exams you will be tested on your knowledge of the points in the summary boxes. These boxes will also help you make notes and answer questions.

Glossary pages

When a new scientific word appears for the first time in the text, it will appear in **bold** type. All words in bold are listed with their meanings in the glossary at the back of the book. Look there to remind you what they mean.

Data sheet pages

When you sit your exams you will be given data sheets. At the back of the book you will find the information that will be on these data sheets.

Contents

Module 4 – Inheritance and selection

Why do you have some of your father's features and some of your mother's features? Some of your characteristics are due to information in your body's cells, which you **inherited** from your parents. Other characteristics are affected by the environment in which you live and grow.

Breeding from animals and plants with desired characteristics has produced many types of pet and farm animals, as well as garden and crop plants. New breeds have been developed with useful characteristics by **selecting** which animals and plants will reproduce.

Scientists think that life on Earth began about 400 million years ago. Since then more species of animals and plants have developed – and are still developing. This is the process of **evolution**.

This module will help you to understand how information can be passed from parents to their offspring. You will study how useful breeds of animals and plants have been developed and how scientists can even control the characteristics of an organism by changing the material of inheritance found inside cells. You will also learn how species of organisms have evolved and why some species no longer exist.

These kittens have many attractive characteristics, which are the result of many generations of breeding.

These children are very different from the orang-utan they are looking at, and different from each other. There are differences between species and between individuals of the same species.

Before you start, try these questions to check what you know about inheritance and selection.

Fossils are formed from animals and plants that lived many years ago. By studying fossils we can find out how organisms have changed over a long period of time.

1 Where in a cell is inherited information stored?

2 What cells pass information from parents to offspring?

3 Give one example of a characteristic that is inherited, and one that is affected by the environment in which people live and grow.

4 Some animals and plants that lived in the past do not exist today. Suggest reasons why some species no longer exist on the Earth.

You are unique

There are many different kinds of animals and plants. We call these **species**. You look very similar to other people around you because you belong to the same species.

Even though you look similar you can still be recognised as different from other people around you. This is because of your **characteristics**, or features, such as your hair colour, eye colour and height. These are just a few of the many characteristics that distinguish you from everyone else. There are millions of people in the world, yet no two people are exactly the same. You are unique!

a What important characteristic do the police use to identify criminals even if they have left the scene of a crime?

Spot the difference

Young animals and plants often look like their parents.

b Give two examples of characteristics the puppy in the photograph has in common with:

i all other dogs

ii the parent dog.

Young animals and plants look like their parents because some characteristics are **inherited** – they are passed from parents to their offspring.

The puppy in the photograph has many similar characteristics to its parents.

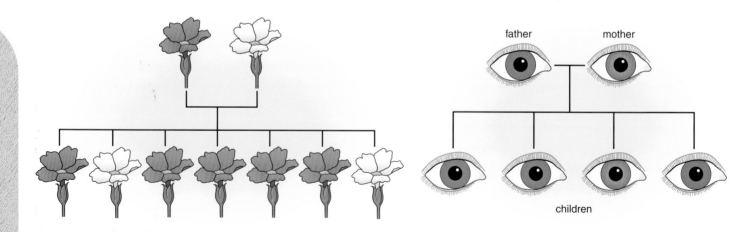

Flower colour is an inherited characteristic.
Some inherited characteristics are more common than others.

Eye colour is a characteristic that is inherited.

Inheritance and selection ◆ Paper 1

Talent or training?

Not all characteristics are passed on from parents. You cannot just be born with all that it takes to become a world class musician, for example – it depends on years of practice as well as having natural talent. This is because some characteristics are affected by the environment in which you live and grow.

The characteristics of individuals may be due to:

◆ inherited causes

◆ environmental causes

◆ a mixture of both.

It takes more than natural talent to become a world class gymnast.

It runs in the family

It is possible to find out if a characteristic is inherited by tracing it in a family tree.

Questions

1 Copy and then complete the table below using words from the list. One example has been filled in for you.

scars   freckles   fingerprints

eye colour   height   body mass

number of tooth fillings   running ability   intelligence

being left- or right-handed

Inherited causes	Environmental causes	Mixture of both inherited and environmental causes
		height

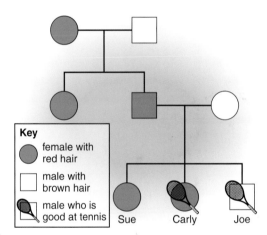

Key

◉ female with red hair

☐ male with brown hair

⬚ male who is good at tennis

Sue   Carly   Joe

Which characteristic of the children in this family has been inherited from their parents?

2 Look at the family tree diagram.

a Which of the children's parents had red hair?

b Which of the children had brown hair?

c Describe the evidence suggesting that red hair is inherited.

3 Carly and Sue are identical twins, which means they developed from the same fertilised egg. Using this information, explain whether or not being good at tennis is an inherited characteristic.

Summary

• Young plants and animals have similar characteristics to their parents.

• Characteristics may be inherited, caused by the environment or caused by both environmental and inherited factors.

4:2 Passing on information

Inheriting features

'Doesn't she have her mother's eyes?' 'Isn't she like her father?' These are typical comments that people make when they first see a baby. Children have similar characteristics to their parents because of the **genes** they inherit. Different genes control the development of different characteristics. For example, the baby in the photograph may have inherited genes that will produce curly hair or freckles.

Children inherit characteristics from their parents.

Genes and chromosomes

The genes that control characteristics are carried on the **chromosomes** contained in the nucleus of a cell. Each chromosome carries a large number of genes.

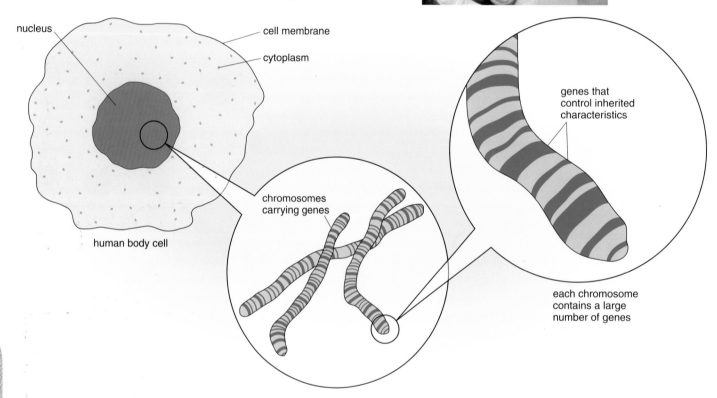

nucleus

cell membrane

cytoplasm

genes that control inherited characteristics

chromosomes carrying genes

human body cell

each chromosome contains a large number of genes

The nucleus of a cell contains chromosomes. Each chromosome is made up of thousands of genes.

Coded information

Each chromosome is made from a very long molecule called **DNA**. Each gene is a section of a DNA molecule.

A section of DNA contains coded information that determines an inherited characteristic. For example, a section of the DNA in your cells controls the production of the substance that gives you your eye colour.

The DNA in your cells is as unique as your fingerprints. In fact, your DNA is your 'genetic fingerprint'.

Passing on genes

Young animals and plants have similar characteristics to their parents because of the genes that are passed on to them.

Genes are passed from parents to their children in sex cells called **gametes**. In male animals, the sex cells are called **sperm** cells. Sperm cells are made in sex organs called **testes**. In female animals, the sex cells are called **egg** cells. Egg cells are made in sex organs called **ovaries**.

a Where are the genes in a sperm cell?

b Why do sperm cells have tails?

Eggs and pollen

Plants also produce sex cells to pass on genes to young plants. Male sex cells are made inside **pollen grains**. Female sex cells are made inside **ovaries**.

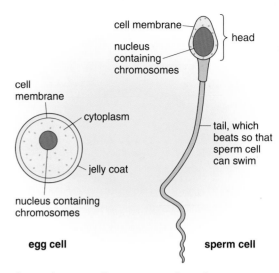

Egg and sperm cells carry genes from the parents.

Flowers are a plant's reproductive system.

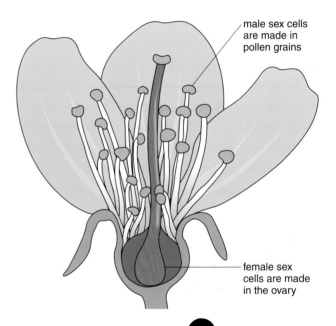

male sex cells are made in pollen grains

female sex cells are made in the ovary

Questions

1 Where are the following cells made?

   a sperm cells in an animal

   b egg cells in an animal

   c female gametes in a plant

   d male gametes in a plant

2 Identical twins are formed from the same fertilised egg. Explain why no two people have the same DNA, except identical twins.

Summary

- The nucleus of a cell contains chromosomes.

- Chromosomes carry a large number of genes.

- Genetic information is passed on from parents to offspring in gametes.

- A gene is a section of DNA.

- DNA contains coded information that determines inherited characteristics.

4:3 Making new cells

The start of life

Your life started from a single cell, formed by the fusion of a sperm and an egg. This single cell contained all the genetic information needed to make you. All the thousands of cells that make up your body developed from this single cell by **cell division**. During cell division, all the genes are copied into new cells so that all the cells of your body contain an exact copy of the genes that were present in the cell formed at fertilisation.

Making copies

When a cell divides a copy of each chromosome is made. One copy of each chromosome then moves into each of the newly formed cells. This means that each new cell formed has exactly the same chromosomes. This type of cell division is called **mitosis**.

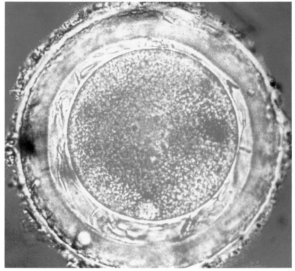

A fertilised egg is the start of a whole new organism.

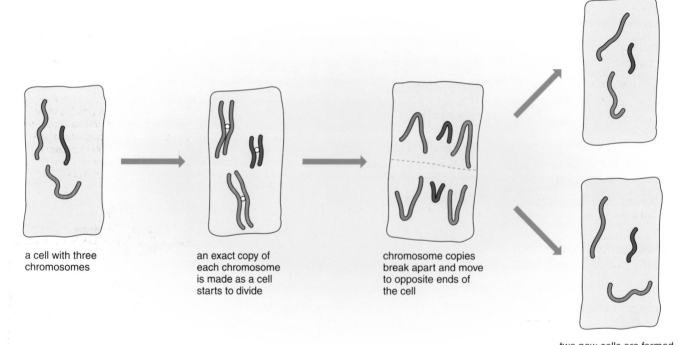

a cell with three chromosomes

an exact copy of each chromosome is made as a cell starts to divide

chromosome copies break apart and move to opposite ends of the cell

two new cells are formed, each containing exactly the same genetic information as the original cell

Producing new cells by mitosis.

Forming gametes

A new life starts when gametes (sperm cells and egg cells) fuse. Producing gametes involves a different type of cell division called **meiosis**. In humans, meiosis takes place in reproductive organs. Cells in the testes divide by meiosis to form sperm cells. Cells in the ovaries divide to form egg cells.

Halving the number of chromosomes

Chromosomes are normally found in pairs. For example, human body cells contain 23 pairs of chromosomes.

During meiosis, the pairs of chromosomes separate from each other. The gametes that are formed contain only one chromosome from each pair of chromosomes. Human sperm cells and egg cells contain 23 *single* chromosomes.

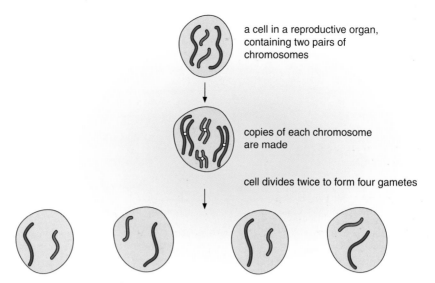

a cell in a reproductive organ, containing two pairs of chromosomes

copies of each chromosome are made

cell divides twice to form four gametes

each gamete contains a single set of chromosomes

Producing new cells by meiosis.

Restoring the number of chromosomes

The first cell of a new individual is formed when male and female gametes fuse at fertilisation. This cell will contain chromosomes from both gametes.

Gametes contain *single* chromosomes. When gametes fuse, a cell is formed containing *pairs* of chromosomes.

For example, in humans at fertilisation a sperm cell containing 23 chromosomes fuses with an egg containing 23 chromosomes. The fertilised egg contains 23 *pairs* of chromosomes.

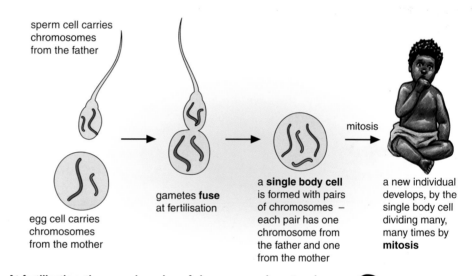

sperm cell carries chromosomes from the father

egg cell carries chromosomes from the mother

gametes **fuse** at fertilisation

a **single body cell** is formed with pairs of chromosomes – each pair has one chromosome from the father and one from the mother

mitosis

a new individual develops, by the single body cell dividing many, many times by **mitosis**

At fertilisation, the normal number of chromosomes is restored.

Questions

The diagram shows a cell from an ovary.

1 a Draw a diagram to show the chromosomes that will be present in an egg cell produced from this ovary.

  b Name the type of cell division involved in producing the egg cell.

2 The ovary cell shows two pairs of chromosomes.

  a How many pairs of chromosomes are present in the body cells of humans?

  b What sex chromosomes will be present in a human ovary cell?

Summary

- There are two types of cell division – mitosis and meiosis.

- Mitosis forms new cells containing the same genetic information.

- Meiosis forms cells called gametes with a single set of chromosomes.

- When gametes fuse at fertilisation, a single body cell is formed with new pairs of chromosomes.

4:4 Chromosomes and genes

Boy or girl?

When a baby is born, one of the first questions people ask is whether it is a boy or a girl. Your sex depends on the chromosomes you inherit.

In your body cells, chromosomes are found in pairs. Human body cells contain 23 pairs of chromosomes. One of these pairs is the **sex chromosomes**. In females, the two sex chromosomes are the same (XX). In males, they are different (XY).

Chromosomes in sex cells

Sex cells (sperm and egg cells) contain only one chromosome from each pair of chromosomes. This means that each sperm and egg cell contains only one of the two sex chromosomes.

a **How many chromosomes do human sex cells contain?**

Your sex was set by the chromosome present in one sperm cell from your father – the sperm cell that fertilised an egg and started your life. The diagram below explains how.

b **Why is there a 50% chance of a baby being a girl?**

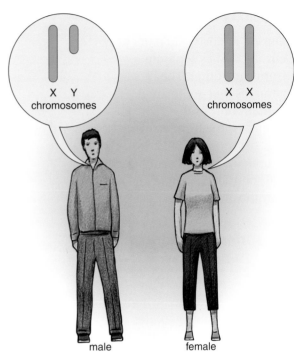

Male humans have XY sex chromosomes. Female humans have XX.

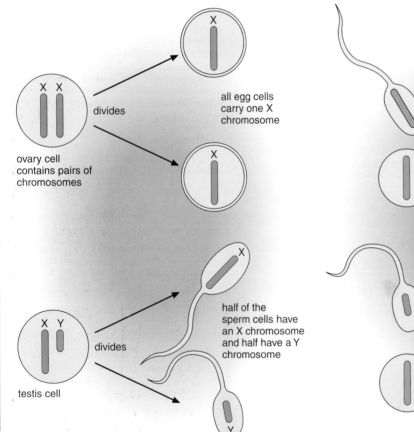

Each sex cell contains only one sex chromosome – an X or a Y.

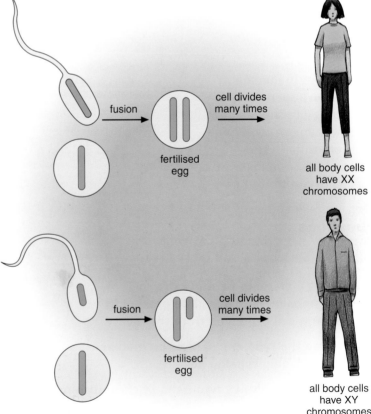

If the sperm cell contains an X, the fertilised egg becomes a female. If it contains a Y, the fertilised egg becomes a male.

Pairs of genes

The diagram shows a pair of chromosomes. Because paired chromosomes are identical, the same genes are carried along the length of each one. This means that genes, like chromosomes, are found in pairs.

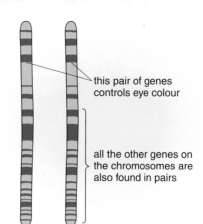

this pair of genes controls eye colour

all the other genes on the chromosomes are also found in pairs

Body cells contain pairs of chromosomes. The genes carried on the chromosomes also come in pairs.

Different forms of genes

Many genes have different forms called **alleles**. For example, the gene that controls the colour of a rabbit's fur has two alleles. The diagram shows the alleles that may be present and the colour of the rabbit's fur.

c **i** Which alleles are present in rabbits with white fur?

ii Which alleles are present in rabbits with black fur?

the letters B and b stand for the two alleles that control fur colour

rabbits are white only when both alleles are bb

rabbits with black fur can have either BB or Bb alleles

The different colours of rabbits are caused by different alleles.

Dominant and recessive

Rabbits will always have black fur if the B allele is present. This is an example of a **dominant** allele.

A rabbit will have white fur only when there is no dominant B allele, and both alleles are b. Allele b is an example of a **recessive** allele.

An individual is described as being **homozygous** when both chromosomes in a pair contain the same allele. When the chromosomes in a pair contain different alleles, the individual is **heterozygous**.

bb

white rabbits are homozygous for the recessive allele

BB or Bb

black rabbits can be homozygous or heterozygous

Homozygous means 'same alleles'. Heterozygous means 'different alleles'.

Questions

For a long time scientists thought that panthers and spotted leopards were different species. We now know that they are the same species and their different coat colours are due to different alleles.

Alleles ss.

Alleles SS or Ss.

1 Which allele is recessive?

2 If two panthers mated and had young, predict what the cubs' coat colour would be. Explain your answer.

3 If a leopard that is heterozygous for the coat colour gene is mated with a panther, predict the ratio of panthers to leopards in their offspring. Draw a diagram to explain your answer.

Summary

- There are 23 pairs of chromosomes in human body cells.

- One pair of chromosomes is the sex chromosomes.

- In human males, the sex chromosomes are XY.

- In human females, the sex chromosomes are XX.

- Some genes have different forms called alleles.

- Alleles may be dominant or recessive.

- Individuals can be homozygous (for example, BB and bb) or heterozygous (for example, Bb).

Forming and fusing gametes

Producing young animals and plants by forming and then fusing gametes is called **sexual reproduction**.

The offspring produced by sexual reproduction show different characteristics from each other and from their parents. This **variation** happens because of the way:

◆ alleles separate during meiosis as gametes are formed

◆ alleles combine when gametes fuse.

The diagram below shows the stages in sexual reproduction. The two parent rabbits in the diagram have the same pair of alleles but the pair of alleles varies in their young.

Young plants can also be formed from sexual reproduction. Plants produce gametes in their flowers. After the gametes have fused, an embryo plant develops inside a seed.

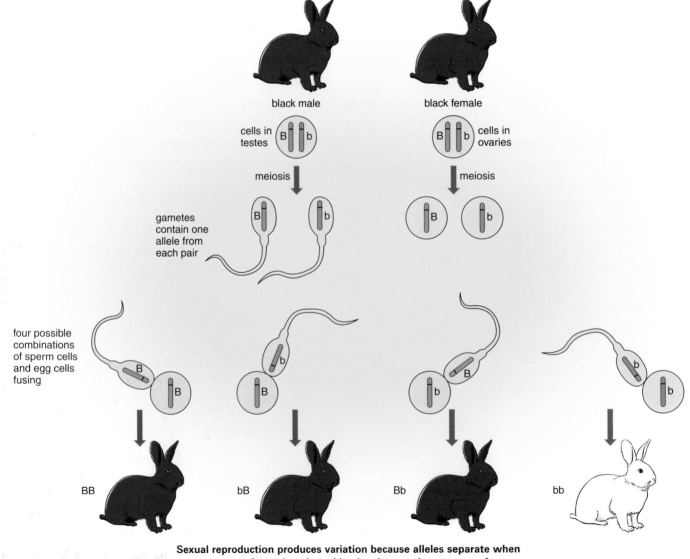

Sexual reproduction produces variation because alleles separate when gametes are formed, and combine by chance when gametes fuse.

Reproducing without gametes

Young plants do not always grow from seeds. They sometimes grow from the ordinary body cells of a parent plant. The diagram shows young strawberry plants being made from one parent plant. The parent plant does not use gametes to reproduce in this way. This type of reproduction is called **asexual reproduction**.

The cells of new plants produced by asexual reproduction are formed by mitosis. They contain exactly the same genes as the parent plant. Such genetically identical individuals form a **clone**.

Young plants from cuttings

Young plants can be grown from older plants by taking **cuttings**. Plants grown from cuttings from the same parent plant will have identical genes. Cuttings can be taken from the stems, leaves or roots of plants.

By taking cuttings, gardeners can produce many young plants with the same characteristics quickly and cheaply.

The strawberry plant can make identical new plants, by asexual reproduction.

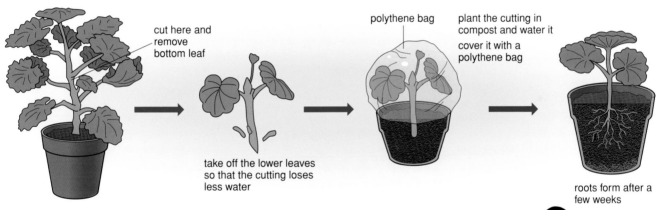

Taking cuttings from a plant.

Questions

1 a Why do gardeners place a polythene bag over cuttings?

   b Explain why cuttings grown from the same plant are identical.

   c Give two advantages of growing plants from cuttings.

2 a Explain why strawberry plants grown from runners are identical.

   b Explain why strawberry plants grown from seeds have different characteristics.

3 When the two black rabbits shown on page 9 were mated, they produced offspring in the ratio of 3 black rabbits to 1 white rabbit. Predict what the ratio in the offspring will be when a heterozygous black rabbit is mated with a white rabbit. Draw a diagram to explain your answer.

Summary

- Sexual reproduction involves the fusion of gametes.

- Sexual reproduction produces variation because alleles separate during meiosis and combine by chance when gametes fuse.

- In asexual reproduction there is no fusion of gametes.

- The cells produced by asexual reproduction are formed by mitosis and have identical genes.

4:6 Controlling reproduction

The start of your life

An egg is released from one of a woman's ovaries about every 28 days. The egg passes out of the ovary into an oviduct (egg duct). The egg moves along the oviduct towards the **womb**.

If sperm cells are present in the oviduct, one of the sperm cells may fuse with the egg cell. This is called **fertilisation**. If an egg is not fertilised it soon dies.

The fertilised egg cell grows to form an embryo, which attaches to the lining of the womb.

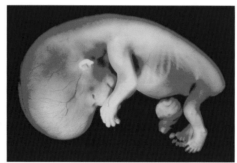

An eight week old embryo attached to the womb of the mother.

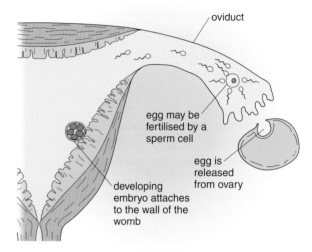

A woman has two ovaries (only one is shown here). Each month, one ovary releases an egg.

- oviduct
- egg may be fertilised by a sperm cell
- egg is released from ovary
- developing embryo attaches to the wall of the womb

Getting the timing right

The lining of the womb needs to be ready to receive a growing embryo. At the same time that an egg is developing inside an ovary, the lining of the womb becomes thicker. The thick lining contains many blood vessels to supply the developing embryo with food and oxygen.

If the egg is not fertilised, the lining of the womb breaks down causing bleeding. This is the woman's monthly period.

The monthly cycle of changes that take place in the ovary and in the womb is called the **menstrual cycle**. Several hormones are involved in controlling this cycle. The action of the hormones involved is summarised in the diagram.

Controlling fertility

The hormones that control the release of eggs and the growth of the womb lining can be used to control **fertility**.

Hormones can be used to:

- ◆ stop a woman becoming pregnant
- ◆ help a woman to become pregnant.

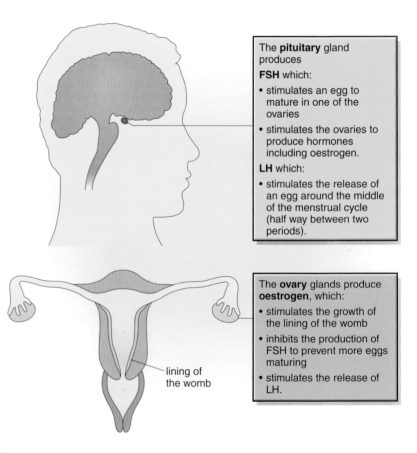

The **pituitary** gland produces
FSH which:
- stimulates an egg to mature in one of the ovaries
- stimulates the ovaries to produce hormones including oestrogen.

LH which:
- stimulates the release of an egg around the middle of the menstrual cycle (half way between two periods).

The **ovary** glands produce **oestrogen**, which:
- stimulates the growth of the lining of the womb
- inhibits the production of FSH to prevent more eggs maturing
- stimulates the release of LH.

lining of the womb

Glands make and release chemical messengers, called hormones, that control the menstrual cycle.

Stopping egg release

Some couples want to have sexual intercourse but do not want the woman to become pregnant. The woman can take the **contraceptive pill**. The pill contains oestrogen to inhibit FSH production in the pituitary gland. This means that no eggs will mature and be released from the ovaries.

The pill has to be taken every day. It is a very reliable method of stopping pregnancy but it can produce side effects. Some women get headaches or feel sick. In a very small number of women, the contraceptive pill can cause heart problems.

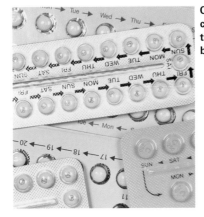

Contraceptive pills contain hormones that stop eggs being released.

Stimulating egg release

Some couples want to have children but the woman cannot become pregnant because her ovaries do not release eggs. She is infertile.

The woman can be treated by having FSH regularly injected into her blood. FSH acts as a **fertility drug** by stimulating the release of eggs from the ovaries.

Fertility treatment does not always work. Or, sometimes, it may cause more than one egg to be released. This can result in twins, triplets, quadruplets or even more!

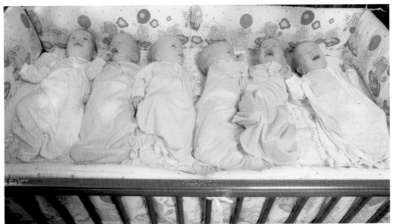

Sometimes fertility drugs do not work – sometimes they work too well!

Questions

1 The graph shows some of the changes that take place during the menstrual cycle.

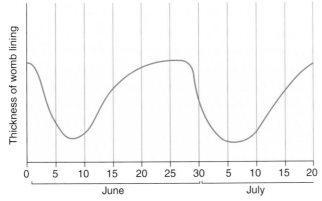

   a i On which date is an egg released?

   ii Name the hormone that stimulates the release of an egg.

   b i Describe how the thickness of the womb changes before an egg is released.

   ii Explain why this change in thickness occurs.

   c Explain how egg release is prevented by taking the contraceptive pill.

2 Copy and complete the table.

	Benefits	Problems
Using hormones as a contraceptive pill		
Using hormones as fertility drugs		

Summary

- The hormones FSH and LH are secreted by the pituitary gland.
- FSH stimulates eggs to mature in one of the ovaries.
- LH stimulates the release of an egg.
- Oestrogen is secreted from the ovaries.
- Oestrogen controls changes in thickness in the lining of the womb, and inhibits the production of FSH.
- FSH is used as a fertility drug.
- Oestrogen is used in the contraceptive pill.
- Using hormones as contraceptives or as fertility drugs can have both benefits and problems.

Early genetics

In the 1860s, Gregor Mendel carried out some very important investigations to find out how characteristics are inherited. At this time, no-one knew about chromosomes or genes because they were not yet discovered.

Gregor Mendel (1822–84) carried out investigations to find out how characteristics are inherited.

Controlling breeding

In his investigations, Mendel used pea plants with distinctive characteristics such as flower colour and height. He also controlled which parent plants produced young plants by transferring pollen from one plant to another. He used hundreds of plants in his experiments.

From his results, he made predictions about the way characteristics are passed from one generation to the next.

a Why did Mendel use very large numbers of plants in his investigations?

b What is transferred when pollen is taken from one plant and put onto the flower of another plant?

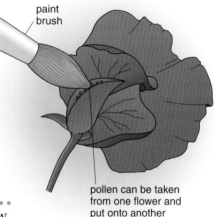

paint brush

pollen can be taken from one flower and put onto another

Pollen from a chosen plant can be transferred to another chosen plant to find out which characteristics are inherited.

Finding a pattern

One of the investigations carried out by Mendel is shown below.

parent plants	first generation	second generation
Mendel crossed red-flowered pea plants with white-flowered plants. He used hundreds of plants	All the plants had red flowers. Mendel then crossed these first generation plants with each other.	Mendel found that three times more plants had red flowers than white. By counting hundreds of plants, he found there was a ratio of 3 red : 1 white.

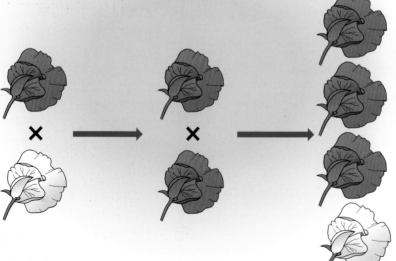

This investigation looked at how flower colour was inherited in pea plants.

DIGGING DEEPER
Tomatoes grown in the UK are usually round. The round shape is due to a single allele. Italian tomatoes found in many cans of tomatoes contain a different allele – they are long rather than round. When plant breeders crossed the two types of tomato, all the tomatoes produced were round. Which is the dominant allele?

Making conclusions

From the results of this investigation, and many others, Mendel concluded that:

- some characteristics, such as flower colour, are controlled by a pair of 'inherited factors'

- only one of these factors is present in a gamete

- 'inherited factors' can be dominant or recessive.

The diagram shows how Mendel explained the results of his investigation with red and white flowered pea plants.

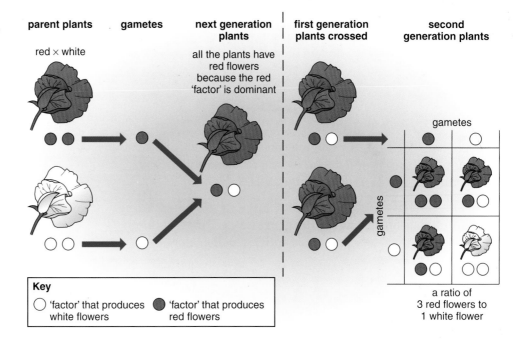

Key
- ○ 'factor' that produces white flowers
- ● 'factor' that produces red flowers

What Mendel called 'factors' we call 'genes' or 'alleles' today.

Testing his ideas

Once Mendel had made his conclusions, he carried out more investigations to make sure his findings were accurate. The diagram on the right shows an investigation carried out with round-seeded and wrinkled-seeded pea plants.

Important findings

The importance of Mendel's work was not recognised until after his death. By then chromosomes had been discovered. Once scientists knew about chromosomes, they could then explain how the 'inherited factors' suggested by Mendel could be passed from parents to their young. We now call these 'factors' genes.

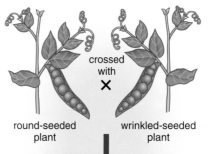

Mendel found when he crossed round-seeded and wrinkled-seeded plants, all the seeds produced grew into round-seeded plants.

round-seeded plant   crossed with ✕   wrinkled-seeded plant

next generation, all plants had round seeds

Questions

The diagram explains the results of the investigation using round-seeded and wrinkled-seeded plants.

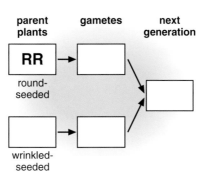

1 Copy the diagram. Fill in the boxes using the letters R and r to represent the alleles for round-seeded and wrinkled-seeded plants. One of the boxes has been filled in already.

2 When plants from this first generation were crossed, the following results were obtained:

   10 wrinkled-seeded plants

   32 round-seeded plants.

   Draw a diagram to explain these results, using the symbols R and r to represent the alleles.

Summary
- Mendel carried out investigations to find out how characteristics are inherited.
- He suggested the idea of 'inherited factors', which we now call genes.
- His discoveries were not recognised until after his death.
- By that time other scientists had discovered chromosomes.

4:8 Harmful genes

Inheriting illness

Most illnesses are caused when microbes get into your body. For example, measles and flu are diseases caused by certain viruses that get inside your body and cells.

There are some diseases that are not caused by microbes. Some health problems are caused by the genes passed on to children from their parents. These are called **inherited disorders**.

Cystic fibrosis

One child in every 2000 is affected by an inherited disorder called **cystic fibrosis**. The photograph below shows a girl who suffers from cystic fibrosis. Her body produces a thick, sticky mucus. This blocks the air passages in her lungs. Because of the blockages, the girl will get a lot of chest infections. She will also have difficulty digesting and absorbing food because a lot of mucus is produced by her digestive system.

Regular physiotherapy and strong antibiotics help, but each time the girl gets an infection she becomes more and more ill.

There is no cure for cystic fibrosis yet. Scientists are working on ways to replace the faulty allele.

Inheriting faulty genes

Cystic fibrosis is caused by a faulty *recessive* allele. The faulty alleles must be passed on from both parents. The parents may be **carriers** of the disease without having the disease themselves.

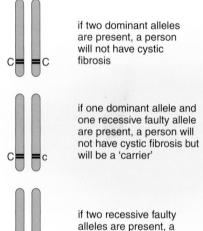

Physiotherapy helps to shift the mucus from the lungs and unblock the air passages.

> **DIGGING DEEPER**
> Scientists in Edinburgh have a sheep called Tracey, who has had a certain gene transferred into her cells. This means her milk contains a substance that can save the lives of children who have cystic fibrosis. The substance can be extracted from human blood, but this produces very small amounts at a very high cost. Tracey makes the substance every day just by eating grass.

if two dominant alleles are present, a person will not have cystic fibrosis

if one dominant allele and one recessive faulty allele are present, a person will not have cystic fibrosis but will be a 'carrier'

if two recessive faulty alleles are present, a person will have cystic fibrosis

Key
C dominant allele
c recessive allele

If both parents are carriers, they may produce a child with cystic fibrosis.

Huntington's disease

Huntington's disease is an inherited disorder that damages the brain and other parts of the nervous system. People with the disease lose control of their movements and cannot remember things.

Sadly, there is no cure. People with Huntington's disease need a lot of care and eventually die from the disease.

Faulty dominant alleles

Huntington's disease is caused by a faulty *dominant* allele, so only one allele needs to be present for the person to have the disease. It is passed on even if only one parent has the disease.

Signs of the disease do not appear until people are 30–50 years old. This means that people may have children before finding out that they have a disease that can be inherited.

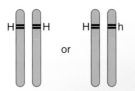

even if just one dominant faulty allele is present, a person will have Huntington's disease

a person will not have Huntington's disease if two recessive alleles are present

Key

H   dominant allele

h   recessive allele

Huntington's disease is caused by a faulty dominant allele.

Questions

The family trees show how cystic fibrosis and Huntington's disease can be inherited. Study the family trees carefully and then answer the questions that follow.

1 a Sue has Huntington's disease. Which of her parents also has the disease?

b What evidence shows that Huntington's disease is inherited?

c Draw Sue's family tree showing the alleles present in the body cells of each person. Use the letters H and h to represent the alleles.

2 a Sammy has cystic fibrosis. Neither of his parents has this disease but they are 'carriers'. Explain what this means.

b Using the letters c and C, draw a diagram to show how Sammy inherited cystic fibrosis even though neither of his parents has the disease.

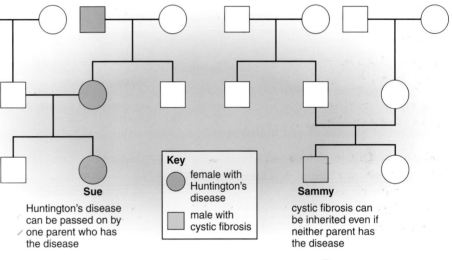

Sue

Huntington's disease can be passed on by one parent who has the disease

Key

● female with Huntington's disease

■ male with cystic fibrosis

Sammy

cystic fibrosis can be inherited even if neither parent has the disease

Summary

- Some diseases are caused by faulty alleles.

- These diseases can be inherited.

- Cystic fibrosis is caused by a faulty recessive allele.

- Huntington's disease is caused by a faulty dominant allele.

- Parents may be carriers of an inherited disease.

4:9 Blood disorders

Blocking blood vessels

Sickle cell disease is an inherited disorder.

People with sickle cell disease have red blood cells containing sickle haemoglobin, which is different from normal haemoglobin. When sickle haemoglobin releases oxygen to tissues, it makes the red blood cells become rigid and sickle-shaped. Healthy red blood cells can bend easily and have a doughnut shape.

Healthy red blood cells can bend to squeeze through small blood vessels, but rigid sickle red blood cells cannot. This causes blood vessels to become blocked and oxygen cannot get to where it is needed. Organs become damaged, causing a lot of pain.

As a result, people with the disorder cannot get enough oxygen from their lungs to their body organs. A shortage of oxygen is called **anaemia**.

a What is the job of red blood cells?

b What happens when red blood cells become rigid and sickle-shaped?

Inheriting sickle cell disease

Sickle cell disease is caused by a faulty allele.

People with sickle cell disease have two faulty alleles. This means that the haemoglobin they make is faulty, causing their red blood cells to be sickle-shaped and rigid.

People can inherit one faulty allele and one 'normal' allele. They will be **carriers** of the disease. They make enough normal haemoglobin to keep their red blood cells flexible. They do not have the symptoms of sickle cell disease, but they have to be careful when they are doing an activity where there is less oxygen available than usual, such as scuba diving or mountaineering.

c What is a 'carrier' of an inherited disease?

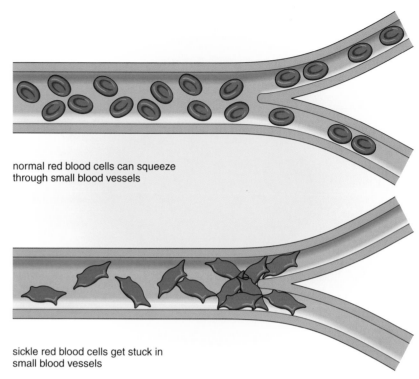

normal red blood cells can squeeze through small blood vessels

sickle red blood cells get stuck in small blood vessels

The shape and stiffness of sickle red blood cells mean they clog up small blood vessels.

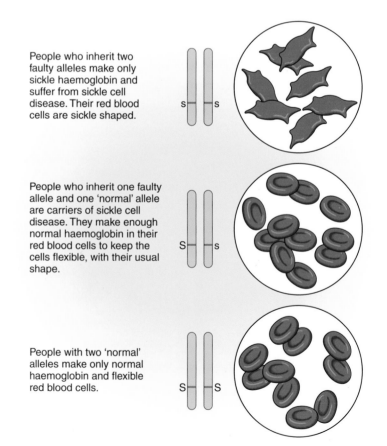

People who inherit two faulty alleles make only sickle haemoglobin and suffer from sickle cell disease. Their red blood cells are sickle shaped.

People who inherit one faulty allele and one 'normal' allele are carriers of sickle cell disease. They make enough normal haemoglobin in their red blood cells to keep the cells flexible, with their usual shape.

People with two 'normal' alleles make only normal haemoglobin and flexible red blood cells.

Sickle cell disease is inherited.

A puzzling pattern

In parts of Africa more babies are born with sickle cell disease than in other parts of the world. Doctors could not explain this for many years. The maps give an explanation.

The maps show that areas where sickle cell disease is common match areas where malaria is common. Malaria is a disease that also affects red blood cells. Thousands of babies die from malaria every year.

People who are carriers of sickle cell disease do not have anaemia and they do not get malaria. In parts of the world where malaria is common it is an advantage to have the faulty allele.

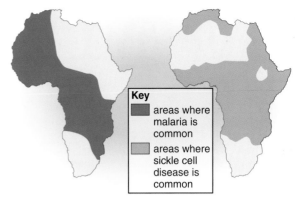

Key
- areas where malaria is common
- areas where sickle cell disease is common

In Africa, sickle cell disease is common where malaria is common.

alleles that may be present	SS alleles	Ss alleles	ss alleles

effects of alleles

SS alleles	Ss alleles	ss alleles
normal red blood cells	normal red blood cells	sickle-shaped red blood cells
no anaemia	slight risk of anaemia	sickle cell disease causing anaemia
no resistance to malaria	resistance to malaria	resistance to malaria

In some circumstances, a 'faulty' gene can be helpful.

Questions

1 a Describe evidence that shows there is a link between malaria and sickle cell disease.

b Explain why it may be beneficial to be a carrier of sickle cell disease in countries in Africa.

2 The diagram shows which members of a family have sickle cell disease.

a Which member of the family has sickle cell disease?

b Which alleles for this disease are present in Farah's cells?

c Joseph and Farah want to have children but are worried that their babies might be born with sickle cell disease. If they do have a child what is the chance that the baby will have sickle cell disease? Explain your answer.

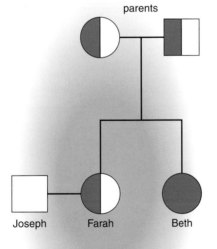

parents

Joseph   Farah   Beth

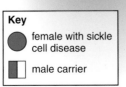

Key
- ● female with sickle cell disease
- ▮ male carrier

Summary

- Sickle cell disease is an inherited disease that affects red blood cells.

- This disease reduces the ability of red blood cells to carry oxygen to body organs.

- It can be beneficial to be a carrier of this disease in countries where malaria is common.

Tasty foods

The shelves of your local supermarket are stacked with a wide choice of good quality foods. This food has been produced from plants and animals bred by farmers.

Farmers choose which plants and animals have useful characteristics and then use them for breeding. This means that these characteristics will be passed on to young plants and animals. Selecting the plants and animals used for breeding is called **artificial selection**. In this way, new varieties of plants and animals have been produced.

We need plants and animals with the best characteristics to produce the foods we buy.

Breeding better plants

The very first plants used to produce food were wild plants. By choosing which plants were used for breeding, farmers produced new varieties.

Broccoli is a plant grown for food. We use the flower heads as a vegetable. The photograph shows the flower head from the modern variety of broccoli. Wild broccoli contains several much smaller flower heads.

a **What characteristic makes the modern variety more useful to farmers than wild broccoli?**

Wheat is a very important plant grown by farmers. It is used to make flour to make bread, cakes and other foods. Modern varieties of wheat have characteristics more useful to farmers than older varieties.

b **The diagram below shows the modern and old varieties of wheat. What characteristics make the modern variety a better plant?**

Many years of breeding have produced more useful varieties of broccoli.

The ears of wild wheat are small and have few seeds.

The ears ripen at different times and can be diseased.
The stalks grow to different heights, making it hard to cut the crops.

wild wheat

This is an ear of modern wheat. It is large and has many seeds. The seeds are used to make flour.

The ears all ripen at the same time and are resistant to disease.

The stalks grow to the same height, making it easier for farmers to cut the crop.

modern wheat

Advantages of modern varieties of wheat.

Breeding better animals

New breeds of farm animals have been produced by choosing which animals are used for breeding. The new breeds have characteristics that are wanted by farmers.

For example, the hens used by farmers many years ago produced about 20 eggs per year. Modern varieties of hen lay eggs for most of the year and produce about 240 eggs per year.

This is what the first hens were like.

Hens have been bred to increase the number of eggs they lay.

More milk

The black and white cows you often see in fields are a breed called Friesian. This breed is used by farmers to produce milk.

Dairy Shorthorns used to be a more common breed used by farmers for milk.

A Dairy Shorthorn cow.

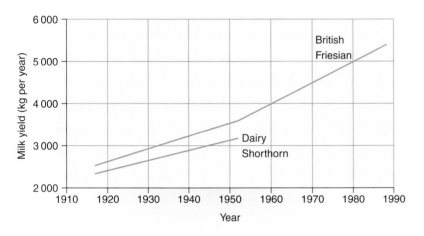

The amounts of milk produced by Dairy Shorthorn and Friesian cows each year during the twentieth century.

A Friesian cow.

Questions

1 a List four characteristics of modern wheat that make this variety more useful than wild wheat.

  b Explain why each characteristic is useful.

2 a Why did farmers stop using Dairy Shorthorn cattle for milk production?

  b Describe how milk yield changed between 1940 and 1990.

  c Explain how breeders were able to increase milk yield year by year.

  d Even though Dairy Shorthorn cattle are no longer used for milk production, breeders still maintain a small herd. Suggest why it is important to keep this breed rather than let it die out.

Summary

- Selective breeding has produced new varieties of plants and new breeds of animals.

- Using modern varieties of plants and breeds of animals has increased food production.

- Choosing which animals and plants are used for breeding is an example of artificial selection.

4:11 High-tech breeding

Modern technology

Selective breeding has been used for many years to produce new varieties of plants and new breeds of animals.

Modern techniques are now used to make breeding more efficient.

Test tube plants

The photograph shows plants growing on a special jelly. Tiny pieces of plant are placed on the jelly, which contains nutrients and hormones. The tiny pieces form roots and shoots and develop into whole plants. This technique is called **tissue culture**.

Using tissue culture, plant breeders can grow large numbers of plants containing the same genes, from just one plant. The new plants form a **clone**.

a Why are the new plants grown from a single plant called a clone?

Tissue culture can be used to produce identical new plants.

Transplanting embryos

Breeders also use **embryo transplants** to produce young animals with the characteristics they want. The diagram shows how embryo transplants are carried out.

All the young animals produced from a single fertilised egg will have identical genes – they will be a clone. This means that a breeder can produce more young animals with chosen characteristics.

b Explain why the embryos that are transplanted contain identical genes.

Dolly the sheep

The birth of Dolly the sheep in 1997 caused a lot of discussion about the rights and wrongs of using embryo transplants ('cloning'). Dolly was cloned by transferring the nucleus of a body cell into an egg cell that had already had its nucleus removed.

During this experiment, 277 embryos were produced. Many of the pregnancies failed and some lambs were stillborn or died at birth.

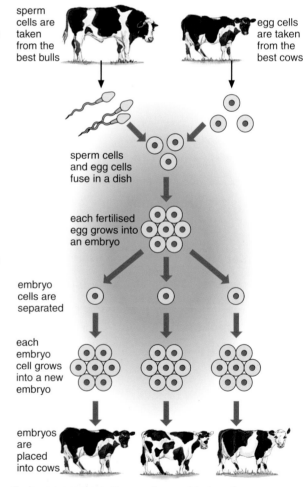

sperm cells are taken from the best bulls

egg cells are taken from the best cows

sperm cells and egg cells fuse in a dish

each fertilised egg grows into an embryo

embryo cells are separated

each embryo cell grows into a new embryo

embryos are placed into cows

Embryo transplantation can be used to breed many animals with chosen characteristics.

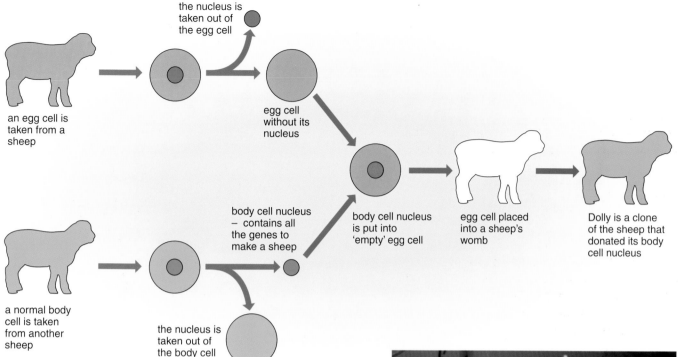

the nucleus is taken out of the egg cell

an egg cell is taken from a sheep

egg cell without its nucleus

body cell nucleus – contains all the genes to make a sheep

body cell nucleus is put into 'empty' egg cell

egg cell placed into a sheep's womb

Dolly is a clone of the sheep that donated its body cell nucleus

a normal body cell is taken from another sheep

the nucleus is taken out of the body cell

How Dolly the sheep was produced.

Cloning – should it be used?

Some people argue that breeding lots of identical animals by cloning is not natural. It is as though the scientists are 'playing God'.

Scientists argue that cloning from embryos is a method of controlling the breeding of animals that can be used to do good.

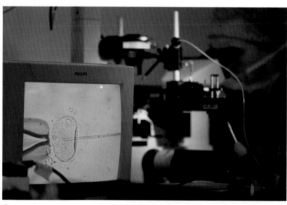

Scientists use an extremely fine pipette to remove the nucleus from a cell under the microscope, during the 'cloning' process.

Questions

1 The following examples describe cases when cloning *could* be used. In each case, explain your views on whether cloning methods *should* be used.

   a A dog breeder wants to use cloning methods to increase the number of pups to sell.

   b Scientists in a developing country in Africa want to use cloning to raise healthy cattle.

   c Scientists working in a zoo want to use cloning methods to breed from an animal of an endangered species that may become extinct.

2 a Explain why Dolly is a clone of the sheep that donated a nucleus from a body cell, and *not* of the sheep that donated the 'empty' egg cell.

   b The birth of Dolly raised hopes that the same techniques could be used to produce farm animals. Give a reason why these techniques should not be used for normal breeding.

Summary

- Plants and animals can be produced using cloning techniques.

- Tissue culture is a cloning technique used to grow new plants from small groups of cells from part of a parent plant.

- Cells from a developing animal embryo can be split apart. The identical embryos that form are then transplanted into host mothers.

4:12 Swapping genes

Missing chemicals

Some illnesses are caused when a person cannot make a substance that is needed for their body to work. For example, some people have **diabetes** because their body cannot make a hormone called **insulin**. This hormone is used in your body to control the amount of sugar in your blood.

a What is the sugar in your blood used for?

b Suggest the effect of a low amount of sugar in someone's blood.

Steve Redgrave (second from right) needs to inject himself with insulin six times a day just to stay alive. But he was determined that his diabetes would not prevent him winning gold at the Sydney Olympic Games.

Treating diabetes

People who have diabetes control the amount of sugar in their blood by injecting themselves with insulin. Regular insulin injections help people who have diabetes to lead a healthy life.

Over a million people in the UK have diabetes, so large amounts of insulin are needed. Insulin can be obtained from cattle and from pigs. Over recent years, scientists have developed methods of producing human insulin from bacteria.

Cutting and sticking genes

You have a gene in your chromosomes that makes insulin. Scientists have been able to cut this gene out of the chromosome that carries it and then stick it into a chromosome of a bacterial cell. This is an example of **genetic engineering**.

DIGGING DEEPER
Before insulin was available, people with diabetes slowly lost more and more weight and eventually died. In 1922, a 14-year-old Canadian boy with diabetes was treated with extract from the pancreas of a dog. After treatment, the teenager was able to eat a normal diet and began to put on weight and lead an active life. Without this treatment he would have died.
Insulin was then extracted from the pancreas of pigs and cattle and made available for the treatment of diabetes. Now human insulin is made by 'genetic engineering' from bacteria.

stage 1
The gene that makes insulin is cut out from the DNA.

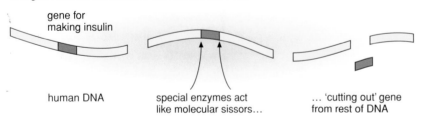

gene for making insulin

human DNA

special enzymes act like molecular sissors...

... 'cutting out' gene from rest of DNA

stage 2
The human gene is inserted into bacterial DNA.

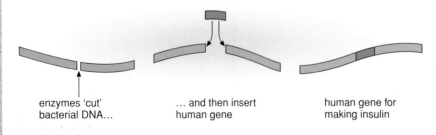

enzymes 'cut' bacterial DNA...

... and then insert human gene

human gene for making insulin

Cutting and sticking the human gene for insulin into bacterial cells.

Bacterial factories

Bacteria containing the human gene that makes insulin can be grown inside massive storage vessels. The temperature and nutrients inside the vessels are controlled so that the bacteria will grow rapidly.

Rapid growth produces millions of bacterial cells inside the vessels, each cell containing the human gene that makes insulin. This means that large amounts of insulin can be made.

c If a bacterial cell reproduces to form two cells every minute, how many cells will be formed in five minutes?

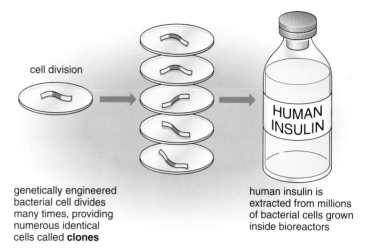

genetically engineered bacterial cell divides many times, providing numerous identical cells called **clones**

human insulin is extracted from millions of bacterial cells grown inside bioreactors

Human insulin produced by bacteria is now available to people with diabetes.

Adding genes to plants

Recently scientists have found ways of cutting genes from bacteria and sticking them into the crops grown by farmers. For example, some bacteria produce a protein that is poisonous to some insects. The gene that makes the protein can be cut out and added to the genes of a crop plant. Because the crop plant makes the poisonous protein, farmers will need to use smaller amounts of insecticides to kill insects that damage the crop.

Other genes can be changed to make crops resistant to disease or to increase their vitamin content.

Crops that have had their genes changed in this way are called genetically modified crops (**GM crops**).

Some people are against the use of GM crops. They say they are unsafe and we do not know the long-term effects of adding and replacing genes.

Questions

1 Describe how crops can be genetically modified to make the plant more useful.

2 GM crops are grown in countries such as the USA. They cannot be grown in the UK except on test sites. Give two reasons:

   a in support of growing GM crops

   b why GM crops should not be grown.

3 What are the advantages of using bacteria to manufacture insulin rather than obtaining insulin from pigs or cattle?

Summary

- Genes from the chromosomes of humans and other organisms can be cut out using enzymes.

- The genes can then be put into bacterial cells.

- The swapped gene makes the same protein in the bacterial cell.

- Bacteria can be grown on a large scale to manufacture drugs such as human insulin.

- Genes can be transferred to the cells of animals and plants to give them useful characteristics.

4:13 Forming new species

Changing species

People used to think that all living things had always remained the same. They also thought that living things had been created at the same time that the Earth was created.

As scientists learned more and more about plants and animals, they suggested that species have *not* always been the same and that new species are being formed. This is the **theory of evolution**.

Early theories

One of the earliest theories of how evolution takes place was proposed by a French scientist called **Lamarck** in 1809. His theory was based on the idea that the more an organ is used, the more it increases in size, from generation to generation.

For example, according to Lamarck's theory, the long legs and long neck of the giraffe are the result of generations of giraffes stretching to feed on the leaves of tall trees. The slightly longer legs and neck produced each generation were passed on to the next generation.

By stretching to feed, each generation of giraffes inherits a slightly longer neck and legs. Over many generations, the giraffe has developed a very long neck and long legs.

Lamarck's theory of evolution.

Changing people's ideas

Charles Darwin was one of the first scientists to explain how the process of evolution takes place.

A five year voyage on board a ship called *HMS Beagle* took Darwin all around the world. During this long voyage Darwin kept careful records of his many observations and collected hundreds of specimens.

After studying all his evidence and discussing his ideas with other scientists, Darwin suggested that new species can be formed by a process called **natural selection**.

a Look at the diagram which summarises the process of natural selection. Why do varieties with poor camouflage have less chance of passing on their genes to the next generation?

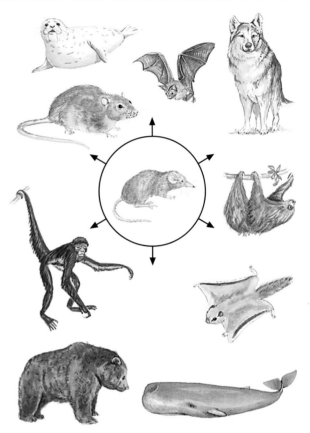

Species gradually change over many generations. This is called evolution.

1 Organisms produce many offspring and have to compete for food.

2 Organisms struggle to survive. They may die from disease or be eaten by predators.

3 Members of a species may have different characteristics.

4 Characteristics that give an organism an advantage are more likely to be passed on to the next generation.

Natural selection means that helpful characteristics are inherited by more offspring.

Darwin was so concerned about how other scientists would react to his ideas that he did not publish his findings for many years. Most people still believed that species were created and did not evolve. To suggest that species evolve went against what many people understood from the Bible to be the 'truth'.

When Darwin's ideas were first presented to a group of well-known scientists, the audience remained in total silence at the end of the talk.

Darwin finally published his ideas in 1859, but his findings were rejected by some scientists for over 50 years afterwards.

Different varieties

On his voyage Darwin visited a group of islands near South America called the Galapagos Islands. He made many recordings of the features of birds on the islands called finches.

When he returned to England, Darwin continued to study his recordings. He realised that many of the birds he had seen were different varieties of the same species of finch. One of the characteristics of each variety was the shape and length of its beak. The shape of its beak enabled each variety to feed on a particular type of food.

Darwin suggested that each of the different varieties was descended from one variety of finch. The diagram shows how different varieties evolved by natural selection.

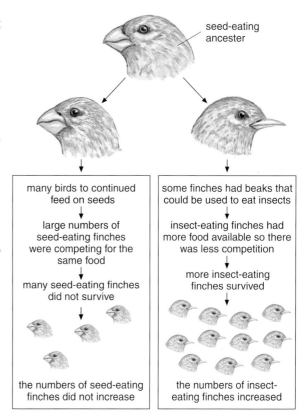

seed-eating ancester

many birds to continued feed on seeds	some finches had beaks that could be used to eat insects
↓	↓
large numbers of seed-eating finches were competing for the same food	insect-eating finches had more food available so there was less competition
↓	↓
many seed-eating finches did not survive	more insect-eating finches survived
↓	↓
the numbers of seed-eating finches did not increase	the numbers of insect-eating finches increased

Some finches had slightly narrower beaks, good for eating insects. These birds got more food than the others, lived longer and had more offspring.

Questions

1 The following sentences summarise how species may change by natural selection. Place the sentences in the right order to show how this process takes place.

- Organisms that survive and breed will pass their genes on to the next generation.

- Individual organisms may have different characteristics.

- Organisms with characteristics most suited to the environment are more likely to survive and breed.

- Organisms may die because of predation, disease and competition.

2 Charles Darwin suggested that the different varieties of finch on the Galapagos islands had evolved from one variety of finch that came from South America.

a Name the process that may have resulted in the evolution of different varieties.

b The finch that came from South America probably had a thick beak. Suggest why birds with thinner beaks that can reach insects in tree bark survived better.

c Suggest how birds could have developed long beaks to reach insects according Lamarck's theory.

Summary
- All species have evolved from simpler organisms.
- Species may evolve by a process of natural selection.
- The theory of natural selection was first suggested by Charles Darwin.
- It took many years before Darwin's ideas were accepted.
- Lamarck's theory of how evolution occurs differs from Darwin's theory.

The first organisms

There is evidence that all species have evolved from simple organisms that lived on the Earth more than three billion years ago. These simple organisms evolved to form larger more complex organisms.

Evolution usually occurs as a result of very small changes taking place over a long period of time. This is why scientists investigate changes in evolution taking place over millions of years.

Evidence from the past

Evidence of the way organisms have changed can be seen in fossils. Fossils are the remains of plants and animals that are found in rocks.

Fossils can be formed from:

◆ the hard parts of animals, which do not decay easily

◆ parts of animals and plants that have not decayed because the conditions for decay were not present

◆ parts of plants and animals that are replaced by other materials as they decay

◆ preserved traces of plants and animals such as footprints and traces of plant roots.

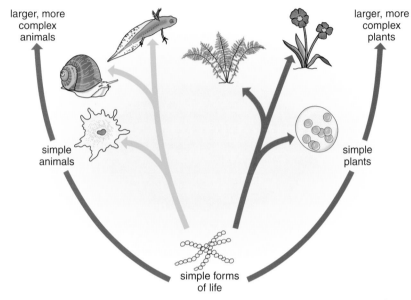

larger, more complex animals

simple animals

larger, more complex plants

simple plants

simple forms of life

Simpler forms of life evolved to form larger and more complex organisms.

If remains can't decay (because there is no water or because it is too cold, for example) then they may form fossils.

Dinosaur footprints at Hanover Point on the Isle of Wight.

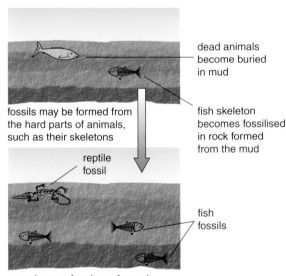

dead animals become buried in mud

fish skeleton becomes fossilised in rock formed from the mud

fossils may be formed from the hard parts of animals, such as their skeletons

reptile fossil

fish fossils

more layers of rock are formed on top of the older rock

Fossils can show us what plants and animals looked like millions of years ago.

Fossil records

The bones, shells, leaves and other remains found in rocks give some idea of what animals and plants looked like when they were alive, perhaps millions of years ago.

The position of a fossil also provides evidence of its age. The deepest rocks are likely to contain the oldest fossils. This means that fossils provide a record that shows how plants and animals have changed over a long period of time.

rocks appear as bands (strata)

younger

older

different types of fossils appear in each band of rock

The fossil record gives us vital information about how organisms have evolved.

Extinct species

The fossil record shows that some species lived in the past but are no longer living – they have become **extinct**. For example, about 100 million years ago there were many more species of reptiles on the Earth than there are today, including many species of dinosaur.

Species may become extinct because:

- ◆ the environment they need to survive changes
- ◆ new predators or diseases kill them
- ◆ they cannot compete with other species.

Using the fossil record

By studying the numbers and types of fossils found in different layers of rocks scientists can build up a record of how living things evolved. The diagram shows the fossils found in layers of rock.

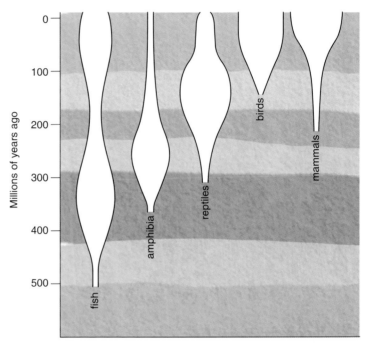

Number of fossils
(the wider the band, the more fossils present)

In this diagram, the wider the bands, the more fossils there are present in that rock layer.

Questions

Look at the diagram showing the numbers and types of fossils found in different rock layers. Use it to answer the following questions.

1 The colours in the diagram represent each layer of rock. Which colour represents the oldest rock?

2 How does the fossil record show that there were more amphibia on Earth 300 million years ago than there were 10 million years ago.

3 About 200 million years ago the Earth was dominated by dinosaurs. This started a period in evolution called 'the age of dinosaurs'.

a How long ago did dinosaurs become extinct?

b Explain how the record shows this.

c One reason suggested for the decrease in the number of reptile species was that reptiles could not compete with mammals. What evidence in the fossil record supports this suggestion?

Summary

- Fossils are the remains of organisms from many years ago.

- Fossils can be formed in various ways.

- Fossils show how much different organisms have changed since life developed on Earth.

- Fossils show that some species have become extinct.

4:15 Changing genes

Mutation

Your cells contain a gene that controls the production of a substance called melanin. **Melanin** gives your skin its colour, and it can even give you a suntan.

The photograph shows a blackbird that cannot make melanin. Animals that cannot make melanin and have no pigment in their skin are called **albinos**.

Albinos cannot make melanin because the gene that controls its production has changed. A change in a gene is called a **mutation**.

Increasing mutations

Mutations occur by chance. Some things, such as ionising radiation and some chemicals, can increase the chance of mutations occurring.

Ionising radiation includes UV light, X-rays, and radiation from radioactive substances.

Chemicals that can increase the chance of mutations occurring include benzene and the hydrocarbons in tobacco smoke.

a Why do radiographers go behind a screen when they are taking an X-ray of someone?

Harmful mutations

When mutations occur in reproductive cells, the young produced from these cells may develop abnormally or even die at a young age.

Mutations in body cells may cause the cells to multiply in an uncontrolled way and invade other body tissues. This is cancer. For example, being exposed to the sun's harmful UV radiation can cause skin cancer. People who spend hours sunbathing to get a suntan are increasing the chances that they will also get skin cancer.

Useful mutations

In rare cases, a mutation occurs that increases the chances of an organism's survival. For example, a mutation in bacteria produces a variety that is resistant to the use of antibiotics. This mutation increases the chance of bacteria surviving – very useful for the bacteria, but a problem for you if you are infected.

The bar charts show how the number of resistant bacteria increases as a result of the over-use of antibiotics.

Not all blackbirds are black! This is an albino blackbird.

X-rays increase the chance of genes becoming damaged, or mutated.

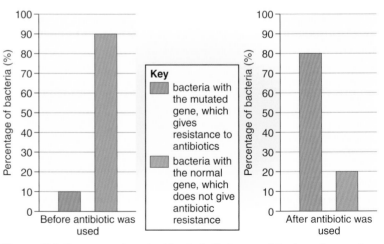

Key
- bacteria with the mutated gene, which gives resistance to antibiotics
- bacteria with the normal gene, which does not give antibiotic resistance

When antibiotics are used, mutant bacteria that are resistant survive much better than the normal bacteria. So a large proportion of the bacteria left afterwards are resistant.

Investigating the effects of radiation

Yeast cells are single-celled organisms that can be grown in the laboratory on nutrient gel. When yeast cells grow they form colonies that can be seen on the surface of the gel. Some gene mutations make the yeast colonies look different.

The diagram shows the effect of putting yeast cells in UV light for different amounts of time.

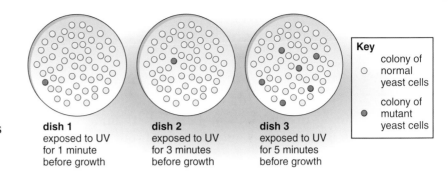

dish 1
exposed to UV for 1 minute before growth

dish 2
exposed to UV for 3 minutes before growth

dish 3
exposed to UV for 5 minutes before growth

Key

○ colony of normal yeast cells

● colony of mutant yeast cells

b What is the effect of increasing the amount of UV light on yeast cells?

The UV light increases the chances of mutations occurring in the yeast cells.

The Chernobyl disaster

In April 1986, a nuclear power station exploded in Chernobyl, in Ukraine. The explosion caused was a major disaster.

The explosion released a radioactive cloud, which spread from Chernobyl across Europe. Heavy rain washed radioactive materials from the clouds into fields in Wales and other parts of the UK.

Sheep feeding in fields ate grass contaminated with radioactive materials. The sale of lamb from contaminated areas was banned. Even now, more than fifteen years after the explosion, some lambs in these areas are found to have high levels of radiation in their bodies.

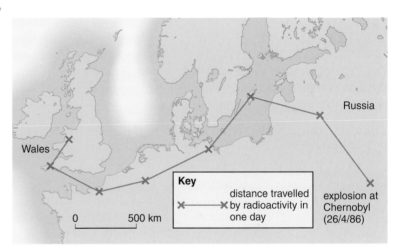

Russia

Wales

Key

✕———✕ distance travelled by radioactivity in one day

✕ explosion at Chernobyl (26/4/86)

0   500 km

Radioactive material from the Chernobyl explosion was carried by the wind for hundreds of miles.

Questions

1 a How long did it take for the radioactivity from Chernobyl to reach Wales?

b Suggest why lamb from contaminated areas was banned from being sold.

2 a Copy and then complete the table by counting the number of normal yeast colonies and mutant yeast colonies in the dishes shown above.

	Number of normal colonies	Number of mutant colonies
Dish 1		
Dish 2		
Dish 3		

b Describe the effect of increasing the amount of time for which yeast cells are exposed to UV light.

3 Explain why using antibiotics too often has led to an increase in the number of bacteria resistant to antibiotics.

Summary

- Mutation results in new forms of genes.
- Ionising radiation and some substances can increase mutations.
- Mutations are usually harmful.
- Cancer can be caused by mutations occurring in body cells.
- Occasionally, mutations occur that increase the chances of an organism's survival.

4:16 The code for life

What will I become?

Will you become an Olympic athlete? Prime Minister? A TV star? Your future depends on many things, but some aspects of your future were set from the start of your life.

A chemical called **DNA** is found in the nucleus of each cell. DNA contains coded information that controls inherited characteristics. Each gene is a section of a DNA molecule.

The DNA in a fertilised human egg has the coded information to make an entire human being.

A double helix

DNA molecules are made of two very long strands. The strands coil into a double helix like a twisted ladder. The two strands are joined together by **bases**.

There are four different types of base, represented by the letters A, T, C and G.

A special code

The sequence of the bases creates a code that controls inherited characteristics. This code controls the production of **proteins** used in the body. Each protein contains a particular arrangement of **amino acids**.

The sequence of bases in DNA controls the order that amino acids are joined together to make a protein. A sequence of three bases is the code for a particular amino acid.

Proteins are the building materials of organisms. By controlling the production of proteins, DNA controls all the inherited characteristics of an organism.

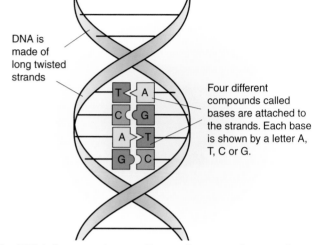

DNA is made of long twisted strands

Four different compounds called bases are attached to the strands. Each base is shown by a letter A, T, C or G.

The DNA in just one of your cells contains a complete set of instructions on how to make and run your body.

DIGGING DEEPER

Police scientists can extract DNA from tiny traces of tissue such as a strand of hair or a drop of blood. The DNA is used to identify criminals because no two people have the same sequence of bases in their DNA (except identical twins). This technique, called 'genetic fingerprinting', was first developed in 1984 and has been used to solve many major crimes.

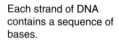

Each strand of DNA contains a sequence of bases.

A sequence of three bases codes for a particular amino acid.

DNA → protein

TAA is the code for this amino acid

CGA is the code for this amino acid

what is the code for this one?

the sequence of bases in DNA... ...acts as a code to control... ...the sequence of amino acids in protein

The type and order of amino acids in a protein are determined by the DNA code.

The body's building blocks

Your body contains many different proteins, each carrying out an essential job in keeping you alive and healthy. Each protein molecule is a chain of amino acids. The properties of each protein depend on the order of amino acids in the chain. A protein may no longer be able to carry out its job if just one amino acid in the chain is changed.

The code in DNA controls *which* amino acids will be in a protein and the s*equence* in which they are joined.

Breaking the code

Amino acids put together in a sequence make a particular protein.

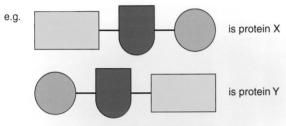

e.g.

is protein X

is protein Y

Each sequence of three bases in a DNA strand codes for each amino acid. So if

A–T–T–G–C–C–T–A–G

is the code for protein X, answer question 1 below to work out the code for protein Y.

A protein molecule may be hundreds of amino acids long. The gene coding for the protein will contain thousands of bases.

Over the past few years, scientists from all over the world have been involved in working out the code in DNA for every protein in the human body. Scientists now know the DNA code for important proteins such as insulin and haemoglobin. This is helping scientists to understand inherited diseases and to find possible cures and treatments.

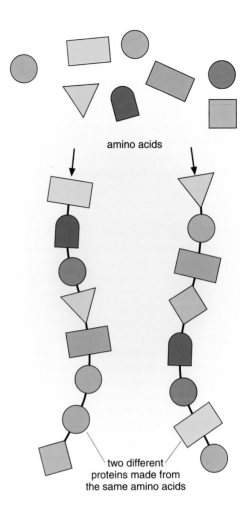

amino acids

two different proteins made from the same amino acids

If amino acids are put together in a different order, a different protein is 'spelled out'.

Questions

1 Using the symbols for amino acids and bases used in the diagram above:

   a write down the DNA code for protein Y

   b show the structure of a different protein using the same amino acids.

2 The DNA code for each of three amino acids is shown below.

   CGA codes for alanine

   ACA codes for cysteine

   CAA codes for valine

   Write down the sequence of bases that codes for the following chain of amino acids:

   valine — alanine — cysteine

Summary

- DNA contains coded information that controls inherited characteristics.

- DNA contains long strands of four bases.

- Each group of three bases codes for a particular amino acid.

- The sequence of bases in DNA controls the sequence of amino acids in a protein.

End of module questions

1 These young kittens have the same fur colour as their parents. This is because information about characteristics is passed from parents to their young.

Choose words from this list to complete the sentences.

    alleles   chromosomes   genes   nucleus

The _____ of a cell contains thread-like strands called _____ . Characteristics that are inherited are controlled by _____ , which may exist in different forms called _____ .

2 Geraniums produce flowers with many different colours.

A gardener wants to grow geranium plants. She decides to grow them from cuttings from one plant.

2.1 Give one condition that cuttings need to grow well.

2.2 Give two advantages of growing the geraniums from cuttings.

3 The diagram below shows some of the parts of a woman's reproductive system.

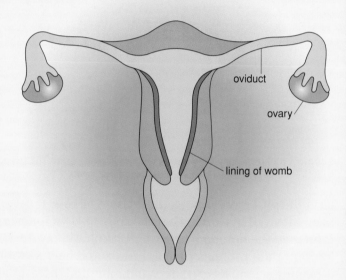

During each month, the thickness of the lining of the womb changes and an egg is released. This is called the monthly menstrual cycle.

3.1 Which part of the reproductive system shown in the diagram produces hormones?

3.2 Which part of the reproductive system releases eggs?

If a woman's reproductive system is not able to release eggs, she can be given fertility drugs to make this happen.

3.3 What do fertility drugs contain?

3.4 Describe a problem that may be caused by using fertility drugs in this way.

4 Huntington's disease is an inherited disease. It is due to a faulty dominant allele. The effects of this allele do not appear until a person is over 30 years old.

The diagram below is a family tree showing the inheritance of Huntington's disease.

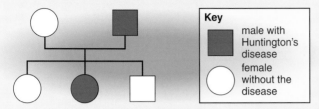

Key

■ male with Huntington's disease

○ female without the disease

Draw a genetic diagram to show the pairings of the alleles for this family. Use H for the allele that causes Huntington's disease and h for the recessive allele.

5 The strawberries that you see in supermarkets remain ripe for several days.

Strawberries used to rot very quickly after ripening. A small number of strawberry plants produced strawberries that were disease-resistant and did not rot quickly.

5.1 Copy and place these sentences in the correct order, to show how to develop more disease-resistant strawberry plants.

- Grow the seeds into new plants.
- Repeat this for many generations of plants.
- Breed plants together to produce seeds.
- Select plants producing strawberries that do not rot quickly.

5.2 Breeding plants to produce seeds involves the fusion of male and female gametes. What type of reproduction involves gametes?

New strawberry plants can also be grown from runners.

5.3 All the new plants grown from the original plant form a clone. Explain why these plants form a clone.

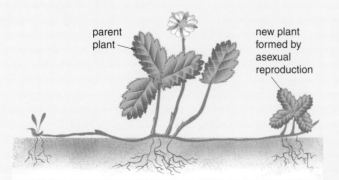

parent plant

new plant formed by asexual reproduction

5.4 One strawberry plant produced pink flowers instead of the usual white flowers. The growers thought this was because of mutation. Explain what 'mutation' means.

6 Kakapos are a species of bird found in New Zealand. They cannot fly, and they live in forests. They make their nests close to the ground.

Rats from visiting ships escaped into the forests and ate birds' eggs. Cats also escaped into the forests. Large areas of forests were cleared to make fields to graze sheep.

A few years ago, there was only a very small number of kakapos remaining.

6.1 Kakapos faced extinction. Explain what is meant by an extinct species.

6.2 Use the information given to suggest reasons why kakapos faced extinction.

7 **7.1** Copy and then complete the following diagram to show how the sex of a child depends on chromosomes.

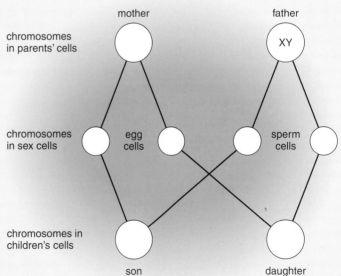

mother   father

chromosomes in parents' cells   XY

chromosomes in sex cells   egg cells   sperm cells

chromosomes in children's cells

son   daughter

7.2 Human body cells contain 46 chromosomes. How many chromosomes are there in human egg cells?

7.3 Explain why both of the children shown on the diagram will have some of their mother's characteristics and some characteristics from their father.

7.4 What type of cell division is involved in the formation of gametes?

8 Cystic fibrosis is an inherited disease that causes the tubes in the lungs to be blocked with sticky mucus.

The disease is caused by a faulty allele, f. People with two faulty alleles suffer from the disease.

People with just one normal allele, F, do not suffer from the disease.

8.1 What term is used to describe people who can pass an inherited disease on to their children but do not suffer from the disease?

8.2 Draw a genetic diagram to show how the normal allele and the faulty allele are passed on when two Ff parents have children. Show on your diagram which children have cystic fibrosis and which do not.

8.3 The faulty allele was caused by a normal gene changing. What are changes in genes called?

8.4 Mucus contains a protein. The normal gene contains coded information to make this protein. Explain how a change in a gene causes a different protein to be made.

9 Diabetes can be treated using insulin produced by genetically engineered bacteria.

9.1 Describe how bacteria are changed to produce human proteins.

9.2 Insulin is made by cloned bacterial cells. Explain what is meant by a clone.

9.3 Cells from a developing embryo can be split apart. The separated cells grow to form embryos, which can be transplanted into host mothers. Explain why the young animals produced form a clone.

10 The diagram below shows some fossils in layers of rock. The rock was formed from mud.

10.1 When animals die bacteria make them decay. Warmth, water and oxygen are needed for decay. Explain why the rocks in the diagram contain fossils.

10.2 Explain why the fossils are of bones but not of soft tissues such as skin.

10.3 Explain how the position of a fossil in the layers of rock shows the relative age of the fossil.

Module 8 – Structures and bonding

Everything in the world is made of chemicals. There are millions of different kinds of chemicals, so how can we possibly know what is going on? Fortunately, we can all benefit from the work of great scientists. Over the last 200 years they have helped to unravel the mysteries of chemistry. They have discovered that all this complexity can be explained by the relatively simple rules that govern the behaviour of just a few different kinds of atoms and sub-atomic particles. In this module you will learn the basic rules that underlie the material world.

You will learn:

- what controls the properties of the different elements;
- how the elements are arranged in the periodic table;
- how the periodic table gives a summary of atomic structure;
- how atoms combine to form compounds;
- why different types of materials have different properties that depend on their structure;
- how to work out chemical formulae and balance chemical equations.

Before you start, check what you remember about the structures and bonding of elements and compounds.

1 **What happens to the particles in a solid when you heat it (without melting)? What effect does this have on the volume of the solid?**

2 **The particles in liquids and gases are both free to move, but what is the difference between the way the particles are arranged?**

3 **What is the difference between an element and a compound?**

4 **Roughly how many different elements are there (10, 50, 100, 500)?**

5 **Which elemental gas is used to kill germs?**

6 **Which gas is used to fill modern lighter-than-air balloons?**

Everything is made of particles. Water is made of water particles, iron is made of iron particles, and so on.

But ice, water and steam are all made of the same particles. Why is ice a solid, water a liquid and steam a gas?

a Why can you pour a liquid but not a solid?

b Why can you squash a gas but not a liquid?

The answer is that it all depends on:

◆ how the particles are arranged;

◆ how big the forces of attraction are between the particles; and

◆ how much movement energy the particles have.

	Properties	Particle arrangement	Forces of attraction compared to movement energy
Solid	Fixed shape and fixed volume	regular close-packed	The particles vibrate but the forces of attraction are strong enough to hold them together
Liquid	No fixed shape but fixed volume	irregular close-packed (some gaps)	The particles vibrate more. Clumps of particles break free and can move about
Gas	No fixed shape and no fixed volume	few, spaced out, random	The forces of attraction have been overcome. The particles spread out and whiz about at high speed

The amount of movement energy the particles have depends on the temperature.

c Do the particles move faster or slower as the temperature goes up?

Solid ice, liquid water or gaseous steam? It all depends on the temperature.

The energy link

The particles in ice have enough energy to vibrate, but they cannot break away from each other as they are held in place by strong forces.

If you heat ice, however, you give the particles more energy, and this makes them vibrate more. The more you heat the particles, the more violently they vibrate. Eventually, they have enough vibration energy to overcome some of the forces that hold them together. As the solid melts, clumps of particles become free to move. For water, this happens when the temperature reaches 0°C. This is the **melting point** of water.

d Iron melts at 1540°C. Are the forces between iron particles stronger or weaker than the forces between water particles? Explain your answer.

If you keep heating liquid water, the particles can move around faster and faster because they get more energy. Some of the particles at the surface of the liquid get enough energy to break free and escape into the air. This is called **evaporation**. Evaporation happens faster and faster as the liquid gets hotter and hotter, because the particles get more and more energy. The gas that forms is **water vapour**.

If you keep heating, the particles will eventually get enough energy to completely overcome the forces that were holding them together. The liquid starts to boil and turns into a gas. For water, this happens when the temperature reaches 100°C. This is the **boiling point** of water.

It's reversible

The changes from solid to liquid and from liquid to gas are called physical changes and they are easily reversed. If you cool steam back down to 100°C, it will **condense** to form liquid water again. The particles lose energy and clump back together. If you continue to cool the water it will **freeze** back to solid ice, at 0°C.

e Alcohol boils at 79°C. At what temperature would alcohol vapour condense back to liquid alcohol?

Questions

1 a Water boils at 100°C. How does washing on a washing line dry when the temperature is only 15°C?

b Why does washing dry faster on a hot day?

2 a Sulphur melts at 114°C. It is often transported by tanker as molten sulphur. What is the advantage of transporting sulphur as a liquid?

b Why isn't iron transported as a liquid?

Data analysis

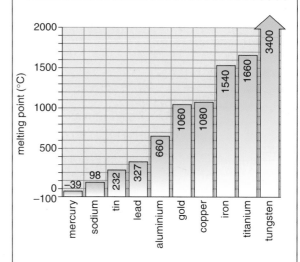

f The filament in a light bulb has to get 'white hot' – over 2000°C. Why can't a filament be made of iron?

g In a Siberian winter the temperature drops below –50°C. Why can't mercury thermometers be used in Siberia?

h Zinc boils at 907°C. Brass is made from copper and zinc. Why can't you make brass by simply heating solid copper and solid zinc until they melt?

Summary

- In solids, the particles are close together and vibrate but are held in place by forces.

- In liquids, the particles are still close together but they are free to move about.

- In gases, the particles have broken free and are whizzing about at high speed.

- The higher the temperature, the more energy the particles have and the faster they move.

Naming the pieces

Everything is made up of particles. For most substances, these particles are built from smaller particles called **atoms**. Groups of two or more atoms joined together are called **molecules**.

There are about 100 different kinds of atoms on Earth. Substances made from only one type of atom are called **elements**. As there are 100 different types of atom, there are 100 different elements.

Many elements, such as oxygen or sulphur, form molecules containing just one type of atom.

a How many atoms of oxygen are there in an oxygen molecule?

Compounds

When *different* elements combine they form **compounds**. The 100 different atoms can combine to give an enormous number of different compounds, but the same compounds are always formed in the same way.

b Which elements combine together to make water molecules and which make methane?

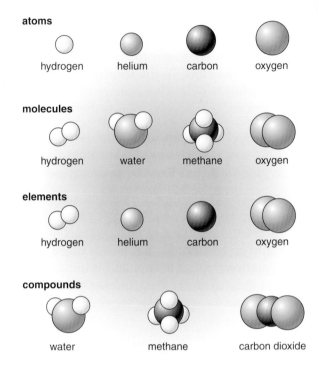

Dalton and the atom

About 200 years ago, John Dalton was studying the way elements combined to form compounds. By careful experimentation, using very accurate balances, he found that the simple compounds he made always contained the same elements in the same proportions.

Dalton explained his results by the idea that elements were made of tiny particles that could not be broken – atoms. This was quite surprising to many scientists at the time, but it was not a new idea. The idea of atoms was first thought up by the Ancient Greeks, 2000 years ago. The Greeks had no experimental evidence to support their idea, so the idea went out of favour!

c What evidence did Dalton use to convince other scientists that everything was made of atoms?

Using symbols for elements

Each of the 100 elements has a unique, internationally recognised symbol of one or two letters. Most of these symbols are 'sensible' choices from the name. Some seem odd, because they refer to older names that are no longer used.

John Dalton (1766–1844).

Symbols for compounds

For compounds, the symbols of the elements that they are made from are simply listed one after another. So iron sulphide, which has one iron atom joined to one sulphur atom, is written as FeS.

If there is more than one atom of a particular element in a compound, this is shown by a small subscript number after its symbol. So water, which has two hydrogen atoms joined to one oxygen atom, is written as H_2O.

Every chemical compound has its own list of symbols and numbers to describe the atoms it is made from. This is called its **chemical formula**.

Remember that each chemical compound always has the same formula. If formula is different, it is a different compound, with different properties.

- ◆ CO_2 is carbon dioxide, the harmless gas that you breathe out and plants take in.

- ◆ CO is carbon monoxide, a deadly poisonous gas.

d How many of each type of atom are there in the compound sulphuric acid, H_2SO_4?

e Why can't sodium use the symbol 'S'?

Spelling it out

It is easy to get confused when thinking about atoms and compounds. Here is a model that might help.

- ◆ Atoms are like the letters of the alphabet.

- ◆ Compounds are like words.

Think how many different words, each with its own specific meaning, you can make from just 26 letters. You should now realise just how many different types of compounds can be made from 100 atoms!

Questions

1 Are the following elements or compounds?

　a Iron oxide, Fe_2O_3

　b Iodine, I_2

　c Ethene, C_2H_4

2 Phosphoric acid is a compound made from three hydrogen atoms joined to one phosphorus (P) atom and four oxygen atoms. What is the chemical formula of phosphoric acid?

3 If you burn magnesium in air, the magnesium combines with oxygen in the simple ratio of 3Mg:2O by mass. You can also make magnesium oxide by reacting magnesium with steam. What is the Mg:O mass ratio in magnesium oxide made using steam?

Some elements and their symbols

Single letters (always capital)	Double letters (first letter capital)
H = hydrogen	He = helium
C = carbon	Mg = magnesium
N = nitrogen	Al = aluminium
O = oxygen	Si = silicon
S = sulphur	Cl = chlorine
I = iodine	Br = bromine
	Ca = calcium
	Zn = zinc

Some 'oddities'

Na = sodium, from the Latin name *natrium*

K = potassium, from the Latin name *kalium*

Fe = iron, iron and steel are the *ferrous* metals

Cu = copper

Pb = lead, *plumbers* used to work with lead pipes

Ag = silver, *argent* is French for coins – 'silver'

Au = gold, from the Latin name *aurium*

Hg = mercury, from the Latin name *hydrargyrum*, which means liquid silver

---

Summary

- All substances are made of atoms.

- There are about 100 different types of atoms.

- A substance which contains only one type of atom is called an element.

- Each element has its own symbol.

- A substance made from different types of atoms joined together is called a compound.

Working out the formula

A chemical formula tells you how many of each type of atom there is in a compound. But why do the compounds form in the way that they do?

For example, why is there only one chlorine atom in sodium chloride (NaCl) but two chlorine atoms in magnesium chloride ($MgCl_2$)?

The answer is that the atoms of different elements can make different number of chemical bonds. It is as if the atoms had different numbers of 'arms' that they could use to join up with 'handshake' bonds. To make a compound, you must use up all of the 'arms'.

Sodium and chlorine have just one 'arm' each, so they join in a simple one to one compound. Magnesium has two 'arms', so one magnesium atom can hold on to two chlorine atoms.

Oxygen also has two 'arms'. Magnesium oxide is just MgO as the atoms join with a 'double handshake'. But oxygen can hold onto two sodium atoms, so sodium oxide is Na_2O.

a Calcium chloride is $CaCl_2$. How many 'bond arms' must calcium have? What is the formula for calcium oxide?

b Potassium oxide is K_2O. How many 'bond arms' must potassium have? Is potassium chloride KCl or KCl_2?

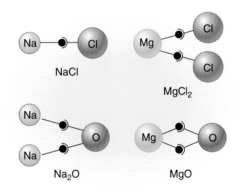

The simple 'handshake' model for bonding can help you work out the formulae of some compounds.

Charge it!

Atoms do not have arms, of course. The way that metals and non-metals form compounds is by becoming charged particles called **ions**.

- ◆ Metals such as sodium and magnesium form **positive ions**.
- ◆ Non-metals such as oxygen and chlorine form **negative ions**.

These opposite charges are attracted to one another, to form an **ionic bond** (see page 50).

In a compound, the charges balance out.

The 2+ charge on a magnesium ion could be balanced out by:

- ◆ one 2– oxygen ion (in MgO); or
- ◆ two 1– chlorine ions (in $MgCl_2$).

c Use the figures in the tables to work out the formulae of silver chloride, zinc oxide and zinc chloride.

d Sometimes groups of atoms form complicated ions that can react with metals. What are the formulae of copper(II) sulphate and potassium nitrate?

1+
sodium (Na^+)	potassium (K^+)
silver (Ag^+)	ammonium (NH_4^+)

2+
magnesium (Mg^{2+})	calcium (Ca^{2+})
lead (Pb^{2+})	iron(II) (Fe^{2+})
copper(II) (Cu^{2+})	zinc (Zn^{2+})

3+
aluminium (Al^{3+})	iron(III) (Fe^{3+})

1–
chlorine (Cl^-)	bromine (Br^-)
iodine (I^-)	nitrate (NO_3^-)
hydroxide (OH^-)	

2–
oxygen (O^{2-})	sulphur (S^{2-})
sulphate (SO_4^{2-})	

The charge on the ion is the same as the 'number of arms' in the simple 'handshake' model.

Chemical reactions and equations

When chemical reactions occur, new compounds are formed as atoms are combined in different ways. These reactions can be written as **word equations**, to show what is happening.

The chemicals you start with (the **reactants**) are written on the left. The chemicals that form (the **products**) are written on the right.

  reactants → products

For example, when the metal magnesium burns in air, magnesium atoms and oxygen atoms are the reactants. They combine to form the new compound magnesium oxide, which is the only product in this reaction. So:

  magnesium + oxygen → magnesium oxide

e Iron reacts with sulphur to form iron sulphide. Write this as a word equation.

Burning magnesium gives off light and heat as the chemical reaction takes place.

Symbol equations

You can get even more information about the chemical reaction if you use the symbols and formulae. Here is the symbol equation for the magnesium/oxygen reaction:

  $2Mg(s) + O_2(g) → 2MgO(s)$

This shows that two magnesium atoms react with one oxygen molecule (which contains two atoms of oxygen) to form two lots of magnesium oxide.

The symbols in brackets tell you that magnesium and magnesium oxide are solids (s), but oxygen is a gas (g). These useful 'state symbols' are:

  ◆ (s) solid;   ◆ (g) gas;   ◆ (l) liquid;

  ◆ (aq) aqueous solution (a solution in water).

f Describe the following reaction in words:

  $Mg(s) + Cl_2(g) → MgCl_2(s)$

Questions

1 Carbon (C) burns in oxygen (O_2) to form carbon dioxide gas (CO_2).

  a Write this as a word equation, then use the symbols to write a symbol equation.

  b Add 'state symbols' to complete the equation.

2 Using either the 'bond arms' model or the idea of ionic bonds, work out the formulae of the following compounds:

  a potassium chloride   **b** silver oxide

  c aluminium chloride   **d** aluminium oxide

3 Hydrogen can form a positive ion, like a metal. The formula of hydrochloric acid is HCl. What is the charge on a hydrogen ion?

Summary

• You can work out the formula of a simple compound if you know how many bonds each element can make.

• For metal/non-metal compounds you can work out the formula if you know the charge on each ion.

• Chemical reactions can be shown as word equations or symbol equations.

8:4 Balancing equations

Keeping in balance

Hydrochloric acid and sodium hydroxide react to make sodium chloride and water.

If you weigh the hydrochloric acid and sodium hydroxide before and after they have been mixed, you will find that there is no change in mass. This follows a fundamental rule of chemistry:

mass of reactants = mass of products

This makes sense, because you still have the same number of atoms – you have just rearranged them! If you keep this in mind, you will find chemical equations easy to follow.

a 20 g of sodium hydroxide and hydrochloric acid produced 15 g of salt. How much water was formed?

Balanced chemical equations

As you have seen, you can write the reaction down using the chemical formulae of the reactants and products instead of the names. If you do this, you must make sure that there are the same number of each type of atom on the two sides of the equation.

$$HCl + NaOH \rightarrow NaCl + H_2O$$

b There are two hydrogen atoms in water. Where did they come from in this reaction?

Balancing equations

To write a balanced chemical equation, you need to follow a series of steps in the correct order. How many steps it takes depends on the reaction. For some reactions, writing a balanced equation can be quite simple.

For example, calcium carbonate breaks down when it is heated to give calcium oxide and carbon dioxide.

Step 1: Write a word equation

calcium carbonate → calcium oxide + carbon dioxide

Step 2: Find out (or work out) the formulae for the reactants and products. Write a symbol equation.

$$CaCO_3 \rightarrow CaO + CO_2$$

Step 3: Count the atoms on each side. Do they balance?

$$1 \times Ca, 1 \times C, 3 \times O \rightarrow 1 \times C, 1 \times C, 3 \times O$$

The answer is yes!

Step 4: Now add the 'state symbols' to complete the equation.

$$CaCO_3(s) \rightarrow CaO(s) + CO_2(g)$$

hydrochloric acid + sodium hydroxide → sodium chloride + water

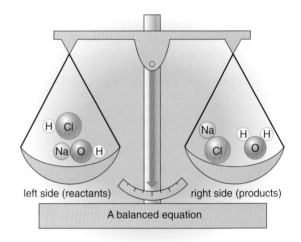

left side (reactants)   right side (products)

A balanced equation

Making salt and water from acid and alkali – it's just a case of rearrangement!

Calcium carbonate breaks down when it is heated.

What if it doesn't balance?

Not all equations balance quite so easily.

For example, sulphuric acid reacts with sodium hydroxide, making sodium sulphate and water.

$$\text{sulphuric acid} + \text{sodium hydroxide} \rightarrow \text{sodium sulphate} + \text{water}$$

Step 1: If you put in the formulae for these chemicals, the numbers do not add up.

$$H_2SO_4 + NaOH \rightarrow Na_2SO_4 + H_2O$$

Step 2: There are two sodium atoms on the right, but just one on the left. You need two lots of sodium hydroxide to start with. Put a large '2' in front of the formula for NaOH.

$$H_2SO_4 + \mathbf{2}NaOH \rightarrow Na_2SO_4 + H_2O$$

Step 3: Now there are four hydrogens on the left but only two on the right. Two molecules of water balances the equation!

$$H_2SO_4 + 2NaOH \rightarrow Na_2SO_4 + \mathbf{2}H_2O$$

d Balance this equation:

$$Ca(OH)_2 + HCl \rightarrow CaCl_2 + H_2O$$

Note: $Ca(OH)_2$ means one Ca with two lots of (OH).

Equations for electrolysis

If you melt sodium chloride and pass an electric current through it, you can split it up into sodium and chlorine. You can write this as a simple equation:

$$\text{sodium chloride} \xrightarrow{\text{electrolysis}} \text{sodium } + \text{ chlorine}$$
$$2NaCl \qquad \rightarrow \qquad 2Na + Cl_2$$

Alternatively, you could show what is happening at the electrodes. This gives you a clearer picture of what is going on.

Sodium chloride is made from ions. When you melt it, it splits up into separate positive sodium ions (Na^+) and negative chlorine ions (Cl^-). These ions are attracted to the electrode with the opposite charge, where the charges are cancelled out.

The positive metal ions go to the negative electrode. The single positive charge on a sodium ion is cancelled out as it picks up an electron:

$$Na^+ + e^- \rightarrow Na$$

The negative chloride ions go to the positive electrode, where they lose their extra electrons. You need two chloride ions to make a chlorine molecule.

$$2Cl^- \rightarrow Cl_2 + 2e^-$$

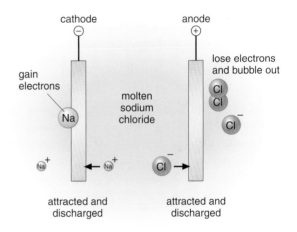

Questions

1 When magnesium (Mg) burns in air it reacts with oxygen (O_2) to form magnesium oxide (MgO). Write a balanced equation for this reaction.

2 Aluminium is made by the electrolysis of molten aluminium oxide. Balance these equations.

   a At the anode: $O^{2-} \rightarrow O_2 + e^-$

   b At the cathode: $Al^{3+} + e^- \rightarrow Al$

Summary

- In a chemical reaction, the mass of the products is equal to the mass of the reactants.

- In a balanced equation, you must have the same number of each type of atom on each side.

- For electrolysis, you can write the equation for each electrode separately.

8:5 Inside the atom

There are millions of different kinds of chemicals in the world. All these chemicals are made from just 100 different kinds of atoms, arranged in different ways. To understand how these atoms join together to make all these different chemicals, you will need to know how the atoms themselves are made.

Sub-atomic particles

Atoms are made from just three kinds of particles, arranged in a particular way. These sub-atomic particles are called **protons**, **neutrons** and **electrons**.

a What form of energy involves the flow of electrons along wires?

At the very centre of an atom is the **nucleus**. The nucleus contains the protons and the neutrons. The protons carry a positive electrical charge. The neutrons are electrically neutral.

The nucleus is very small compared to an atom, so how does the atom get its shape? Whizzing around the nucleus are even smaller particles, the electrons. Electrons carry a negative electrical charge.

When you look at a TV picture, there is just a moving dot of light, but it moves so fast that you see a complete picture. In a similar way, the electrons move so fast around the nucleus that they make an outer shell for the atom. This outer shell gives the atom its shape. But, surprising as it may seem, most of every atom is just empty space!

b In 1911 a scientist called Rutherford fired tiny radioactive particles at a thin sheet of gold. He was very surprised to find that most of the particles passed straight through! How could this happen?

More about sub-atomic particles

As well as having different electrical charges, the different particles have different masses. These are too small to usefully measure in grams, so they are simply compared to the mass of a hydrogen atom. On this model, protons and neutrons both have a mass of 1, but electrons are so small that their mass is usually ignored!

c What is the mass of the helium atom shown in the diagram?

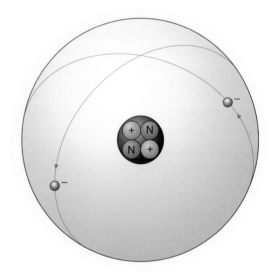

An atom of helium has two negatively charged electrons whizzing around a nucleus. The nucleus is made of two positively charged protons and two neutrons.

	Mass	Charge
proton	1	positive
neutron	1	neutral
electron	0	negative

Atoms of the same element always have the same number of protons in the nucleus. If the number of protons is different then it is a different element!

Putting atoms in order

The number of protons an element has is called its **proton number** or **atomic number**. We use the symbol Z for the proton number.

- ◆ Hydrogen is the simplest atom, with just one proton, so it is atomic number 1.

- ◆ Helium has two protons, so it is atomic number 2.

- ◆ Uranium has ninety-two protons, so it is atomic number 92.

The more protons there are in the nucleus, the more neutrons are needed. Neutrons act like a kind of sub-atomic packaging that helps to keep the nucleus stable. So the higher the atomic number, the bigger the mass of the atom compared to hydrogen. You can find this **relative atomic mass** (symbol: A_r) by adding the number of protons and neutrons together.

Remember, the atomic number (Z) tells you the number of protons, while the relative atomic mass (A_r) tells you the overall mass. To find the number of neutrons you must take the smaller number from the bigger one!

Finally, remember that atoms are neutral overall. So the number of electrons whizzing around an atom is equal to the number of protons in its nucleus.

d For each of the six elements in the photograph, state how many protons, neutrons and electrons there are in an atom.

The atomic number and relative atomic mass of some common elements.

Isotopes

For atoms of most elements, the number of neutrons in the atoms is usually the same. Some elements, however, have different numbers of neutrons. These alternative versions are called **isotopes**.

For example, chlorine always has 17 protons. But chlorine atoms can have either 18 or 20 neutrons. As the '18' isotope is three times as common as the '20' isotope, the average relative atomic mass comes out as 35.5!

e Most carbon has an A_r of 12. But carbon has another isotope, with an A_r of 14. In what way is this similar to and different from the carbon in the photograph above?

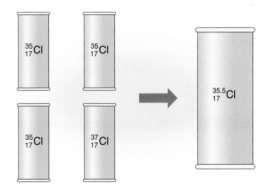

The two isotopes of chlorine.

Questions

1 Aluminium has 13 protons and 14 neutrons. What is its atomic number and its relative atomic mass?

2 Bromine has two isotopes, ^{79}Br and ^{81}Br, but bromine is usually given as ^{80}Br. What does this tell you about the relative amounts of each isotope found naturally?

3 How can you tell that rubidium ($A_r = 85.5$) has more than one common isotope?

Summary

- Atoms are made from three sub-atomic particles: protons, neutrons and electrons.

- Protons (positive) and neutrons (neutral) are found in the nucleus.

- Electrons (negative) whiz around the nucleus.

- Isotopes are versions of the same element, with different numbers of neutrons.

8:6 Electrons rule chemistry

Energy levels (electron shells)

The electrons whiz round the nucleus of an atom forming an 'electron cloud'. This electron cloud gives the atom its shape. But the electron cloud is not haphazard. The electrons can only fit into certain zones. These zones are called **energy levels** or **electron shells**.

In a neutral atom the number of electrons is the same as the number of protons. These electrons normally fit into levels closest to the nucleus. For the first 20 elements, the pattern is a simple one:

◆ level one: 1 or 2 electrons only;

◆ level two: up to 8 electrons;

◆ level three: up to 8 electrons;

◆ level four: 1 or 2 electrons fit in, then the pattern becomes more complicated.

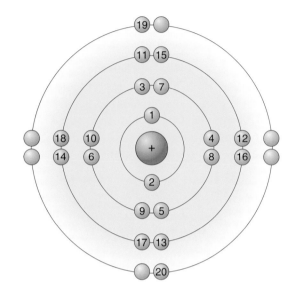

How the first 20 electrons fit in the energy levels. You can mark a cross (×) to show the position of an electron.

If you know the number of electrons in the atoms, you can work out how the electrons are arranged in the levels.

a How many electrons does an atom of magnesium have ($Z = 12$)? How many electrons will fit in each energy level?

This is called the **electronic structure** of the atom. It can be drawn on a 'flat' version of the atom like this, or written as the numbers in each level, in turn.

Filling them up

◆ Hydrogen's single electron fits in the first level.

◆ Helium's two electrons fill up the first level completely.

◆ At number 3, lithium's third electron must start the next level.

◆ Carbon is number 6, so it half-fills the second level.

◆ Neon has ten electrons, which fill up levels one and two.

◆ Sodium starts a third level for its 11th electron.

◆ Elements number 12 to 18 fill up level three.

◆ Calcium, at number 20, is the last element to show this simple pattern. Its last two electrons are found in the fourth level.

b Draw the electron structures of fluorine ($Z = 9$), aluminium ($Z = 13$), sulphur ($Z = 16$), argon ($Z = 18$) and potassium ($Z = 19$).

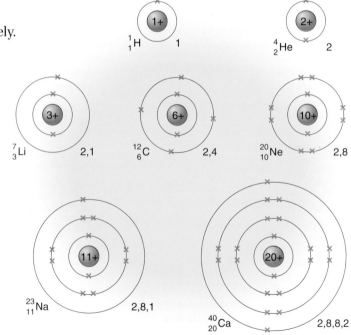

Electrons usually fit into the lowest available energy levels.

Making compounds

Most substances are compounds. It is the electrons in the outer energy levels of the atoms that decide how a compound is formed.

◆ A compound made of metals and non-metals is usually made by a process of 'give and take'.

◆ A compound made of just non-metals has to make do with sharing.

Give and take

Sodium is a metal. Sodium ($Z = 11$) has just one electron in its outer shell. If it loses this electron, it becomes an ion with a single positive charge. The sodium ion has a single positive charge because it has 11 protons but only 10 electrons. This ion is smaller than the atom, as it has one fewer electron shells.

c Explain why a sodium ion has an overall positive charge.

Chlorine is a non-metal. Chlorine ($Z = 17$) has seven electrons in its outer shell. It can gain an extra electron to form an ion with a single negative charge. The chlorine ion has 17 protons but has 18 electrons.

d Explain why a chlorine ion has a negative charge.

All metals are able to lose electrons and form positive ions. Reactive non-metals can gain electrons and form negative ions.

Oppositely charged ions will attract each other and can join together to form **ionic compounds**. An example is sodium chloride.

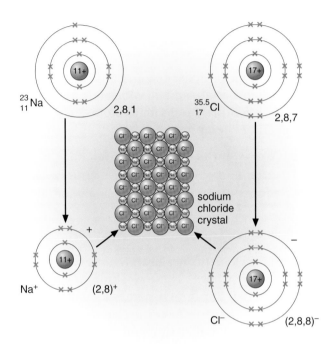

Sodium chloride (common salt) is built from ions.

Sharing

Non-metals can form compounds on their own by sharing outer electrons rather than making ions. These compounds are called **covalent compounds**. Many covalent compounds form small particles called molecules.

Sodium chloride is an ionic compound.
Water is a covalent compound.

e Is carbon dioxide likely to be an ionic compound or a covalent compound? Explain your answer.

Questions

1 a Write out the electronic structure of the first 20 elements in the form

'Number 20: 2, 8, 8, 2'.

b Use the data sheets at the back of the book to add the names and symbols for these elements.

2 a Why does a sodium atom get smaller when it becomes an ion?

b How do chlorine ions differ from sodium ions?

Summary

• Electrons are arranged in energy levels (electron shells) around the nucleus.

• The way the electrons are arranged controls the way an atom reacts to form compounds.

• Metals form ionic compounds with non-metals after a 'give and take' of electrons.

• Non-metals share electrons to form covalent compounds.

8:7 More about ionic compounds

Happiness is a full energy level

Helium ($Z = 2$), neon ($Z = 10$) and argon ($Z = 18$) belong to a family of elements called the **noble gases**. They have this name because they keep to themselves and do not join in chemical reactions at all. What is it that makes them so stable and unreactive?

If you look at the electronic structure of the noble gases, you will see that they all have full outer energy levels. This appears to be a very stable arrangement, which is not easy to upset. Or to put it in a less scientific way, as far as atoms are concerned, 'happiness is a full outer energy level'!

a Atoms of the element krypton have eight electrons in their outer energy level. What predictions can you make about the properties of krypton? Explain your answer.

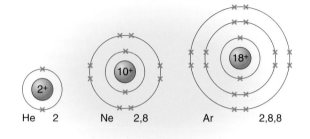

He 2   Ne 2,8   Ar 2,8,8

The full outer energy levels of the noble gases makes them very unreactive.

Why form ions?

Metallic elements usually have just one or two electrons in their outer energy level. These electrons are quite 'loose' and are easily lost, so that the atom becomes a smaller ion with one less energy level. Ions like this have the electronic structure of a noble gas, so they are very stable. But, unlike the noble gases:

◆ their electric charges are not balanced;

◆ they have an overall positive charge.

b Atoms of zinc have two electrons in their outer energy level. Is zinc a metal or non-metal? What sort of ion does zinc form?

Many non-metallic elements have five, six or seven electrons in their outer energy level. They can capture extra electrons to fill the energy level and so form an ion. These ions also have the electronic structure of a noble gas, so they are very stable. However:

◆ their electric charges are not balanced;

◆ they have an overall negative charge.

c Atoms of iodine have seven electrons in their outer energy level. Is iodine a metal or non-metal? What sort of ion does iodine form?

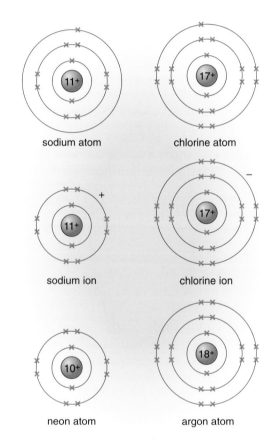

sodium atom   chlorine atom

sodium ion   chlorine ion

neon atom   argon atom

Ions have the electronic structure of a noble gas. They also have electrical charges, so they can make ionic bonds.

The atomic dating agency

You may have spotted the obvious connection. Metallic atoms want to lose electrons so that they can become stable ions. Non-metallic elements want to gain electrons so that they too can become stable ions. They are made for each other! The oppositely charged ions then attract one another to form a strong **ionic bond**.

d How many iodine ions could be made by one zinc atom?

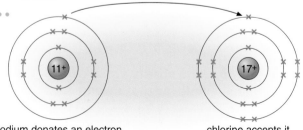

sodium donates an electron   chlorine accepts it

Charges in balance

The overall charges in an ionic compound must balance out.

- A sodium ion (Na^+) joins with just one chlorine ion (Cl^-) in NaCl.

- Magnesium ($Z = 12$) loses two electrons and so forms a double positive ion (Mg^{2+}). This can balance out two single negative chlorine ions to form magnesium chloride, $MgCl_2$.

e Calcium ($Z = 20$) has a structure similar to magnesium. Draw energy level diagrams to show how calcium chloride forms.

Oxygen ($Z = 8$) has six electrons in its outer energy level. It can gain two electrons to form an ion with a double negative charge. So when magnesium and oxygen form a compound, you only need one oxygen ion for every magnesium ion. The formula of magnesium oxide is MgO.

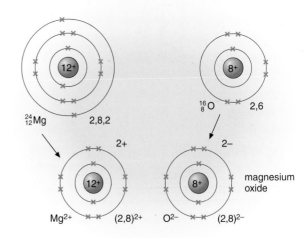

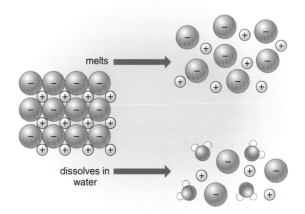

Giant ionic structures

Ionic compounds such as sodium chloride stack up in a regular way to form a **giant ionic structure** (an **ionic lattice**). Every ion is held in place by strong electrostatic forces from its oppositely charged neighbours. These strong forces are called ionic bonds.

Ionic compounds:

- have high melting points and high boiling points;

- are quite hard but brittle, so they shatter easily;

- do not conduct electricity when solid because the charged particles are held tightly in place;

- will conduct electricity if the ions are freed from the lattice, by melting or dissolving in water, and the charged particles themselves carry the current.

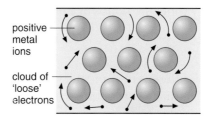

Ionic compounds will only conduct electricity if their ions are freed up by melting or dissolving.

Metals

Metal atoms can also stack up in a regular way to make a giant structure. All metal atoms have 'loose electrons' in their outermost electron energy levels. In the metal structure these outer energy levels merge and the electrons are free to move throughout the material. That is why metals conduct electricity.

positive metal ions

cloud of 'loose' electrons

This 'cloud' of electrons also binds the structure together in a strong but flexible way. If a force is applied to the atoms, they can slide over one another without breaking. This is why metals can be beaten or stretched into shape. The electrons are also responsible for heat conduction.

f How could you tell a metal from an ionic compound using a hammer?

Question

1 Draw up a table to compare the properties of ionic solids and metals, in terms of melting points, electrical conductivity, hardness and flexibility.

Summary

- A full outer electron energy level gives stability.

- Ions form when atoms lose or gain electrons to reach this stable state.

- Ionic compounds often form giant structures.

- Metals are held together by electron clouds.

8:8 Share and share alike

Fair shares

Non-metals cannot form ionic compounds on their own, but they can get together to share electrons. When non-metals share electrons, the electron energy levels join together in the same way that bubbles sometimes join up in groups of two or three.

When the electron energy levels join, the two atoms form a strong chemical bond called a **covalent bond**. This is how molecules form.

a Many gases such as hydrogen and oxygen usually exist as 'double bubble' molecules (H_2, O_2). What kind of bonding is there within these molecules?

Chlorine atoms are just one electron short of a full outer energy level, so they need to share just one pair of electrons to form Cl_2 molecules. This is a **single covalent bond**.

b Draw an electron structure diagram for an H_2 molecule. (Remember, the first energy level can only take two electrons.)

Oxygen atoms are two electrons short of a full energy level, so they share two electron pairs. The O_2 molecule has a **double covalent bond**.

The bonds in these molecules can be shown in different ways. You can show how the outer energy level electrons are shared, or simply show the bonds as linking bars.

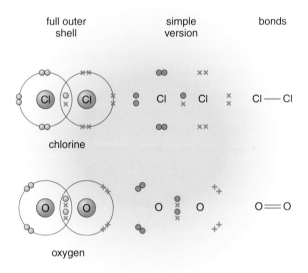

Chlorine and oxygen molecules shown in different ways. Electrons from one atom are shown as 'dots' and electrons from the other are shown as 'crosses'.

Covalent compounds

Atoms of different non-metallic elements can also join together to make compounds.

◆ Chlorine can form a single covalent bond with hydrogen to make hydrogen chloride (HCl).

◆ Oxygen needs to share two electrons and so can join with two hydrogen atoms to make hydrogen oxide – better known as water (H_2O).

c Draw an electron structure diagram for an HCl molecule.

Nitrogen is three electrons short of a full outer energy level. It can share a pair of electrons with each of three hydrogen atoms to make an ammonia molecule (NH_3).

Carbon is four electrons short of a full outer energy level. It can share a pair of electrons with each of four hydrogen atoms to make a methane molecule (CH_4).

d Carbon can also combine with two oxygen atoms, forming two double covalent bonds. Draw an electron structure diagram for a CO_2 molecule.

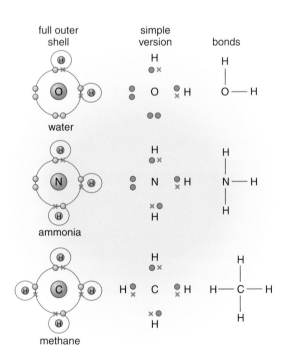

Small molecules

The bonds within covalent molecules are very strong. However, as the molecules have no electric charges, there are only very weak forces between them.

Because of this, molecular compounds have low melting points and low boiling points. Small covalent molecules form gases at room temperature, while larger covalent molecules may be liquids or soft solids.

e Sulphur reacts with oxygen to form small sulphur dioxide (SO_2) molecules. Is sulphur dioxide likely to be a solid, a liquid or a gas?

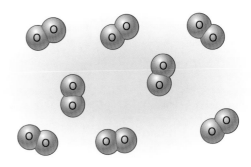

Oxygen is a gas at room temperature because there are only weak forces between the molecules.

Giant covalent structures

Some non-metals can make giant structures by sharing electrons. In these, every atom is joined to its neighbour by a strong covalent bond. The materials they form have high melting points and high boiling points, forming hard and strong solids at room temperature. Carbon can form diamond and graphite like this.

f Silicon and oxygen form silicon dioxide (silica), which has a giant covalent structure. Suggest what the properties of silica are likely to be.

Diamond and graphite have some very different properties. This is because the carbon atoms are joined in different arrangements.

In diamond, each carbon atom has all four of its outer electrons paired up in covalent bonds with neighbouring atoms. This makes a rigid and hard three-dimensional structure. As there are no 'spare' electrons, diamond does not conduct electricity.

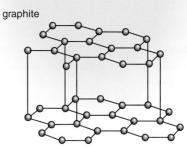

diamond

graphite

Diamond and graphite are very different. It's just down to the arrangement of carbon atoms.

In graphite, the carbon atoms are arranged in two-dimensional sheets, with each atom joined to just three neighbours. This leaves one electron 'unpaired' in each atom. These electrons can be made to move, so graphite does conduct electricity. Also, there are only weak forces between the carbon sheets. Graphite as a whole is a weak solid because the sheets can slide over one another.

g Pencil 'lead' is made from graphite. Why does a pencil leave a trail of carbon when rubbed across paper?

Questions

1 Fluorine ($Z = 9$) can form an F_2 molecule by sharing one pair of electrons.

  a Draw an outer energy level electron diagram for this molecule.

  b Is fluorine likely to be a solid or a gas at room temperature?

2 Rocks such as granite are made from silicate minerals. From what you know about rocks like this, what kind of internal structure must silicate minerals have?

Summary

- Atoms of non-metals can combine by sharing electrons in covalent bonds.

- Small molecules made from covalently bonded atoms are likely to form gases because the forces between the molecules are weak.

- Some non-metals form giant covalent structures where every bond is a strong covalent bond.

- Giant covalent structures are hard and have high melting points.

8:9 Ordering the elements

Looking for patterns

a What pattern can you see in this jumble of black and white?

When you first turned this page, the black and white picture probably appeared to be a complete jumble. It is, in fact, a picture of dalmatians in the snow. Now that you know that, it probably looks obvious!

Early chemists faced an even worse problem as they searched for patterns in the mass of information they were uncovering about the different elements.

◆ They did not know how many elements there were, so they did not know how much information was still missing.

◆ They had no idea why elements were different, because the structure of the atom had not yet been discovered.

It is only thanks to their pioneering work that you are now in the fortunate position of knowing what to look for!

Ordering the elements

A few elements have been known for thousands of years – gold, copper, sulphur and mercury for example. However, most of the 90 elements that occur naturally on Earth were only discovered in the nineteenth century.

Some early chemists found that elements could be grouped in families – the reactive non-metals chlorine, bromine and iodine, for example. However, it was only when it became possible to arrange the elements in order of increasing relative atomic mass (A_r) that real progress was made. Once they did this, a pattern started to emerge.

b What pattern can you see in this list of elements?

The first 20

When the first 20 elements (by relative atomic mass) are listed in order, they show a repeating pattern. This pattern was first spotted by the British chemist John Newlands in 1864. He compared this to the repetition of notes on a musical scale and called it the 'law of octaves'. The chart clearly shows this repetition, particularly in the very reactive gas/unreactive gas/very reactive metal sequence that appears three times (1/2/3, 9/10/11, 17/18/19). Between these sequences the pattern is not quite so clear, though carbon and silicon are similar.

c Which elements were missing from Newland's scale (shown right)?

Z	A_r	Element	Properties
1	1	hydrogen	very reactive gas
2	4	helium	unreactive gas
3	7	lithium	very reactive metal
4	9	beryllium	reactive metal
5	11	boron	non-metal
6	12	carbon	non-metal
7	14	nitrogen	non-metal
8	16	oxygen	reactive gas
9	19	fluorine	very reactive gas
10	20	neon	unreactive gas
11	23	sodium	very reactive metal
12	24	magnesium	reactive metal
13	27	aluminium	metal
14	28	silicon	non-metal
15	31	phosphorus	non-metal
16	32	sulphur	reactive non-metal
17	35.5	chlorine	very reactive gas
18	40	argon	unreactive gas
19	39	potassium	very reactive metal
20	40	calcium	reactive metal

The first 20 elements.

Mendeleev's table

The simple pattern described above breaks down after the first 20 elements. Because of this, Newlands' ideas were not taken up immediately by other scientists. But just 5 years later, in 1869, the Russian chemist Dimitri Mendeleev extended these ideas. He arranged the similar elements in vertical groups on a table.

Mendeleev's table also had its problems. He needed to put iodine out of position compared to its relative atomic mass in order to keep it in the same group as chlorine. Many scientists did not like this.

d Which elements from the 'first 20' table are misplaced according to their relative atomic masses? Why didn't this pair cause problems for Mendeleev?

But Mendeleev had realised that some elements were missing. He thought they had not yet been discovered, so he left gaps in his table. He was so confident that he even used his table to predict the properties of these 'unknowns'. When some of the missing elements were discovered, the accuracy of his predictions gave great support to his ideas.

Dimitri Mendeleev (1834–1907).

Introducing the periodic table

A modern table of the first 20 elements arranged like this clearly shows the repeating (or periodic) pattern, and so is called the **periodic table** of the elements. Now that we understand the sub-atomic structure of the elements, they are arranged according to their proton number (Z). Ordered in this way, iodine and potassium are clearly in the correct positions.

The numbered rows across the table are called **periods**. They are numbered using Arabic numerals, from 1 to 4. The main vertical columns are called **groups**. They are also numbered using Arabic numerals, from 1 to 7, then 0 (sometimes Roman numerals are used, from I to VII, then 0 or VIII).

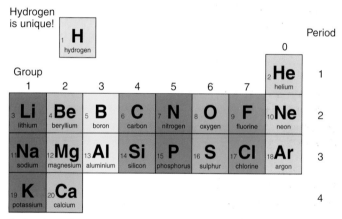
A simple periodic table for the first 20 elements.

Questions

1 **a** How many metals and how many non-metals are there in the first 20 elements?

  b How are they arranged?

2 Look at the full periodic table (see pages 56 and 57).

  a Krypton is below argon. Predict the properties of krypton.

  b Rubidium is below potassium. Predict the properties of rubidium.

3 Vanadium is a metal similar to iron. Mendeleev predicted that a 'missing' element would fit into his group below vanadium. The missing element was later discovered and found to be an iron-like metal, which was called molybdenum. Explain how this discovery helped to support Mendeleev's ideas.

Summary
- If the elements are arranged in order of relative atomic mass, a repeating pattern of properties can be seen.
- The modern periodic table arranges the elements into eight groups with similar properties, based on their proton number.

Here is the modern periodic table. This periodic table is ordered by proton number (Z). Beyond the first 20 elements, the simple pattern of vertical groups and horizontal periods is wedged apart by a block of metals with similar properties (the transition metals). The additional blocks that wedge in after elements 57 and 89 have been left out here, including element 92, uranium.

Example: uranium

relative atomic mass —— (A_r) 238

atomic number —— (Z) 92

U

a Which element is in group 4, period 2?

The electron link

The pattern of the periodic table links in precisely with the way the electrons are arranged around the atoms of each element. This was, of course, unknown to Mendeleev.

- ◆ The period number tells you how many energy levels the element has.

- ◆ The group number tells you how many electrons an element has in its outer energy level.

For example, all the elements in period 2 have two energy levels. Lithium is in group 1, so it only has one electron in its outer energy level; carbon is in group 4, so it has four electrons in its outer energy level; neon is in group 0, so it has eight electrons in its outer energy level, which is therefore full.

Hydrogen and helium stand alone, as the first energy level can only take two electrons. But as helium's two electrons give it a stable 'full energy level', it is usually put in with the other unreactive gases in group 0.

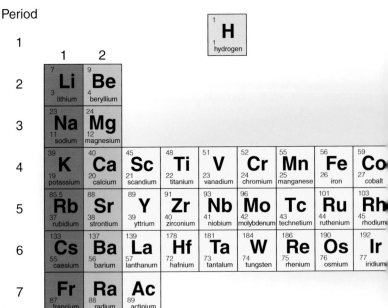

b How many electrons does iodine (I) have in its outer energy level?

c Which element has two electrons in its fifth energy level?

The power of the periodic table is the way it can be used to predict the chemical properties of elements. This is because the chemical properties of elements are governed by their electronic structure.

Metals

More than three-quarters of the elements are metals. Metals are found in the middle and on the left of the full periodic table.

Groups 1 and 2 contain very reactive but quite soft metals with low melting points. Examples are sodium (group 1) and calcium (group 2).

The block of metals that wedges in between groups 2 and 3 in period 4 is called the **transition metals**. This block contains the typical 'everyday' metals such as iron and copper. They are not as reactive as those in groups 1 and 2 but they are harder and stronger and have higher melting points.

d What kind of a metal is nickel (Ni)?

Elements between

Groups 3 to 5 have less clear-cut properties. You find non-metals at the top of these groups, but the elements grade into metals lower down the groups. The boundary between metals and non-metals steps down to the right. Elements on the boundary show intermediate properties. The boundary is shown as a thick line in the periodic table.

e Is bismuth (Bi) a metal or a non-metal?

				Group					0
				3	4	5	6	7	4 He 2 helium
				11 B 5 boron	12 C 6 carbon	14 N 7 nitrogen	16 O 8 oxygen	19 F 9 fluorine	20 Ne 10 neon
				27 Al 13 aluminium	28 Si 14 silicon	31 P 15 phosphorus	32 S 16 sulphur	35.5 Cl 17 chlorine	40 Ar 18 argon
59 Ni 28 nickel	63.5 Cu 29 copper	65 Zn 30 zinc	70 Ga 31 gallium	73 Ge 32 germanium	75 As 33 arsenic	79 Se 34 selenium	80 Br 35 bromine	84 Kr 36 krypton
106 Pd 46 palladium	108 Ag 47 silver	112 Cd 48 cadmium	115 In 49 indium	119 Sn 50 tin	122 Sb 51 antimony	128 Te 52 tellurium	127 I 53 iodine	131 Xe 54 xenon
195 Pt 78 platinum	197 Au 79 gold	201 Hg 80 mercury	204 Tl 81 thallium	207 Pb 82 lead	209 Bi 83 bismuth	Po 84 polonium	At 85 astatine	Rn 86 radon

Non-metals

Less than a quarter of the elements are non-metals. All the non-metals are found to the right of the periodic table.

Groups 6 and 7 contain reactive non-metals. Examples are oxygen (group 6) and chlorine (group 7). Elements in these groups are gases at the top of the groups but solids further down.

Group 0 contains the noble gases, a family of completely unreactive non-metals.

f Is fluorine (F) a solid, a liquid or a gas?

Questions

1 Describe the likely chemical properties of:

  a xenon (54)   **b** strontium (38)   **c** cobalt (27)

  d fluorine (9)   **e** rubidium (37)

2 Why is helium put in group 0, even though it only has two electrons in its outer shell?

3 To which group (or block) are the following elements likely to belong?

  a X is a silver-grey solid that conducts heat and electricity. It is very hard and will not melt in a Bunsen flame.

  b Y is a silvery solid that tarnishes in air. It fizzes in water giving off hydrogen gas. The atoms lose two electrons to form double positive ions.

  c Z is a brown liquid. Its atoms join together in pairs to form covalent molecules. Its atoms can also gain an electron to form a single negative ion.

Summary

- The periodic table has the elements arranged in groups according to their proton number.

- The pattern follows the arrangement of the electron structure of the atoms.

- Elements in the same group have similar properties.

- The periodic table is a powerful tool for predicting how elements react.

8:11 The noble gases

Group 0 (or 8) of the periodic table is the **noble gas** family. These are typical non-metals in many ways:

- they have very low melting points and low boiling points;
- when solid they are soft and crumbly;
- they do not conduct electricity.

But unlike many non-metals they are completely unreactive. You may think that such unreactive gases will not be of much use. However, sometimes their very inactivity is just what is required.

a How many electrons do group 0 atoms have in their outer energy level (helium excepted)?

Group 0

4	**He**
2	helium
20	**Ne**
10	neon
40	**Ar**
18	argon
84	**Kr**
36	krypton

Introducing the noble gases

Helium is not very soluble in water, even under pressure. This makes it an excellent substitute for nitrogen in the 'air' that deep-sea divers breathe. Nitrogen bubbling out of the blood can cause divers to suffer from the 'bends' when they return to the surface. Helium doesn't do this. It does have the side-effect of making you sound like Donald Duck when you talk!

Neon is most commonly used for another reason. Neon glows if an electric current is passed through it. Neon tubes can be coloured, making them ideal for flashy neon signs!

Argon is the cheapest of the noble gases to produce, because it makes up 1% of air. Argon is used inside ordinary light bulbs, to stop the filament from burning. Argon is also used to give an unreactive atmosphere for welding. Welding can be dangerous in air.

Krypton is used in lasers.

b Where do you use noble gases at home?

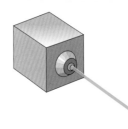

Helium and hydrogen

One other useful property of helium is that it has a very low density – much less than that of air. This makes helium a safe alternative to hydrogen for modern airships – or party balloons.

The explosive property of hydrogen is used as a test for hydrogen gas. If you put a lighted splint next to a tube of hydrogen, it will burn with a squeaky pop.

c Why is helium a better gas to use in airships than hydrogen?

Why are they unreactive?

All the noble gases have full outer electron energy levels. This gives the atoms great stability and so they will not try to lose, gain or share electrons. This means that they will not form chemical bonds at all.

d Draw the electron configurations of helium, neon and argon to show that they all have full outer energy levels.

Because the noble gases are so stable, they always exist as single atoms – they are **monatomic gases**. This is unlike the other gases in the atmosphere, which form molecules.

e Spot the noble gas in this close-up picture of air. (How can you tell?)

f Radon is also found in group 0. Draw a diagram showing a close-up view of pure radon gas.

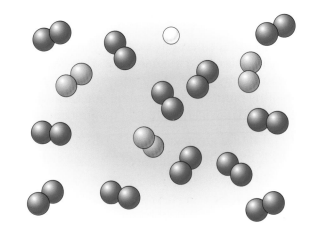

Discovering the noble gases

Air is approximately 20% oxygen (which is reactive) and 80% nitrogen (which is unreactive). But what was unsuspected until 100 years ago was that, hidden within the air, there was about 1% of a truly unreactive gas – what we now know as a noble gas.

In 1892, scientists discovered that nitrogen from the air was denser than nitrogen produced experimentally. They also found that they could react nitrogen with hot magnesium. When this reaction was performed with the 'nitrogen' from the air, about 1% of the gas would not react. That 1% was identified as other gases, which became known as the 'noble gases' because they were so unreactive.

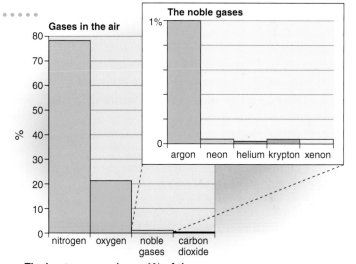

The inert gases make up 1% of the air – but most of that is argon.

g How much neon is there in the air? More than 1%, 1%, 0.1% or less than 0.1%?

h Why did it take so long to discover the noble gases?

i What was the clue that suggested that nitrogen from the air had something 'hidden' in it?

j What reaction finally left the noble gases on their own?

Questions

1 a What would happen to a light bulb when it was switched on if it were filled with air rather than argon?

   b Why is argon used rather than helium?

2 Peter had a test-tube full of hydrogen and another full of helium. How could he tell them apart?

3 Nitrogen and oxygen form *diatomic molecules* but argon is a *monatomic* gas. Explain the terms in italics.

Summary

- Group 0 contains the unreactive noble gases.
- Noble gas atoms have full outer energy levels, which makes them stable and unreactive.
- Noble gases exist as single atoms
- The noble gases have other properties that make them useful.
- Hydrogen gas 'pops' with a lighted splint.

8:12 The halogens

Group 7 of the periodic table contains a family of very reactive non-metals called the **halogens**. This group contains chlorine, bromine and iodine. Like other non-metals they have low melting points and low boiling points, form soft crumbly solids (if cooled down enough) and do not conduct electricity at all.

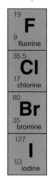

Group 7

Chlorine is a green gas that was used as a poison gas in World War I. Today its is used to kill germs in swimming baths and drinking water.

Bromine is a brown liquid that vaporises easily to form a brown gas.

Iodine is a soft, purple-black solid that gives off a purple vapour. Iodine stains the skin brown because it dissolves in skin oils. This reaction is used to develop fingerprints on paper.

a Consider iodine, bromine and chlorine. Are they solids, liquids or gases? What pattern can you see as you go up the group? Fluorine is the first member of the group. Is fluorine likely to be a solid, a liquid or a gas?

How they react

All the halogens are just one electron short of a full outer shell. This is what makes them reactive non-metals.

On their own, the halogens form simple molecules with two atoms joined by a single covalent bond.

The halogens can also share electrons in covalent bonds with other non-metals. For example, chlorine forms carbon tetrachloride with carbon.

b What type of bond would form between oxygen atoms and chlorine atoms? Explain your answer.

With metals, however, the halogens can capture electrons to form single negative ions. The halogens can form ionic compounds such as sodium chloride, Na^+Cl^-.

Note how the name of a halogen changes as it forms an ion:

◆ chlor**ine** forms chlor**ide** (Cl^-) ions;

◆ brom**ine** forms brom**ide** (Br^-) ions;

◆ iod**ine** forms iod**ide** (I^-) ions.

c What is the ion that will form from fluorine?

fluorine   chlorine   bromine   iodine

The halogens form coloured gases.

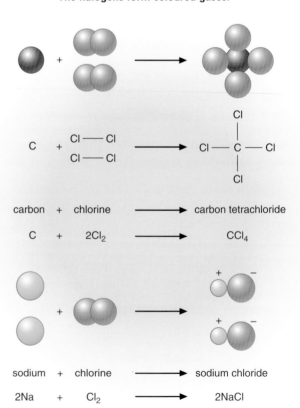

carbon + chlorine → carbon tetrachloride

$$C + 2Cl_2 \longrightarrow CCl_4$$

sodium + chlorine → sodium chloride

$$2Na + Cl_2 \longrightarrow 2NaCl$$

The halogens form covalent compounds with non-metals, but form ionic compounds with metals.

What's the trend?

The melting points and boiling points of the halogens get higher as you go down the group. That is why chlorine is a gas, bromine is a liquid and iodine is a solid at room temperature.

The halogens get less reactive as you go down the group. For example:

◆ chlorine and hydrogen explode together in sunlight;

◆ bromine and hydrogen only react if heated;

◆ iodine and hydrogen only partially react even if heated.

Because of this difference in reactivity, chlorine can displace bromine and iodine from solutions of their compounds. For example:

chlorine + sodium bromide → bromine + sodium chloride
(green)   (colourless)   (brown)   (colourless)
Cl_2 + $2NaBr$ → Br_2 + $2NaCl$

d Write an equation for the displacement reaction between bromine and sodium iodide.

e Could iodine displace chlorine from sodium chloride? Explain your answer.

Why this trend?

All the halogens have seven electrons in their outermost electron energy level. They react by capturing an extra electron and so form negative ions. The better they are at capturing an electron, the more reactive they will be.

At the top of the group, the atoms are small. Passing electrons can get close to the positive nucleus and so are easily captured. As you go down the group, the atoms get bigger and passing electrons cannot get so close to the nucleus, because they are shielded from the nucleus by the inner shells. Because of this, the bigger the atom the less easy it is for them to capture electrons and so the less reactive they are.

Questions

1 Draw the electron configuration for fluorine and chlorine.

2 What type of bonding would you expect to find in the following compounds:

a calcium bromide ($CaBr_2$)

b nitrogen tri-iodide (NI_3)

Explain your answers.

3 Sea water contains bromide ions. Bromine is made by bubbling chlorine gas through sea water. Explain why this reaction works.

4 Explain why fluorine is the most reactive halogen.

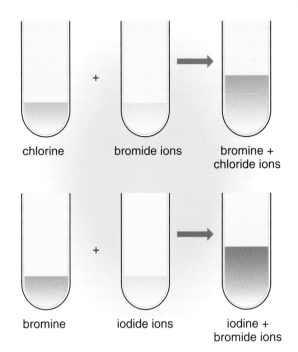

chlorine   bromide ions   bromine + chloride ions

bromine   iodide ions   iodine + bromide ions

Halogen displacement reactions. Iodine can form a dark brown solution in water.

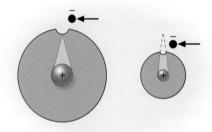

A smaller atom, a bigger force, so more chance of electron capture.

Summary

• Group 7 contains a family of very reactive non-metals with coloured vapours.

• As you go down the group, the elements change from gases, through a liquid to a solid.

• As you go down the group, the elements become less reactive.

• The larger atoms are less reactive as it is harder for them to capture an electron.

8:13 The alkali metals

The metals in group 1

Group 1 of the periodic table contains a family of very reactive metals. This group includes lithium, sodium and potassium.

Like all metals they:

◆ have a typical shiny metallic appearance when fresh (but they tarnish rapidly in air and have to be stored under oil);

◆ are good conductors of heat and electricity.

In other ways they are unlike ordinary 'everyday' metals such as iron or copper.

◆ They are very soft and can be cut easily with a knife.

◆ They have low densities and can float on water.

◆ For metals, they have very low melting points and low boiling points.

a Give two physical differences between lithium and iron.

Group 1 metals are very soft.

Positive ions

When group 1 metals react, each atom loses an electron to form a single charged positive ion. These ions can then form ionic compounds with non-metals. For example, lithium forms Li^+ ions when it reacts with oxygen:

lithium + oxygen → lithium oxide
$$4Li(s) + O_2(g) \rightarrow 2Li_2O(s)$$

b Oxygen ions are O^{2-}. Explain why there must be two lithium ions (Li^+) for every oxygen ion in lithium oxide.

The alkali metals

The elements in group 1 react with water. They form soluble metal hydroxides which give strongly alkaline solutions. Because of this, group 1 metals are also called the **alkali metals**. Hydrogen gas is given off during this reaction.

For example, with sodium:

sodium + water → sodium hydroxide + hydrogen
$$2Na(s) + 2H_2O(l) \rightarrow 2NaOH(aq) + H_2(g)$$

c What colour would pH paper turn in sodium hydroxide solution?

d What test would show that the gas is hydrogen?

e What do the symbols (s), (l), (aq) and (g) mean?

Lithium burns in air with a bright red flame.

Group 1

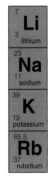

7	
Li	
3	lithium

23	
Na	
11	sodium

39	
K	
19	potassium

85.5	
Rb	
37	rubidium

What's the trend?

The alkali metals become softer and have lower melting points and lower boiling points down the group. They also get more and more reactive down the group. This is seen in the reaction with water.

Lithium fizzes steadily.

Sodium reacts so rapidly that the heat given out by the reaction melts the metal. The metal whizzes around the surface of the water. The hydrogen gas may catch fire, giving a yellow flame (because of the sodium).

Potassium reacts even more violently. The hydrogen catches fire instantly and burns with a lilac flame (because of the potassium).

f What do you think would happen if you put rubidium (Rb) in water?

Why this trend?

All the alkali metals have just one electron in their outermost energy level. They react by losing this electron, forming positive ions. The 'looser' this outer electron is, the more reactive they will be.

As you go down the group, the atoms get bigger as more and more energy levels are added. This means that the lone outer electron is further away from the positive nucleus that is holding it in place. The outer electron is increasingly screened by the inner electron shells. So the bigger the atom, the 'looser' the outer electron, and the more reactive the metal.

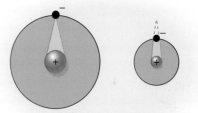

bigger atom, weaker force, 'looser' electron

Questions

1 In what way are group 1 metals 'typical metals'? In what ways are they unusual?

2 Using the equations on these pages as models, write balanced chemical equations for the reactions of:

   a sodium and oxygen;

   b potassium and water.

3 Group 2 metals lose two electrons to form double positive ions. Calcium atoms have more energy levels than magnesium atoms. Will calcium be more or less reactive than magnesium? Explain your reasoning.

Summary

- Group 1 contains soft but very reactive metals called the alkali metals.

- Group 1 metals react with water to give strongly alkaline solutions.

- Group 1 metals form single positive ions.

- Group 1 metals get more reactive down the group.

- The larger atoms lose their lone outer electron more easily and so are more reactive.

8:14 Metal halides

Making salt

Sodium is an alkali metal. It is dangerously reactive, fizzing violently in water, leaving a strongly alkaline solution.

a What gas is given off in this reaction?

Chlorine is a halogen. It is a dangerously reactive and deadly poisonous gas. If you put damp litmus paper in chlorine it turns red then bleaches to white as the chlorine reacts with the dye.

If you put hot sodium into a jar of chlorine you get a violent reaction as the two elements combine to form an ionic compound. A great amount of heat is given out.

b Is this reaction exothermic or endothermic?

So what is the result of combining these two dangerously reactive chemicals? You get a white crystalline solid which dissolves in water to give a neutral solution. It is *sodium chloride* – common salt. You need it in your diet and sprinkle it on your chips to improve the flavour...

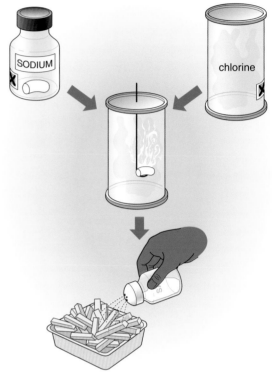

Salt can be made by combining the reactive elements sodium and chlorine.

Useful chemicals from salt

Salt occurs naturally in solution in the sea (**brine**) and in large beds of rock underground (**rock salt**).

When salt is dissolved in water, its splits up into its ions (Na^+ and Cl^-). These ions are free to move about. Because the ions can move about, brine conducts electricity. This is used in industry to split the brine apart by the process of **electrolysis**. The electrolysis of brine makes three useful products.

◆ *Chlorine gas* forms at the positive electrode. Chlorine is used to kill bacteria in swimming pools and drinking water. It is also used to make disinfectants, bleach and plastics such as PVC.

◆ *Hydrogen gas* forms at the negative electrode. Hydrogen is used to make ammonia for fertilisers, and change oils into fats for margarine and chocolate.

◆ *Sodium hydroxide* is left in solution. This strong alkali (also known as caustic soda) is used to make soap, paper and ceramics. It is also used to clean ovens!

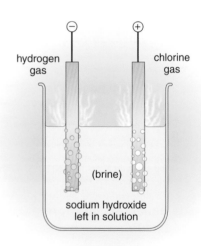

Three useful products are made by the electrolysis of brine.

$$\text{sodium chloride} + \text{water} \xrightarrow{\text{electrolysis}} \text{chlorine} + \text{hydrogen} + \text{sodium hydroxide}$$

$$2NaCl + 2H_2O \longrightarrow Cl_2 + H_2 + 2NaOH$$

c Why do the chloride ions go to the positive electrode?

Metal halides

Compounds of metals with halogens are called **halides**.

Sodium is a very reactive metal, so sodium halides are stable compounds that can only be broken apart by electrolysis.

Silver is an unreactive metal. Silver forms halides such as silver chloride, silver bromide and silver iodide. These compounds are much weaker than sodium chloride and can be split up easily.

Radioactivity, X-rays and even light can break up these silver halides. If you shine light onto a film containing a silver halide, the compound is reduced to silver. This leaves a dark spot where the light fell. The stronger the light, the darker the spot. For example:

$$\text{silver bromide} \xrightarrow{\text{light}} \text{silver} + \text{bromine}$$
$$\text{(colourless)} \qquad\qquad \text{(black)}$$

This reaction is used in black and white films and photographic papers. The first reaction produces a negative image – black where the light was brightest and white where no light fell.

d Why is it a waste to throw old X-ray photographs away?

Hydrogen halides

Halogens react with hydrogen to form covalent molecules called the *hydrogen halides*. The hydrogen halides form colourless gases which are very soluble in water and give acidic solutions.

Hydrogen burns in chlorine to give hydrogen chloride, a colourless gas.

$$\text{hydrogen} + \text{chlorine} \rightarrow \text{hydrogen chloride}$$
$$H_2 \quad + \quad Cl_2 \quad \rightarrow \quad\quad 2HCl$$

When hydrogen chloride dissolves in water it changes. The molecules split up and become ions instead. This makes a very strong acid – hydrochloric acid.

$$HCl \rightarrow H^+ + Cl^-$$

e What is unusual for a non-metal in the way that hydrogen ionises?

Questions

1 How could you tell chlorine gas and hydrogen chloride gas apart using damp pH paper?

2 Why can't you get sodium metal by electrolysing brine? (Think what would happen if you put sodium in water.)

3 Iodine is much less reactive than chlorine. Which compound would be easier to split apart, silver chloride or silver iodide? Explain your answer.

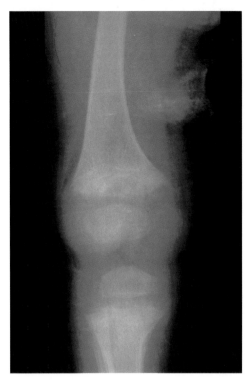

Silver halide films give a negative image with light – or X-rays!

Hydrochloric acid is made by dissolving hydrogen chloride gas in water.

Summary

- Halogens react with metals to form ionic compounds called halides.

- Three useful products can be made by the electrolysis of sodium chloride: chlorine, hydrogen and sodium hydroxide.

- Silver halides are used in photography.

- Hydrogen halides form acid solutions.

1 Water can be broken up into its component elements by passing electricity through it.

a What is the name of this process?

b Copy and complete the table.

Substance	Test for the substance
water	turns white anhydrous copper sulphate blue
hydrogen	
oxygen	

c State one important product that is made from hydrogen.

2 a Copy and complete this table, showing some non-metals and their compounds.

Element	Symbol	Electron structure	Formula of compound with hydrogen
carbon	C	(2,4)	
nitrogen	N	(2,5)	NH_3
oxygen	O	(2,6)	H_2O
fluorine	F	(2,7)	

b What type of bonding holds all these compounds together?

3 About 200 years ago, John Dalton was studying the way elements combined to form compounds. By careful experimentation, he found that the simple compounds he made always contained the elements in the same proportions. Dalton explained his results by the idea that elements were made of tiny particles that could not be broken – atoms.

Some students burnt magnesium in air (oxygen) and worked out how much of each element reacted to form magnesium oxide. Here are their results.

Student	Weighed mass of magnesium (g)	Weighed mass of magnesium oxide (g)	Calculated mass of oxygen (g)	Mg:O ratio
Derek	2.4	4.0	1.6	3:2
Jasmin	1.2	2.0	0.8	3:2
Petra	1.5	2.5	1.0	3:2

Show how Derek, Jasmin and Petra's results support Dalton's findings and explain how this leads on to the idea of atoms.

To gain full marks in this question you should write your ideas in good English. Put them into a sensible order and use the correct scientific words.

4 Sodium metal reacts with water, forming hydrogen gas and sodium hydroxide solution. The symbol equation shows the reaction.

a Balance the equation and add the state symbols.

$$Na + H_2O \rightarrow NaOH + H_2$$

b Sodium, along with chlorine, can be made by the electrolysis of molten sodium chloride.

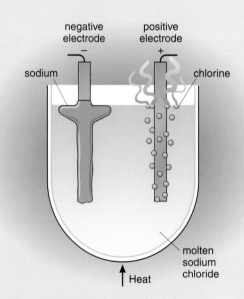

i Why must the sodium chloride be molten before electrolysis can work?

ii Complete these half-equations for the reactions.

at the negative electrode: $Na^+ + \boxed{} \rightarrow Na$

at the positive electrode: $2Cl^- \rightarrow Cl_2 + \boxed{}$

c Potassium is in group 1 of the periodic table and is in the period below sodium. Explain why potassium is more reactive than sodium.

5 The diagrams show the structure of two non-metal elements, diamond and oxygen.

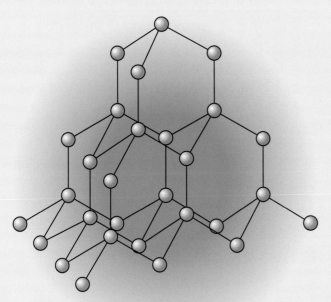

a i What type of bonding holds the carbon atoms together in diamond's giant structure?

   ii Explain why diamond has a very high melting point.

b i What kind of bonding (force) exists *within* the molecules of oxygen?

   ii What kind of bonding (force) exists *between* the molecules of oxygen?

   iii Explain why oxygen is a gas at room temperature.

6 a Draw the electronic structure of sulphur ($Z = 16$).

b How many electrons does sulphur need to fill its outer shell?

c What is the charge on a sulphur ion when it fills its outer shell?

d Which noble gas has the same electronic structure as the sulphur ion in part **c**?

e Draw the electronic structure of beryllium ion ($Z = 4$).

f How many electrons does beryllium need to lose to empty its outer shell?

g What is the charge on a beryllium ion when it has emptied its outer shell?

h Which noble gas has the same electronic structure as the beryllium ion in part **g**?

i What type of compound could beryllium and sulphur form?

j What would the formula be for the compound in part **i**?

7 a Draw the electronic structures of potassium ($Z = 19$) and fluorine ($Z = 9$).

b Use the diagrams from part **a** to show how potassium fluoride (KF) would form.

8 Describe the following in terms of electronic structure and electron transfer or electron sharing.

a Fluorine ($Z = 7$) and lithium ($Z = 3$) can form the ionic compound lithium fluoride (LiF).

b Fluorine can form an F_2O molecule with oxygen ($Z = 16$).

9 For each of the examples below, state whether the substance described is metallic, ionic, molecular covalent or giant covalent in structure.

a W is a volatile liquid which easily vaporises in a warm room. It does not conduct electricity.

b X is a hard but brittle solid that does not conduct electricity. X dissolves in water and the solution conducts electricity.

c Y forms very hard crystals which melt at 700 °C. Neither the solid nor the liquid conduct electricity.

d Z is a dense, fairly hard solid which can be flattened out if hammered. It melts at about 1100 °C and conducts electricity as both a solid and a liquid.

10 The table below shows the melting points of the first 20 elements.

Atomic number (Z)	Element	Melting point (°C)	Boiling point (°C)
1	H	−259	−253
2	He	−272	−269
3	Li	181	1342
4	Be	1278	2970
5	B	2300	2550
6	C	3652	4827
7	N	−210	−196
8	O	−218	−183
9	F	−220	−188
10	Ne	−248	−246
11	Na	98	883
12	Mg	649	1107
13	Al	660	2467
14	Si	1410	2355
15	P	44	227
16	S	119	445
17	Cl	−101	−35
18	Ar	−189	−186
19	K	63	760
20	Ca	839	1484

a By hand or using a computer, plot graphs of melting point and boiling point against atomic number.

b Describe the pattern you see.

c How many elements are solid at room temperature (25 °C)?

d Which gaseous element would liquefy in a Siberian winter (−50 °C)?

e The peak melting points are found in which group of the periodic table?

f The lowest boiling points are found in which group of the periodic table?

11 **a** Copy and complete this table:

Atomic number (Z)	Metal or non-metal?	Atom	Atom electron structure	Ion	Ion electron structure
8	i ____	O	2,6	O^{2-}	ii ____
11	iii ____	Na	2,8,1	Na^+	iv ____
12	metal	Mg	2,8,2	Mg^{2+}	2,8
17	non-metal	Cl	2,8,7	Cl^-	2,8,8
20	v ____	Ca	vi ____	Ca^{2+}	vii ____

b What do you notice about the electron structure of:

  i O, Na and Mg ions?

  ii Cl and Ca ions?

c What is different about the ions?

d From the table, explain why:

  i sodium chloride is NaCl but magnesium chloride is $MgCl_2$.

  ii calcium oxide is CaO, but sodium oxide is Na_2O.

12 Here are some unbalanced equations:

  i Write them out as word equations.

  ii Balance them.

  iii Add state symbols.

  a $K + H_2O \rightarrow KOH + H_2$

  b $CaCO_3 + HCl \rightarrow CaCl_2 + H_2O + CO_2$

  c $LiOH + H_2SO_4 \rightarrow Li_2SO_4 + H_2O$

  d $CH_4 + O_2 \rightarrow CO_2 + H_2O$

Module 12 – Waves and radiation

In this module, you will be finding out more about two topics you have studied before – light and sound. You have probably heard people talking about light waves and sound waves. But why do we picture these things as waves?

We will look at waves on water and on springs and ropes, as a way of understanding how waves behave. Then we will see how the same ideas apply to light and sound.

In this module, you will also learn more about many different types of radiation. You may think that anything called 'radiation' must be dangerous. This isn't necessarily so. The radio waves used by mobile phones and the infrared radiation coming from a heater are both forms of radiation which we need not fear. And by learning about the more hazardous forms of radiation, including X-rays and gamma rays, we can understand how to use them safely and avoid any harm they might do us.

We are surrounded by radioactive substances – fortunately, usually only in small quantities, so that their radiation is quite weak. When radioactivity was first discovered, a little over a hundred years ago, it gave scientists a new way of looking at atoms. By using alpha radiation, Ernest Rutherford was able to show that every atom has a tiny nucleus at its centre.

Waves carry energy. These giant breakers carry vast amounts of energy, but not quite enough to knock down the lighthouse.

Before you start this module, check that you can recall the answers to the following questions about sound and light.

1 What do we call a sound which is reflected back to us from a hard surface?

2 The *frequency* of a sound is the number of complete vibrations each second. What are its units?

3 If you increase the *amplitude* of a sound, how does the sound change?

4 When a ray of light travels from one material into another, it may be *refracted*. What does this mean?

5 When white light passes through a prism, it may be split up to form – what?

Waves are a disturbance travelling across the surface of the sea.

Scientists talk about light waves and sound waves. But if you see light or listen to sounds, you won't notice anything very wavy about them. So why do we call them waves?

To answer this, we have to think about waves on water. The photograph shows waves on the surface of the sea. On a calm day the surface of the sea is flat and undisturbed. On a rough day, the waves travel across the surface, making the boat go up and down.

Measuring waves

Water waves are a disturbance which moves across the surface of the water. The diagram shows how we can represent waves. It is like a cross-section of the surface of the water. There are two quantities we can measure on this diagram:

The **amplitude** of the wave: this is the maximum amount by which the surface of the water moves upwards from its undisturbed position.

The **wavelength** of the wave: this is the distance from the crest of one wave to the crest of the next.

(The small diagram shows that there are other ways to measure the wavelength: from one trough to the next, or from any point on one wave to the same point on the next wave.)

The amplitude and wavelength of a water wave are both measured in metres (m).

a Look at the diagram of the wave. Which is greater, its amplitude or its wavelength?

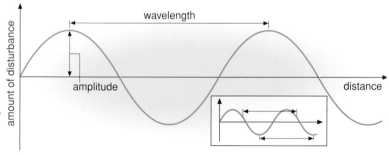

Take care! The amplitude of a water wave is measured from the undisturbed level of the surface.

Making waves

You can see waves on the surface of water using a ripple tank. A straight bar vibrates up and down, disturbing the surface of the water so that waves travel across it. An image of the waves is projected onto the floor, or onto a screen. To find the wavelength, measure across several waves.

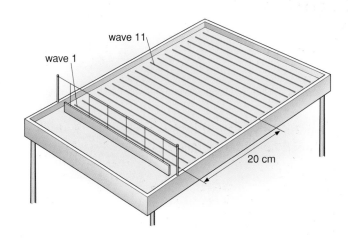

In the picture, there is 20 cm between wave 1 and wave 11. There are 10 waves in this distance. So:

wavelength = 20 cm/10 = 2 cm

Stretching strings and springs

Fix one end of a long spring, and move the other from side to side. A wave travels along the spring. (You can do this with a string or rope, too.)

By moving your hand from side to side more rapidly, you will make more waves each second. You have increased the frequency of the wave.

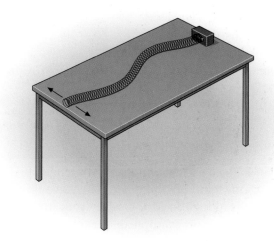

The **frequency** of a wave is the number of waves which pass a point each second. It is measured in hertz (Hz). One hertz (1 Hz) means one wave per second.

b If you move the end of the spring from side to side once every half-second, what is the frequency of the waves produced?

Questions

1 Look at the diagram of a wave.

  a What is its amplitude, in cm?

  b What is its wavelength, in cm?

2 On squared paper, draw a diagram to show a wave with the following measurements:

  amplitude = 2 cm

  wavelength = 8 cm

3 Jo stands on the end of the pier, timing the waves as they go past on the surface of the sea. She counts 6 waves in 1 minute.

  a How many seconds is it from one wave crest to the next?

  b What is the frequency of the waves?

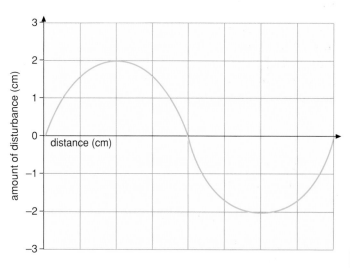

Summary

- Waves can travel across the surface of water, and along strings and springs.

- Waves can be measured to find their amplitude, wavelength and frequency.

Imagine that you are sitting in a small boat on the open sea. It is a windy day, and waves are travelling across the surface of the sea. As the waves pass under the boat, you move up and down.

This shows that a wave on water is a disturbance which makes the surface of the water move up and down. The wave itself moves along horizontally.

Making transverse waves

You can make a similar wave on a stretched spring by moving your hand up and down. The wave travels horizontally along the spring, while your hand moves vertically. This is an example of a **transverse wave**.

In a transverse wave, the disturbance is at right angles to the direction in which the waves themselves are travelling.

a Using the spring in the picture, you could make a wave along the spring by moving your hand from side to side, instead of up and down. Would this wave be transverse?

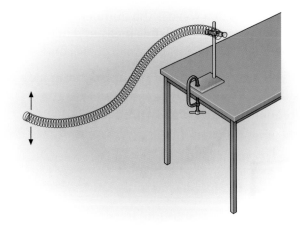

Making longitudinal waves

There is another way of making a wave on a stretched spring. Push the end back and forth, along the length of the spring. The wave looks different from a transverse wave. A region of squashed-up spring travels along, followed by a region of stretched-out spring. This is an example of a **longitudinal wave**.

In a longitudinal wave, the disturbance is back and forth, along the direction in which the waves themselves are travelling.

b Are water waves transverse or longitudinal? Explain your answer.

The speed of waves

Some waves travel quickly; others travel more slowly. Waves on the sea move at a few metres per second; the water in a ripple tank is much shallower, and the waves travel more slowly.

The diagram shows a line of waves. After 1 s, the red wave has moved 6 m to the right. The speed of the waves is 6 m/s.

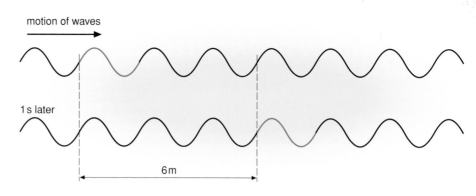

motion of waves

1 s later

6 m

From the diagram, you can see that the waves have wavelength = 2 m, and their frequency = 3 Hz. We can calculate the speed of the wave by multiplying these two quantities together:

Wave speed (m/s) = frequency (Hz) × wavelength (m)

To calculate frequency and wavelength:

$$\text{Frequency} = \frac{\text{wave speed}}{\text{wavelength}}$$

$$\text{Wavelength} = \frac{\text{wave speed}}{\text{frequency}}$$

Worked example

Some waves on the sea have a wavelength of 20 m and are travelling at 4 m/s. What is their frequency?

Choose the correct version of the formula and substitute in the values:

$$\text{Frequency} = \frac{\text{wave speed}}{\text{wavelength}} = \frac{4\ \text{m/s}}{20\ \text{m}} = 0.2\ \text{Hz}$$

c Some waves are travelling along a spring. Their wavelength is 0.1 m and their frequency is 12 Hz. What is their speed?

A surfer can ride along on the top of a breaking wave. It can be quite a fast ride!

DIGGING DEEPER
It is easiest to think of waves on the sea as transverse. However, they are really a mixture of transverse and longitudinal. As waves pass beneath a small boat, it goes both up and down and back and forth, so that it moves around in a vertical circle.

Questions

1 Copy the table. Write **transverse wave** or **longitudinal wave** in the first column.

Type of wave	Description
	disturbance in same direction as wave moves
	disturbance at right angles to direction in which wave moves

2 Describe how you would make a longitudinal wave travel along a horizontal stretched spring.

3 A vibrating motor sends waves along a string. It produces 20 waves each second, and 10 waves occupy 5 m of the string.

a What is the frequency of the waves?

b What is their wavelength?

c What is their speed?

4 Ripples of wavelength 3 cm are travelling across the surface of water in a ripple tank. They move at 12 cm/s. What is their frequency?

Summary
- Waves transfer energy without any matter being transferred.
- Waves may be transverse or longitudinal.
- Wave speed = frequency × wavelength

Waves on the sea are whipped up by the wind. The wind transfers energy to the water, and the waves carry the energy across the sea. The energy of waves can cause a lot of damage when they strike the shore.

If you make waves on a stretched spring, you are transferring energy to the spring. The energy is carried along the spring by the waves, though the spring itself does not move along.

All waves transfer energy from their source to other places, without any matter being transferred.

The high winds of a hurricane transfer a lot of energy to waves on the sea.

Bouncing off barriers

If you send a single wave along a stretched spring, you will see it bounce off the fixed end and come back towards you. This is an example of **reflection**.

You can see waves on water being reflected by a barrier in a ripple tank. In the diagram, ripples are travelling from the left. The reflected ripples are travelling upwards.

a When might you see waves on the sea being reflected?

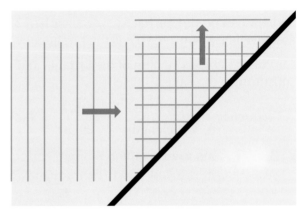

Refraction of ripples

By placing a sheet of glass in the water in a ripple tank, you can make it shallower. The ripples travel more slowly in shallow water because they drag on the bottom. How do the waves change when they move more slowly?

Ripples changing direction is an example of **refraction**. Refraction happens when waves change their speed. You should recall that light can be refracted, too. This suggests that light changes speed when it enters glass. The diagrams will remind you about what happens when a ray of light enters glass.

b Look at the second diagram of the light ray entering glass. Does it bend towards the normal, or away from it? Does light speed up or slow down when it enters glass?

Sound and light

Sounds can be reflected – an echo is a reflected sound. Sound can also be refracted.

Light can be reflected, for example, by a mirror. It can also be refracted when it travels from one material to another.

Here you can see that the ripples are closer together because they are moving more slowly.

When the ripples enter the shallow water at an angle, they become bent. They move in a different direction

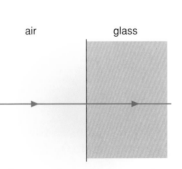

A ray travelling along the normal is not refracted.

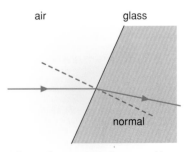

A ray at an angle to the normal is refracted.

This suggests that both sound and light travel as waves. That is why scientists talk about **sound waves** and **light waves**.

It also suggests that sound and light travel at different speeds in different substances. Scientists have made measurements and found that this is true.

Longitudinal or transverse?

The cone of a loudspeaker moves back and forth to make a sound. It pushes the particles of the air back and forth, making a longitudinal wave in the air. This is just like a longitudinal wave you make on a spring by pushing the end back and forth. Sound waves can travel through solids, liquids and gases.

Light is a form of **electromagnetic radiation**. Light waves are transverse waves. They do not need a material to travel through – they can pass through a vacuum.

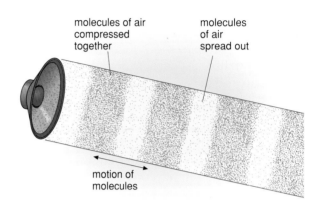

molecules of air compressed together

molecules of air spread out

motion of molecules

c How could you show that sound waves can travel through solids?

d How do we know that light waves can travel through a vacuum (empty space)?

Questions

1 Which of the following are transverse waves, and which are longitudinal?

    water waves   **sound waves**   **light waves**

2 **a** Do ripples speed up or slow down when they enter shallower water?

  b What name is given to the change of direction caused when waves change speed?

  c In what special circumstances do waves **not** change direction when they change speed?

3 Which of the following statements are true, and which are false?

  a Light waves can be reflected. TRUE/FALSE

  b Light waves can be refracted. TRUE/FALSE

  c Light waves can travel through a vacuum. TRUE/FALSE

4 Which of the following statements are true, and which are false?

  When you listen to the radio:

  a Sound waves travel from the loudspeaker to your ear. TRUE/FALSE

  b Sound energy travels from the loudspeaker to your ear. TRUE/FALSE

  c Air particles travel from the loudspeaker to your ear. TRUE/FALSE

5 Explain why scientists think that light waves travel at different speeds in different materials.

Summary

- Waves transfer energy without any matter being transferred.

- Waves on water can be reflected and refracted.

- Because light and sound can also be reflected and refracted, this suggests that they travel as waves.

12.4 Diffraction of waves

A harbour can provide protection from big waves on the open sea. The photograph shows what happens when waves enter a harbour. They spread out as they enter the harbour mouth into the space beyond, so that boats in the furthest corners are rocked up and down.

You can make a model of this using a ripple tank. Straight ripples approach a gap in a barrier, just like the mouth of the harbour. As they pass through the gap, they spread out into the space beyond.

In a similar way, ripples spread around the corner as they pass an obstacle, to fill the space behind it.

This spreading out of waves as they pass through a gap or around an obstacle is known as **diffraction**. Diffraction is an effect which is only observed with waves. Particles move in straight lines, and their paths do not bend when they pass through a gap. As we shall see, both sound and light can be diffracted, and this is further evidence that they travel as waves.

Longer wavelengths

The diagrams show how waves of different wavelengths are diffracted as they pass through a gap. Waves with a longer wavelength are diffracted more strongly.

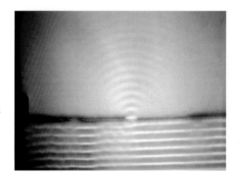

short wavelength (ripples close together): very little diffraction

longer wavelength: more diffraction

longest wavelength: strongest diffraction

a Look at the first diagram of ripples being diffracted. What do you think would happen if the gap was made narrower? Would the ripples be diffracted more, or less?

b Look closely at the diagrams of waves being diffracted. Does their wavelength change when they are diffracted? How can you tell?

Diffracting sound and radio waves

If you are in the next room to someone who is speaking to you, you may be able to hear them even though you cannot see them. The sound waves of the voice are diffracted as they come through the doorway and spread out around the room you are in.

Because sounds can be diffracted, this supports the idea that sound travels as waves.

Radio waves are a form of electromagnetic radiation (like light). They have long wavelengths, usually over 1 m and sometimes as much as 1 km. There may be a hill between you and the transmitter, but the waves are diffracted round the hill so that you can still pick up its signal.

Light waves have a very short wavelength. When they are diffracted, the effect is usually too small for us to see.

Because electromagnetic radiation can be diffracted, we believe it travels as waves.

c **Which radio waves are more likely to reach the radio aerial, those for FM (wavelength 3 m) or those for AM (wavelength over 200 m)? Explain your answer.**

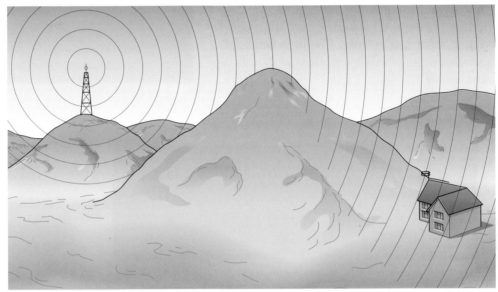

Questions

1 **Copy this table and complete the definitions in the second column.**

Reflection	Waves change direction when ...
Refraction	Waves change direction when ...
Diffraction	Waves spread out when ...

2 **a Draw a diagram to show how straight, parallel ripples are diffracted when they pass through a narrow gap.**

b Draw a second diagram to show how the situation would be altered if the ripples had a longer wavelength.

3 **You are standing at your friend's front door. Explain how you can hear someone mowing the lawn in the back garden.**

4 **You receive radio signals from a transmitter a few kilometres away. Explain how your radio set can pick up these signals even though there may be a block of flats in the way.**

DIGGING DEEPER
Light can be diffracted by mist on a window or car windscreen. That's why we sometimes see a halo of light around streetlamps on a foggy night.

Summary
• Waves spread out when they go through a gap or past an object. This is diffraction.

• The longer the wavelength, the more strongly the waves are diffracted.

When you are listening to the radio, you can tune it into different stations. When you turn the dial, you are changing the frequency of the radio waves you are tuning in to. On the FM scale, the frequencies range from about 88 MHz to about 107 MHz. They make up a **spectrum** of frequencies from which you can select the frequency of the station you want to hear.

You can make a spectrum of light by passing white light through a prism or diffraction grating. The light is broken up into different colours, from red to violet. The light waves of each colour have a different frequency and wavelength.

a Which colour of light has the longest wavelength? Which colour has the shortest wavelength?

longer wavelength   shorter wavelength

More waves

Light and radio waves are just two types of electromagnetic wave. There are several others, and together they make up the **electromagnetic spectrum**. The spectrum shows all types of electromagnetic radiation, arranged in order of their wavelengths and frequencies.

You will have heard of each of these types of radiation, but you may not have realised that they all belong to one big family of electromagnetic waves.

b Which type of electromagnetic wave has the longest wavelength? Which has the shortest wavelength?

highest frequency						lowest frequency
gamma rays	X-rays	ultraviolet rays	visible light	infrared rays	microwaves	radio waves
shortest wavelength						longest wavelength

Top speed

Light waves travel very fast. So do all other types of electromagnetic wave. They travel fastest in empty space, where there is nothing to slow them down. In empty space, they all travel at the same speed:

Speed of electromagnetic waves in space = 300 000 000 m/s

That's 300 million metres per second, or over 7 times round the Earth in one second. Most scientists think that nothing can travel faster than this – it's the speed limit of the Universe.

Getting warm

If you lie in the sun, three types of electromagnetic radiation fall on your skin: light, infrared rays and ultraviolet rays. You can tell that these are all absorbed by your skin – you can feel yourself getting warmer. The energy carried by the waves is transferred to your body.

All electromagnetic waves carry energy, and when they are absorbed their energy makes the substance which absorbs them get warmer.

We have another way of absorbing radio waves. We use a metal aerial. The waves make an electric current flow up and down in the aerial. This is an alternating current (because it flows back and forth), and it has the same frequency as the radio waves.

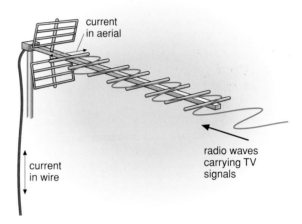

Television signals are carried by high frequency radio waves. They make an alternating current flow in the aerial, and this flows down a wire to the TV set.

c Sometimes we use microwaves to heat things up. Give an example of this.

Questions

1 Copy and complete this version of the electromagnetic spectrum; label the ends with the longest and shortest wavelengths:

		infrared rays				

2 Copy the following statements, choosing the correct word from each pair:

a Gamma rays have a higher/lower frequency than ultraviolet rays.

b Microwaves have a higher/lower frequency than radio waves.

3 A mobile phone uses radio waves to receive and transmit messages. There is a danger that your brain will be heated when you use such a phone. Explain why this is.

4 a How fast do radio waves travel in empty space?

b If a spacecraft sent radio waves and microwaves through space to Earth, which would get there first?

c Radio telescopes detect radio waves coming from the Sun. How long does it take such waves to travel from Sun to Earth?

Summary

- Electromagnetic waves all travel through space at the same speed.

- They form a continuous spectrum:
  highest frequency
  shortest wavelength
    gamma rays
    X-rays
    ultraviolet rays
    light
    infrared rays
    microwaves
    radio waves
  lowest frequency
  longest wavelength

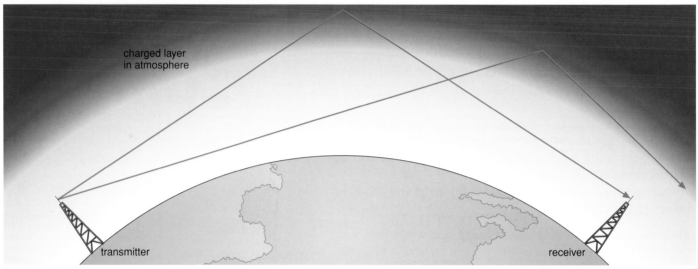

Longer wavelength radio waves reflect off an electrically charged layer in the upper atmosphere.

charged layer
in atmosphere

transmitter

receiver

We make use of electromagnetic waves every day. By knowing how they are reflected and absorbed, we can discover new ways of using them.

Guglielmo Marconi was the first person to send messages using radio waves. In 1901, he sent the first radio message across the Atlantic. Many people thought his signal would travel straight out into space, because the Earth is curved. However, he was lucky. Radio waves are reflected by the upper atmosphere, and so they can be sent between distant points on the Earth's surface.

Radio stations use long-wavelength radio waves to broadcast over large areas. On holiday, you might be able to pick up a station from your home country even if you are thousands of kilometres away. Television stations use much shorter wavelength radio waves which do not travel so far.

Using microwaves

A microwave oven uses microwaves, of course. They have a wavelength which is easily absorbed by water molecules. Since most foods contain water, this is a good way to transfer energy to food. China plates and plastic containers do not absorb the microwaves.

Microwaves are also used by mobile phone networks to transmit messages over long distances. Radio waves from a mobile phone are picked up at a base station. The signal is then carried by microwaves to another distant base station, close to the receiving phone. Then it is sent by radio waves to the phone.

Some wavelengths of microwaves can pass easily through the atmosphere. They are not reflected (unlike radio waves). This means that they are useful for sending messages up to satellites

Marconi sent the first transatlantic radio messages. One of his signals helped catch Dr Crippen, a murderer who had escaped from England on a liner. Detectives were ready to arrest him when he arrived in New York.

DIGGING DEEPER
Astronomers look at radio waves coming from space. Radio and TV broadcasts can interfere with this. There are some wavelengths which broadcasters are not allowed to use, so that astronomers can have a clearer view of space.

which are orbiting high above the atmosphere. Satellites can also use microwaves to send signals back down to Earth.

a In a microwave oven, a plastic plate remains cool even while the food is being heated. Explain why this is so.

Infrared radiation

Infrared radiation is given out by warm objects. The hotter they are, the more radiation they give out. The glowing element in an electric toaster is very hot, and it gives out intense infrared radiation. This is absorbed by the bread which is being toasted, so that it becomes hot and burns gently. Grills and radiant heaters also emit infrared radiation.

We cannot see infrared radiation. It is used in remote controls for TVs and video recorders. When you press a button, an invisible infrared signal is flashed to the appliance. Some security keys for cars also use infrared; others use radio waves.

In fact, even very cold objects emit infrared. A block of ice taken from the deep freeze (temperature –40 °C) gives out small amounts of infrared, but its surroundings are warmer and give out more, so that it absorbs more than it emits.

b Some stoves are fitted with electric grills. You can see them glowing as they cook the food. What type of electromagnetic radiation do you see? What other type of electromagnetic radiation does a grill produce?

Questions

1 Name three types of electromagnetic radiation whose wavelength is longer than that of visible light.

2 Radio waves are reflected by a charged layer in the atmosphere. This means that we can pick up radio signals from distant transmitters.

   a Draw a diagram to show how this happens.

   b In the summer, the reflecting layer is higher. Add to your diagram to show why we pick up signals from different stations in the summer.

   c Explain why, in the UK, we rarely pick up television signals from overseas stations.

3 List some uses in the home for:

   a microwaves;

   b infrared radiation.

4 **a** How do satellites orbiting high above the Earth make use of microwaves?

   b Why can we not use radio waves to communicate with satellites?

These 'dishes' are microwave aerials; masts like this are usually found on hilltops. They form part of a mobile phone network. The dishes send microwave signals horizontally to other dishes many kilometres away.

This satellite is in orbit far above the Earth. It receives microwave signals sent up from Earth, and broadcasts television programmes back down to Earth.

The element in this toaster is hot – about 700 °C. It emits two types of electromagnetic radiation – light and infrared.

Summary

- Radio waves and microwaves are used for communications systems.
- Microwaves and infrared radiation are used in cooking.
- Remote controls use infrared radiation.

12:7 Radiation and life

The ozone layer in the atmosphere protects us from the Sun's most harmful rays, but there is a man-made hole in it. This has been caused by chemicals such as CFCs from refrigerators and aerosol sprays, which destroy the ozone. Even if you have dark skin, you need to take care to avoid being exposed to too much ultraviolet radiation. Some people use sunbeds to give themselves a tan, but it isn't very sensible to increase the amount of ultraviolet radiation to which you are exposed.

Suntan lotion contains chemicals which absorb ultraviolet radiation.

Short wavelengths

Ultraviolet radiation is like light, but with shorter wavelengths. It is invisible to the human eye (though some other creatures can see it). Fluorescent lamps produce ultraviolet radiation; it is absorbed by the white coating inside the tube, and then re-emitted as visible light.

a Explain why a special lamp is needed to show up the security marking on the banknote in the photo.

X-radiation is very penetrating. It can pass easily through flesh and plastic, but not so readily through bone or metal. People who work with X-rays use lead shields and even lead aprons to protect themselves from the radiation.

This banknote has a security marking which only shows up under ultraviolet (UV) radiation. The marking (lamb at lower left) absorbs the UV and re-emits it as visible light.

b Explain how X-rays would be useful if a small child swallowed a coin. Why would they be less useful if the child swallowed a plastic pen top?

Damaging cells

The more radiation you are exposed to, the more harm it may do you.

- ◆ Low doses of ultraviolet, X-radiation and gamma radiation can damage normal cells so that they become cancerous.
- ◆ Higher doses of these types of radiation can kill normal cells.

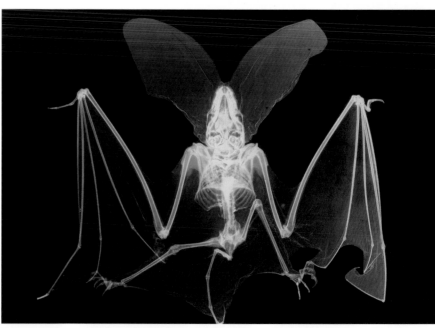

X-rays produce a shadow picture, revealing the bones of creatures such as this bat.

Sometimes we want to kill cells. Some foods are exposed to radiation to kill harmful bacteria. The food can then be safely given to seriously ill people or taken on space flights. In the same way, surgical instruments and sanitary towels and tampons are sterilised using gamma radiation.

The paler your skin, the deeper ultraviolet radiation can penetrate, and the greater the chance that a cancer may be caused. In Australia, where the damage to the ozone layer has been most severe, there has been a steep increase in the occurrence of skin cancer.

Gamma radiation has been used to sterilise these plastic syringes inside their packaging.

c Why is it important to sterilise surgical instruments before use? What type of electromagnetic radiation is usually used to do this?

Other types of radiation can affect living tissue:

◆ All living cells contain water, and this can absorb microwaves. The cells are heated and may die.

◆ Infra red is absorbed by the skin; you feel warm. Intense infrared can cause burns.

Questions

1 Copy the table; in the first column, write the name of a type of electromagnetic radiation which causes the effect shown in the second column.

Type of radiation	Effect
	causes tanning of skin
	produces shadow picture of bones in flesh
	kills harmful bacteria
	absorbed by water in cells; causes heating

DIGGING DEEPER
Permission has been given for some irradiated foods, particularly spices, to be sold in the UK. They have to be labelled to indicate that they have been irradiated.

2 When a dentist takes an X-ray of a patient's teeth, she stands outside the room, or behind a protective metal screen.

a Why might she leave the room?

b Why should the protective screen be made of metal?

3 Describe what happens when:

a infrared radiation lands on your skin;

b ultraviolet radiation lands on your skin.

4 Why does the tube of a fluorescent lamp have a special coating inside it?

5 Design a leaflet explaining the hazards of over-exposure to ultraviolet radiation. Your leaflet should be designed to inform UK holidaymakers who are visiting Australia. It should explain why the hole in the ozone layer has increased the hazard, and why protective suntan lotion should be used.

Summary
- Radiation may be absorbed by living tissue, or it may pass through.

- When radiation is absorbed by cells, they may be killed by it; lower doses may cause the cells to become cancerous.

A doctor may use an instrument called an endoscope to look inside a patient. To see inside the patient's stomach, a long, flexible device is passed down their throat. This contains a bundle of **optical fibres**. Light rays which enter one end of a fibre bounce along inside it until they emerge at the other end.

Some of the fibres in an endoscope carry light downwards, to provide illumination; others carry light rays back upwards to show an image of the stomach.

a What scientific term could be used for the 'bouncing' of light rays as they travel along an optical fibre?

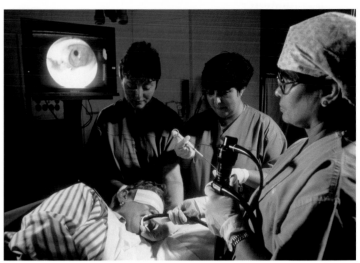

The image of the patient's insides appears on a monitor screen, so that all of the medical team can see it.

Inside glass

Optical fibres are made of very pure glass. They are quite flexible, so that they can be bent into a curved shape. The diagram shows how a ray of light is reflected when it strikes the inside surface of the fibre. The good thing about this reflection is that 100% of the light is reflected. The inside surface of the fibre behaves like a perfect mirror.

This type of reflection is known as **total internal reflection (TIR)**. It is called *internal* because it happens *inside* the glass.

b Why is it called total?

The diagrams show what happens when a ray of light travels from glass (or Perspex or water) into air.

TIR occurs when the angle between the ray and the normal is greater than a certain angle called the **critical angle**.

c Using a protractor, draw accurate versions of the two diagrams.

Diagram A: Angle of incidence = 35°; angle of refraction = 60°

Diagram B: Angle of incidence = 45°

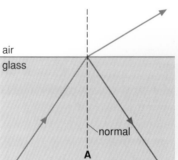

The ray of light strikes the surface of the glass at a narrow angle. Some of the light is refracted as it passes through; some is reflected.

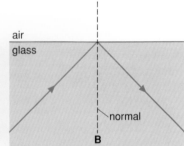

Here the ray strikes the surface at a greater angle. There is no refracted ray; all of the light is reflected.

Up and over

The diagram shows how a telescope can be made using two prisms. (Binoculars are often made like this.) The light is totally internally reflected inside each prism. This makes the telescope much shorter than it would otherwise be.

d How many times is the light totally internally reflected between the two lenses?

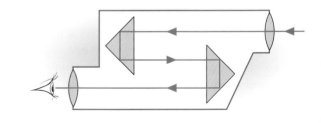

Getting the picture

Today, many houses are connected to a cable TV network which also provides a telephone system. Optical fibres are used to transmit television, radio and telephone signals to the user. The signals are carried by rays of light. This is better than using electrical signals in cables (wires):

◆ Light rays in a thin fibre can carry much more information than electrical signals in a cable of the same thickness.

◆ The light signals can travel much farther than electrical signals before they become too weak to detect.

This technician is adjusting an array of optical fibres.

Questions

1 Copy and complete the two diagrams which show what happens when a ray of light strikes the inside of a Perspex block.

2 A periscope allows the user to see over an obstacle in front. Some periscopes are made with two mirrors; others use two glass prisms to reflect the light. Copy and complete the diagram to show how the light rays reach the user's eyes.

3 Why would you expect to see a brighter image using a periscope which contains two prisms, rather than one with two mirrors?

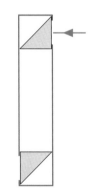

4 Copy the sentences below, which explain why cable TV systems use optical fibres instead of electrical cables. Use the words **more** or **less** to fill the gaps.

An electrical cable can carry ____ information than an optical fibre of the same thickness.

There is ____ weakening of the signal in an electrical cable than in an optical fibre.

Summary

• When a light ray strikes the inside surface of glass (or another transparent material), it is partly reflected and partly refracted, provided the angle between the ray and the normal is small.

• If the angle is greater than the critical angle, it is totally internally reflected.

• Total internal reflection occurs in optical fibres, which are used in endoscopes and periscopes, and for transmitting information over long distances.

Today, we are surrounded by information – pictures, speech, music, text, data. It reaches our eyes and ears in the form of light waves and sound waves.

Information travels around in many forms – it may be carried by radio waves or microwaves through the air, as electrical signals along wires and cables, or as light or infrared signals along optical fibres.

a **What type of electromagnetic waves are used to transmit television signals through the air?**

A computer with Internet access can connect you to many sources of information, including text, data, images and music.

Waves of information

Information is transferred as a signal; signals can have two forms, **analogue** or **digital**. An analogue signal varies like a wave, to carry the information. The amplitude or the frequency of the wave changes continuously, like a sound wave. The diagrams show two forms of analogue signal.

A loudspeaker makes use of analogue signals. The electric current in the wires varies in the same way as the sound wave produced by the loudspeaker.

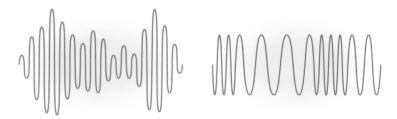

Two analogue signals.

b **In the diagram, which signal has a varying amplitude? Which has a varying frequency?**

Dot dash dot

A digital signal is similar to Morse code. The information is coded as a series of pulses (on and off). A source of light or infrared radiation, such as a laser, is flashed on and off to send the signal down an optical fibre. Later it must be converted back to sounds and pictures which we can understand.

A digital signal is a series of on–off pulses.

Digital quality

Signals become weaker as they travel, and they may become 'noisy' when they pick up random additions.

In many ways, digital signals are a better way of transmitting information than analogue signals.

- ◆ Digital signals are of higher quality, because they do not get distorted as easily as analogue signals. They retain their information better as they are transmitted from place to place. Analogue signals become distorted as some frequencies weaken more than others. Distortions and noise are amplified each time the signal is amplified.

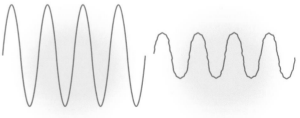

original signal   after transmission

As the signal travels, it becomes weaker and noisier.

- Digital signals may become weaker and distorted, but it is still possible to recognise the 'ons' and 'offs'. This means that, when the signal is amplified, it can be returned to its original form.

- Digital signals can carry more information than analogue signals. A single optical fibre can carry over a hundred TV channels as digital signals, many more than a similar analogue system. This is why much of television and radio broadcasting is changing to make use of digital signals.

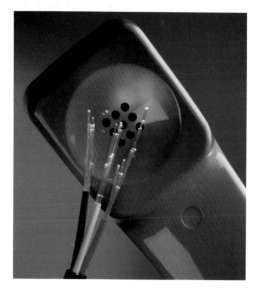

A conventional telephone wire can carry just one conversation, in the form of an analogue signal. If it is replaced by an optical fibre, hundreds of conversations can be carried simultaneously. This photograph shows how fine individual optical fibres are.

c A digital signal can be carried along an optical fibre by light waves. What other form of electromagnetic radiation can be used?

Questions

1 Copy the table. Write **analogue** or **digital** in the first column.

Type of signal	Description
	a series of on–off pulses
	a wave whose frequency or amplitude varies

2 Computers can send information to one another along cables. Which can transfer information more rapidly, analogue or digital signals?

3 Look at the diagrams.

  a Which represents an analogue signal?

  b Which represents a digital signal?

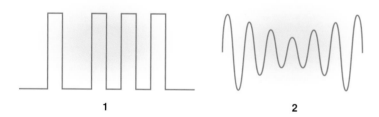

1   2

4 Copy the following sentences, choosing the correct word from each pair.

  a When any signal travels, it becomes weaker/stronger.

  b When an analogue signal is amplified, the noise is not/also amplified. The noise can/cannot be removed.

  c When a digital signal is amplified, the noise can/cannot be removed to return the signal to its original form.

DIGGING DEEPER

An analogy is when we say one thing is like another, so an analogue signal is one which has some of the same characteristics as the original information it carries. For instance, in a loudspeaker the current in the wires gets bigger or smaller to make a louder or quieter volume of sound. Digital is to do with fingers (digits). We count on our fingers; each finger is a unit or whole number. So a digital signal is one which consists only of whole numbers.

Summary

- Information can be transferred in the form of a signal. Signals can be carried by varying electric currents, by electromagnetic waves, or by light or infrared waves along optical fibres.

- Signals can be digital (on-off pulses) or analogue (varying amplitude or frequency).

- Digital signals retain their quality over greater distances.

12:10 Alpha, beta, gamma

There are radioactive substances all around us, and they give out radiation all the time. We can't see the radiation that they give out. That's why it took scientists a long time to discover radioactivity.

The first person to observe the radiation coming from a radioactive substance was a French scientist called Henri Becquerel, in 1896. He was studying rocks which contained uranium. Some of these rocks glow in the dark. He noticed that they made a photograpic film go dark, even when the film was wrapped in black paper to stop light getting at it. Some kind of radiation was getting through the paper.

Becquerel discovered that uranium gives out radiation at the same rate even if you heat it or cool it, or change its chemical form. There is no way to switch on or off the radiation from a radioactive substance.

a Henri Becquerel invented the word 'radio-activity'. Look at the two parts of the word. Why do you think he chose this word?

Detecting radiation

In the lab, your teacher can show you some radioactive sources. Remember that these give out radiation all the time, even when they are not in use. That is why they must be stored securely – there is no on–off switch.

One way to detect the radiation emitted by a radioactive source is to use a Geiger counter. The detector is a Geiger tube; a counter shows how much radiation has been detected. If the tube is moved further away from the source, the reading on the counter goes up more slowly. This shows that the radiation spreads out from the source; it is weaker further away from the source.

b How will the reading on the counter change if the tube is moved towards the source? Give a reason for your answer.

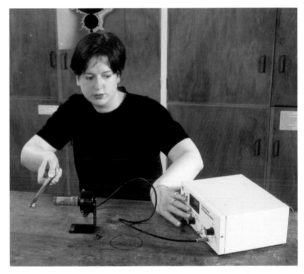

The teacher is using a Geiger counter to detect the radiation from a radioactive source.

Absorbing radiation

Henri Becquerel discovered that he could make the radiation from uranium weaker by putting a metal coin in the way. Some of the radiation was absorbed by the metal. The thicker the metal, the greater the absorption.

With experiments like this, it was possible to show that radioactive substances emit three types of radiation:

◆ alpha (α) radiation – stopped by a thin sheet of paper, or a few centimetres of air;

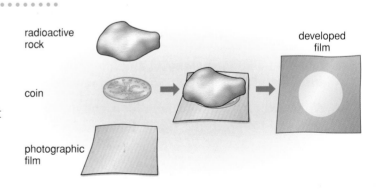

radioactive rock

coin

photographic film

developed film

- ◆ beta (β) radiation – passes easily through air or paper, but stopped by a few millimetres of metal;

- ◆ gamma (γ) radiation – needs many centimetres of lead, or metres of concrete, to absorb it.

This is summarised in the diagram.

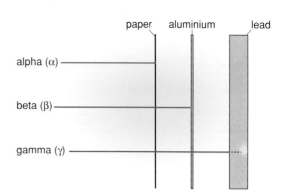

c Which type of radiation is the most penetrating? Which is the least penetrating?

d Which type of radiation is most easily absorbed?

Monitoring thickness

Many factories make use of radiation to check the thickness of materials they are producing. For example, beta radiation can be used to check the thickness of plastic sheeting.

- ◆ If the sheeting is too thick, less beta radiation passes through it. The machine goes faster to make the sheeting thinner.

- ◆ If the sheeting is too thin, more beta radiation gets through to the detector. This tells the machine to go slower.

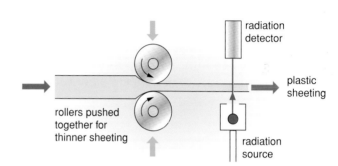

e The thickness of metal sheeting can be monitored in the same way. Which type of radiation should be used for this? Give a reason for your answer.

Questions

1 The diagram is of an experiment to show how radiation from a radioactive source is absorbed by a sheet of metal.

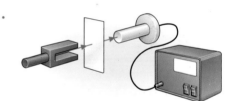

   a Copy the diagram; add the following labels:

   radioactive source   radiation   absorber
   detector   counter

   b Write a sentence or two to say what you would do to show that the metal absorbs some of the radiation from the source.

2 Copy the table.

   a In the spaces in the first column, write **most** or **least**.

_____ easily absorbed	alpha radiation	α
	beta radiation	
_____ penetrating	gamma radiation	

   b Complete the last column by writing the correct symbols for beta and gamma radiation.

3 Which types of radiation are being described here? Choose from alpha, beta and gamma.

   a Absorbed by a few millimetres of aluminium

   b Passes easily through air and through a centimetre of metal

   c Absorbed by a thin sheet of paper

Summary

- Radioactive substances give out radiation all the time, no matter what is done to them.

- Radioactive substances emit three types of radiation:

  — alpha (most easily absorbed, least penetrating)

  — beta

  — gamma (most penetrating, least easily absorbed)

There are radioactive substances all around us. This means that we are exposed to a low level of radiation all the time. This is called **background radiation**. The diagram shows the sources of background radiation.

Cosmic rays come from sources far out in space. They are mostly absorbed by the atmosphere, but they are a serious problem for astronauts.

The food we eat contains small amounts of radioactive substances.

The air around us contains radon and other radioactive gases. In some parts of the country, people have fans under their floors to blow out the radon as it seeps up from underground.

Building materials (stone and brick) contain radioactive substances such as uranium. The radiation from these substances adds to background radiation.

a Make a list of the sources of background radiation mentioned above.

Cell damage

It is right to be cautious about radiation. It can cause cancer. The more radiation you are exposed to, the greater the chance that you will get cancer. Here is how it does it.

◆ Radiation is energetic and fast-moving. When radiation smashes into neutral (uncharged) atoms or molecules, they may be left in a charged state – they are **ionised** (they have become ions).

◆ In the nucleus of each living cell are the molecules of DNA, the substance which controls how the cell works and divides. If radiation damages a DNA molecule, the cell may go out of control and start to divide over and over again. This is how a tumour (a cancer) develops.

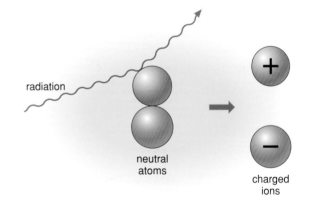

b Each living cell contains billions of molecules. Only a few are DNA molecules. Why is it especially harmful if a DNA molecule is damaged by radiation?

Radiation protection

Because we understand radiation, we can find ways to protect ourselves from its effects. We can understand which are the most dangerous radioactive substances.

When a source of radiation is outside our bodies, we are safe from alpha radiation. It cannot penetrate the layer of dead skin cells which covers us. Beta and gamma radiation are more dangerous because they can penetrate the skin. Then they may damage the cells of organs within our bodies.

A source of alpha radiation is much more dangerous when it is inside our bodies. Then we are not protected by dead skin cells. The alpha radiation can easily damage cells and trigger the development of cancer.

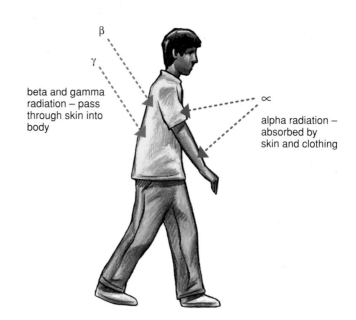

β

γ

beta and gamma radiation – pass through skin into body

∝

alpha radiation – absorbed by skin and clothing

c Our skin is covered with a layer of dead cells. Which type of radiation does this protect us from? Why does it not protect us from the other two types?

Questions

1 Copy the sentences which follow; use words from the list to fill the gaps.

   cancer   ions   background   neutral

   We are constantly exposed to _____ radiation.

   Radiation can damage _____ atoms and molecules, so that they become charged _____ .

   If a molecule within a living cell is damaged, this may cause _____ .

2 We are exposed to background radiation from many different sources. The pie chart shows the contributions which different sources make to background radiation in the UK. Put them in order, from biggest contributor to smallest.

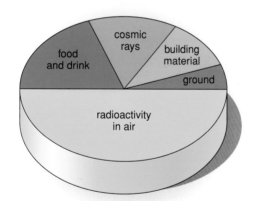

cosmic rays

food and drink

building material

ground

radioactivity in air

3 If you fly in an aircraft, you are exposed to greater amounts of background radiation. Which source of background radiation will increase, the higher you fly?

4 The air contains a radioactive gas called radon. Radon is a source of alpha radiation. In some parts of the country, there is a lot of radon in the air. Explain why people in these areas are more likely to develop lung cancer.

DIGGING DEEPER
As well as natural sources of background radiation, we are also exposed to a significant amount of radiation from medical sources, mostly X-rays. This adds about 15% to our annual radiation dose, on average.

Summary

- We are always exposed to background radiation from radioactive substances around us.

- If radiation damages molecules inside our cells, a cancer may start to develop.

12:12 Radioactive decay

Radioactive substances don't stay radioactive forever. As they give out their radiation, they gradually **decay**. At first, they give out radiation at a high rate. Then the rate gradually declines.

Some of the radioactive sources used in school labs decay quite quickly. After a few years, new ones have to be ordered because the old ones are giving out radiation at a very slow rate. Others give out radiation at a rate which decreases only very slowly, so they never have to be replaced.

Representing radiaoctive decay

The **count rate** tells us the amount of radiation which is detected coming from a radioactive substance. As the substance decays, the count rate gets less.

We can show the pattern of radioactive decay as a graph. From the graph you can see:

◆ at first, the count rate is high;

◆ after a while, the count rate is less;

◆ the count rate gradually gets closer and closer to zero as the substance decays away.

a **Look at the graph. How would you describe the shape of this curve?**

This teacher is demonstrating how the amount of radiation coming from a particular radioactive substance decreases quickly.

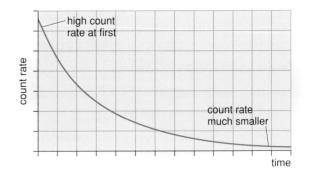

Half-life

When the Earth formed, about four and a half billion years ago, it contained more uranium than it does now. Uranium is radioactive, and about half of it has decayed away.

Other radioactive substances decay much more quickly than uranium. To describe how quickly they decay, we give their half-life. The meaning of this is illustrated by the graph.

The **half-life** of a radioactive substance is the time it takes for half of the original substance to decay away.

The second graph shows that, after twice this length of time, one quarter of the original substance will still remain. (We cannot say when all of the substance will have decayed.)

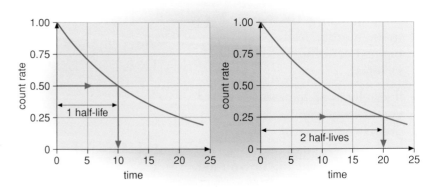

b **A scientist measures the count rate for a sample of a radioactive substance. At first it is 40 counts per second. After 5 minutes, the count rate is 20 counts per second. How long is the half-life of the substance? What would the count rate be after 10 minutes?**

Careful counting

Because background radiation is around us all the time, it adds to all our measurements. To find the correct count rate, the background rate must be measured and subtracted from all readings.

Radioactive decay and atoms

It is useful to picture the atoms in a radioactive substance. When an individual atom decays, it gives out a tiny burst of radiation. Now it has become an atom of a different substance.

◆ The original atoms are called **parent atoms**.

◆ The atoms which remain when the parent atoms decay are called **daughter atoms**.

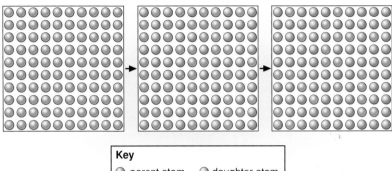

Key

◉ parent atom (undecayed)   ◉ daughter atom (decayed)

The diagram shows what happens when we start with 100 parent atoms (shown in green). After one half-life, the number of parent atoms has halved.

c How many daughter atoms (red) are there after one half-life? And after two half-lives?

Questions

1 Only one of the graphs shows correctly the pattern of radioactive decay. Copy the correct graph.

2 Copy out the sentences which follow, choosing the correct word from each pair.

The half-life of a radioactive substance is the time taken for the number of parent/daughter atoms in the substance to fall to half/zero.

The half-life of a radioactive substance is the time taken for the count rate from the original substance to fall to half its original/final value.

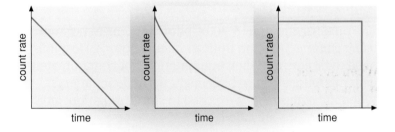

3 A radioactive substance has a half-life of 20 minutes. A sample of the substance initially contained 100 000 parent atoms. Copy and complete the table to show how the number of parent atoms decreases.

Number of parent atoms	100 000			
Time in minutes	0	20	40	60

Summary

- The count rate for a sample of a radioactive substance decreases rapidly at first, then more and more slowly.

- The half-life is the time taken for the count rate to halve; after this time, half of the parent atoms have decayed.

Many people have to use radioactive substances at work. They must know how to use them safely, and how to check that they haven't been exposed to too much radiation.

People who work with radioactive substances often wear a special badge. This does not protect them from radiation, but it does measure how much radiation they are exposed to.

The badge contains a small piece of photographic film. Radiation affects the film inside the badge. When the film is developed, it is grey or black. The more radiation the worker has been exposed to, the darker the film appears. If someone is exposed to a high level of radiation, they may have to stop working with radioactive substances.

a Look at the holder for the film badge. It has different 'windows' which allow radiation to reach the film. This allows the wearer to know which types of radiation they have been exposed to.

One window has a thin layer of lead. Explain why only gamma radiation can penetrate through this window.

b Why does one window have no metal or plastic for the radiation to pass through?

Killing microbes, destroying cancer

The medical equipment in the photo is going to be sterilised using gamma radiation from an intense source. Hospitals need to be sure that their equipment is not contaminated with microorganisms which might harm their patients. When the equipment is exposed to strong radiation, any microorganisms are killed.

Other items, such as tampons, can be sterilised in this way. Some food is also sterilised; this is useful for some hospital patients, and for astronauts.

c Explain why alpha radiation would be no good for sterilising the syringes. Why is gamma radiation a good choice?

Radiation may cause cancer, but it can also be used to cure it. When a patient has cancer, their tumour may be given a high dose of radiation to kill the cancer cells.

The film is contained inside the blue plastic holder. The darker the developed film, the greater the amount of radiation to which the wearer has been exposed.

Gamma radiation is used to sterilise hospital equipment.

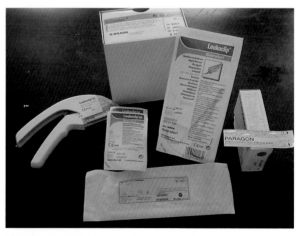

Veterinary equipment is also sterilised using gamma rays.

A look inside

You already know that one way to see inside a patient's body is to use X-rays. Another makes use of gamma radiation.

A radioactive substance which produces gamma radiation is pumped into the patient's bloodstream. It is designed to accumulate in cancerous tissue. The radiation emerging from the patient is recorded on a film or electronic detector.

The substance has a half-life of a few hours. In an application like this, it is important to choose a radioactive substance which has a suitable half-life, and which gives out a suitable form of radiation.

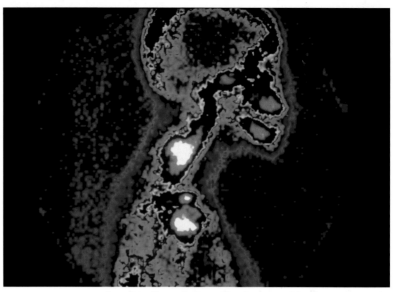
A radioactive substance has been used to show up a cancer in this patient.

d Explain why gamma radiation is a good choice for this.

e Explain why a substance with a half-life of a few minutes would not be suitable for this. Why would a substance with a half-life of several days also be unsuitable?

Questions

1 Copy out the following sentence, adding the correct ending:

   People who work with radioactive substances often wear a radiation badge ...

   ... to absorb any dangerous radiation.

   ... to see how much radiation they are exposed to.

   ... to warn others that they may be radioactive.

2 Explain how radiation from radioactive substances:

   a can cause cancer;

   b can help to cure cancer.

3 The photo shows a bridge being inspected using gamma radiation. The bridge is made of concrete and steel; the machine produces an image which shows up any cracks in the bridge. Explain why gamma radiation is a good choice for this.

4 The sterilising plant shown on the opposite page uses a radioactive form of cobalt with a half-life of 5 years.

   a Explain why the source must be replaced every 10 years or so.

   b Explain why a substance with a half-life of 5 days would be unsuitable.

Summary

- A radiation badge can show how much radiation the wearer has been exposed to.

- High doses of radiation can be used to kill harmful microorganisms and cancer cells.

- Radioactive substances are chosen according to the type of radiation they produce, and their half-life.

12:14 Inside the atom

To understand more about radioactivity, we need to have a picture of the particles which make up an atom. Like all scientific ideas, our idea of the structure of atoms has changed over the years. Experiments have revealed more and more about the world of the atom.

The drawings show two different pictures, or **models** of the atom. One is old and out of date; the other is still useful.

The model on the left is called the **plum pudding model** of the atom. Scientists knew that atoms were made up of positive and negative charge. They thought that an atom might be made up of a sphere of positive charge (the 'pudding'), with negatively charged electrons dotted around inside it (the 'plums').

This model was replaced by the model on the right, known as the **nuclear model**. The atom is shown with a tiny, positively charged **nucleus** at its centre. The electrons orbit around outside the nucleus.

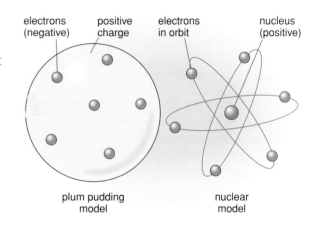

plum pudding model

nuclear model

a In the plum pudding model, what charge has the pudding, positive or negative? What charge have the 'plums'?

b In the nuclear model, what charge has the nucleus? What particles orbit the nucleus?

Rutherford's experiment

To understand why scientists changed their minds about the model of the atom, we need to study a famous experiment. It was thought up by Ernest Rutherford, and carried out by his assistants Geiger and Marsden, at Manchester University, in 1905.

They directed a beam of alpha radiation from a piece of radioactive material at a thin gold foil. The foil was so thin that most of the radiation went straight through it. However, Geiger and Marsden found a most surprising thing: some of the alpha radiation was reflected back towards the source. It appeared to be bouncing off something in the foil – this 'something' was the atomic nucleus.

Rutherford argued that the energetic alpha radiation would pass straight through 'plum pudding' atoms. He realised that the alpha radiation, which has positive electric charge, must be being repelled by the positive charge of the atom, concentrated in a tiny nucleus. In addition, he deduced that most of the mass of the atom must be concentrated in the nucleus.

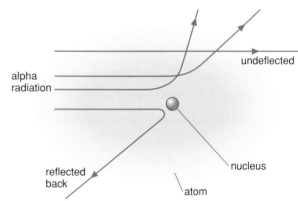

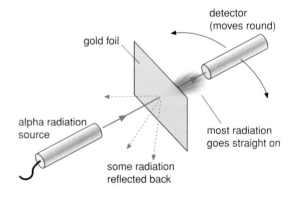

Today's picture

Rutherford's idea of the atom was soon accepted. Other experiments followed which supported his idea, and he used his model to explain what happens during radioactive decay.

Today, we know much more about atoms than was known 100 years ago. We picture each atom as being made up of three types of particles, protons and neutrons (in the nucleus), and electrons (orbiting outside the nucleus). The table gives details of these particles.

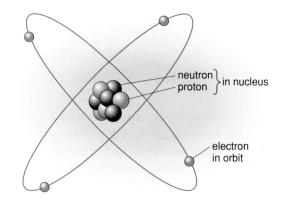

Particle	Mass	Charge	Position
proton	1	+1	in nucleus
neutron	1	0	in nucleus
electron	negligible	−1	outside nucleus

c An atom has equal numbers of protons and electrons. Use the information in the table to explain why this means that it has no overall charge – it is neutral.

Radiation from the nucleus

The radiation (alpha, beta or gamma) from an atom of a radioactive substance – comes from the nucleus of the atom. We now know that alpha and beta radiation are in the form of particles, whilst gamma radiation is a form of electromagnetic radiation with a very short wavelength.

Alpha particle	two protons + two neutrons (the nucleus of a helium atom)
Beta particle	an electron
Gamma ray	electromagnetic radiation

Questions

1 Copy and complete the following sentences; use words from the list to fill the gaps.

> neutral   positive   negative   electrons
> neutrons   protons   nucleus

The _____ of an atom contains _____ and _____ . It has a _____ charge.

Around this orbit the _____ . These have a _____ charge.

Because the amounts of positive and negative charge balance, an atom is _____ .

2 Which particles are being described here?

  a Smaller than an atom; neutral

  b Also known as a beta particle

  c Positively charged; made of two protons and two neutrons

3 This question is about Rutherford's experiment which showed the existence of the nucleus.

  a What radiation did he direct at the metal foil?

  b What metal was the foil made of?

  c What happened to most of the alpha radiation?

  d What did he discover that suggested that most of the mass of the atom was concentrated at its centre?

4 Suggest two reasons why Rutherford's model of the atom rapidly replaced the earlier plum pudding model.

Summary

- Rutherford's alpha particle-scattering experiment revealed that the atom has a nucleus at its centre.

- We can picture an atom as having a positively charged nucleus, with negatively charged electrons orbiting it. The nucleus consists of protons and neutrons, and contains most of the mass of the atom.

- Alpha, beta and gamma radiations are emitted by the nuclei of radioactive atoms.

If you could look very closely at an atom, how could you tell which element it was? Simple; count the number of protons in its nucleus. The number of protons in the nucleus tells you what element it is, because every atom of a particular element has the same number of protons. For example:

◆ An atom with 1 proton in its nucleus is an atom of hydrogen.

◆ An atom with 2 protons in its nucleus is an atom of helium.

◆ An atom with 6 protons in its nucleus is an atom of carbon.

◆ An atom with 92 protons in its nucleus is an atom of uranium.

And so on. (If you look at the Periodic Table, you will see that hydrogen is element number 1, helium is number 2, and so on.)

a **A neutral atom has 6 electrons orbiting its nucleus. How many protons has it in its nucleus? Of what element is it an atom?**

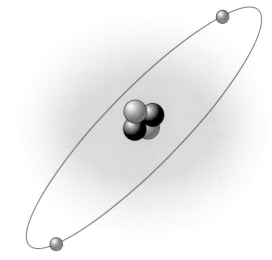

This atom has 2 protons and 2 neutrons in its nucleus; it is an atom of helium.

Isotopes

All carbon atoms have 6 protons in the nucleus. However, they are not all identical. Some have 6 neutrons, some have 7, and some have 8. The illustration shows these atoms. They are known as **isotopes** of carbon.

The **nucleon number** of an isotope is the total number of protons and neutrons (nucleons) in its nucleus.

$$\text{Nucleon number} = \text{number of protons} + \text{number of neutrons}$$

So the isotopes of an element all have the same number of protons but different nucleon numbers.

b **An atom of oxygen has 8 protons and 8 neutrons in its nucleus. What is its nucleon number?**

c **Another atom has 8 protons and 9 neutrons in its nucleus. Is it an isotope of oxygen, or a different element?**

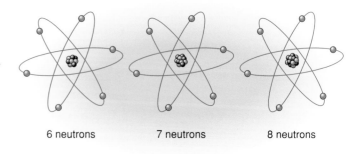

6 neutrons   7 neutrons   8 neutrons

Atoms of three isotopes of carbon.

Changing elements

In radioactive decay, an atom changes from one element to another. Why is this?

Radioactive isotopes are atoms with unstable nuclei. (They are also known as *radioisotopes* or *radionuclides*.) To become more stable, the nucleus of a radioactive isotope emits radiation. The radiation carries away mass and energy, and the nucleus of the atom is lighter. It has a different number of protons, so it has become an atom of a different element.

In alpha decay, the nucleus is left with two fewer protons.

In beta decay, a neutron becomes a proton, so the number of protons increases by 1.

(Gamma radiation only occurs alongside alpha or beta emission.)

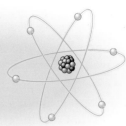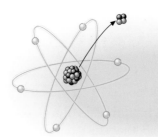

during radioactive decay   after radioactive decay

Nuclear fission

The reactor in a nuclear power station uses the process of **nuclear fission** (splitting). (So do some nuclear bombs.) Their fuel is usually uranium. Uranium atoms have very large nuclei, with over 230 nucleons.

◆ When a uranium nucleus is bombarded with neutrons, it splits into two smaller nuclei.

◆ More neutrons are released, together with energy.

◆ These neutrons can go on to cause more uranium nuclei to split – a **chain reaction**.

The new atoms formed are radioactive. These make the hazardous waste produced by nuclear power stations.

The energy released when an individual uranium nucleus splits is more than a million times greater than the energy released when a chemical bond forms between two atoms.

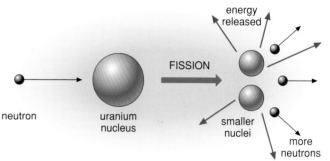

neutron   uranium nucleus   smaller nuclei   more neutrons   energy released   FISSION

Questions

1 Copy the table; put the words from the list in the correct places in the first column.

radioactive isotope   nuclear fission
nucleon number   number of protons

	the same for all atoms of a particular element
	different for isotopes of a particular element
	an atom with an unstable nucleus
	when a large nucleus splits

2 The table shows the particles which are found in the nuclei of three different atoms.

Atom 1	7 protons	7 neutrons
Atom 2	6 protons	7 neutrons
Atom 3	7 protons	6 neutrons

a Which two are isotopes of the same element?

b Which two have the same nucleon number?

3 On page 97, you learned about the composition of alpha and beta particles. Use this information to explain why:

a an atom loses two protons during alpha decay;

b there is one more proton in a nucleus after beta decay.

DIGGING DEEPER
There are many different models of the atom today. Each has its own uses. If you study chemistry, you will come across the idea that electrons do not behave as tiny particles in an atom; rather, they can be thought of as being smeared out into a cloud around the nucleus.

Summary

• All atoms of an element have the same number of protons; isotopes of an element have different nucleon numbers.

• Radioisotopes are atoms with unstable nuclei. They decay to become atoms of a different element.

The Earth is about 4.5 billion years old. How do we know that? What was the clock that started as the Earth formed, and which now tells us how long has passed?

The answer lies in the radioactivity of the rocks around us. When the Earth formed, from a swirling cloud of dust and gas, there was much more radioactivity around. The rocks of the new Earth contained much more uranium, radium and other radioactive isotopes than they do today. The Earth would have been a very dangerous place to live, with high levels of background radiation.

Today, the Earth is much safer because many of the radioisotopes in the rocks around us have decayed away to become stable atoms.

This geologist is collecting rock samples. By measuring their radioactivity, he can determine the age of the rocks.

The decay of uranium

Uranium is a radioactive substance which comes in several different forms (isotopes). Each isotope decays to become a radioisotope of another element, which in turn decays, until eventually a stable isotope of lead is formed. The diagram shows this series of decays.

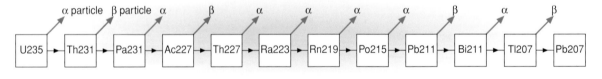

The decay series for one radioisotope of uranium. (The number next to the symbol for each element is the number of nucleons in its nucleus.)

a How many steps are there in the decay series shown? How many alpha decays are there, and how many beta decays?

It is interesting to realise that most of the lead in the Earth started off as uranium. Medieval alchemists tried to turn lead into gold; we now know that the reason we find lead in the Earth is that it is a stable element, that cannot easily be changed into any other.

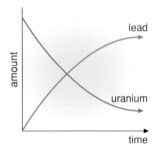

The amount of uranium in the Earth's rocks has gradually declined; the amount of lead has increased.

Now we can understand the radioactive 'clock' which allows geologists to find the age of the Earth. As time passes – billions of years – the amount of uranium in the Earth's rocks has gradually declined, and the amount of lead has increased. Geologists measure and compare the amounts of all the isotopes in the decay series. Because we know the half-life of each decay in the series, it is possible to work out how long the decay has been going on for.

This meteorite is a rock from the planet Mars. Geologists have measured the amounts of different isotopes within it to find its age. It is 4.5 billion years old, the same age as the Earth.

Igneous rocks

Another radioactive decay can be used to find the age of some types of igneous rocks. Igneous rocks form from hot, molten material. This often contains the radioisotope potassium-40, which slowly decays to become argon-40, a stable isotope.

At first, the newly formed rock contains no argon, because argon is a gas which escapes from the molten rock. As the potassium decays, argon is formed and remains trapped within the solid rock. Geologists take samples of the rock; they heat it to release the argon. By comparing the amounts of potassium-40 and argon-40, they can work out the age of the rock (how long it is since the rock was molten).

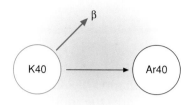

Potassium-40 (K40) decays to become argon-40 (Ar40).

b Sketch a graph to show how the amount of potassium-40 declines, and the amount of argon-40 increases, as a rock ages.

Dating other materials

Material from an organism which was once alive contains radioactive carbon-14 which it took in from the atmosphere. Once the organism has died, the carbon-14 gradually decays away. This can be used to date the material. Radiocarbon dating is used by archaeologists to find the age of material which is up to 50 000 years old.

> **DIGGING DEEPER**
> An ancient 'mummy' found in Iran in 1999 was shown to be less than 10 years old, by radiocarbon dating. It was a clever fake, offered for sale on the art market for millions of dollars.

Questions

1 Why is there less background radiation today than there was when the Earth formed, 4500 million years ago?

2 The decay of potassium-40 to argon-40 can be used to find the age of some rocks.

   a Read the sentence below and explain the meaning of each of the words in **bold**.

   The proportions of the **radioisotope** potassium-40 and its **stable** decay product argon can be used to **date** samples of an **igneous** rock from which the gaseous argon has been unable to escape.

   b Explain why it is important that the decay product argon is gaseous.

3 The graph shows the decay of the radioisotope potassium-40.

   a From the graph, deduce the half-life of potassium-40.

   b Measurements of a sample of igneous rock show that it contains 1 atom of argon-40 for every atom of potassium-40. What fraction of the potassium-40 originally in the rock has decayed?

   c Use the graph to estimate the age of the rock.

4 Geologists measure and compare the amounts of different radioisotopes of uranium and stable isotopes of lead in a sample of rock. Explain how this allows them to determine the age of the rock.

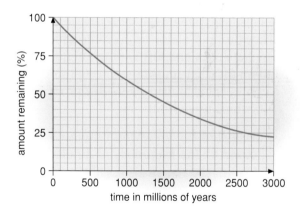

Summary

- We can find the age of rocks and other materials by measuring their radioactivity. The older the material, the less radiation it emits.

- The decays of uranium to lead, and of potassium-40 to argon-40, are used for dating igneous rocks.

We cannot see sounds, but we can use an oscilloscope to show us pictures of sound waves. The microphone turns the sound into an electrical signal, and this appears as a wiggly line on the oscilloscope screen.

Oscilloscope traces allow us to compare different sounds.

a **Look at the four oscilloscope traces in the diagrams (red, green, blue, black). Which sound has the greatest amplitude? Which has the lowest frequency? Explain your choices.**

Beyond hearing

Any sound which is too high for us to hear is called ultrasound. The frequency of **ultrasound** is higher than the upper limit of our hearing range, which is about 20 kHz (kilohertz).

Electronic systems can generate ultrasound. They produce electrical currents which oscillate back and forth at high frequencies. When these currents flow through a device such as a tiny loudspeaker, they produce ultrasonic waves in the air.

b **Which of the following frequencies could be the frequency of an ultrasound wave? 150 Hz, 15 kHz, 300 Hz, 30 kHz**

Ultrasound in medicine

Ultrasound is used to produce an image (a 'scan') of a baby in the womb. The operator moves the probe over the mother's stomach, and a picture appears on the screen. The same technique can be used for other medical purposes, such as looking for gallstones. Ultrasound is better than X-rays for this purpose; there is a slight risk to mother and baby from X-rays (which can cause cancer), but there is no evidence of any risk from ultrasound.

How does pre-natal scanning work? The probe sends ultrasound waves into the mother's body. When the waves reach a boundary between two different media, they

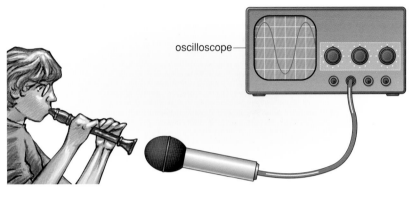

oscilloscope

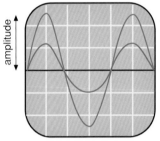

amplitude

The red trace has a greater amplitude than the green trace. It sounds louder.

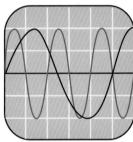

The blue trace has a higher frequency than the black trace (more waves per second). It would sound higher – it has a higher pitch.

Many creatures, such as this bat, produce ultrasound. Young people can hear sounds with frequencies up to about 20 kHz.

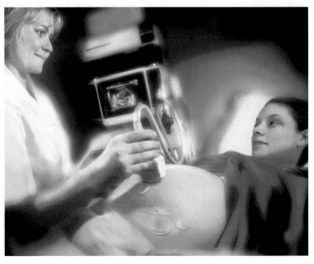

Pre-natal scanning: ultrasound waves reflect off the baby in the womb and are detected, to produce an image on the screen.

are partly reflected. (For example, the two media might be the fluid around the baby, and its flesh. A fraction of the wave is reflected; the rest continues onwards.) The probe also contains the detector, which picks up the reflected waves. It measures the time taken for the reflected waves to bounce back, and (knowing the speed of the waves) the distance from probe to boundary can be calculated.

A computer collects this information and processes it to build up the picture on the screen.

Ultrasound in industry

In a similar way, ultrasound can be used in industry to check for flaws in solid objects. For example, ultrasound waves can show up the presence of defects in railway lines; these cannot be seen from the outside. This is known as quality control.

Ultrasound is also used for cleaning. A jeweller may place a greasy, dirty item in a bath of cleaning fluid. Ultrasound waves are then used to shake the dirt off the item, without damaging it in any way. Delicate mechanisms can be cleaned in this way, without the need to take them apart.

c Explain why it would be better to check for a defect in a car axle using ultrasound, rather than cutting it open.

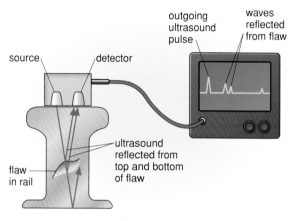

Ultrasound waves are passed into the rail; some of them reflect back from the flaw, and are detected.

Using ultrasound to check for defects in a large gear wheel.

Questions

1 Sketch an oscilloscope trace to represent two sound waves. Wave A has a greater amplitude than Wave B; it also has a higher frequency. Label the two waves.

2 Explain why cleaning using ultrasound is useful in industry.

3 Copy the diagram which shows how ultrasound waves can be produced. Label it with words from the list.

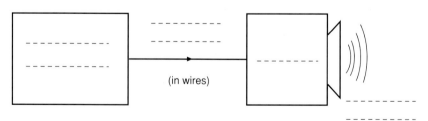

(in wires)

electrical oscillations   loudspeaker
electronic system   ultrasound waves

4 Ultrasound waves are used in pre-natal scanning.

a What does 'pre-natal' mean?

b Why is ultrasound scanning safer than using X-rays?

c Ultrasound waves are partly reflected when they pass from one medium to another. Explain how this allows us to see organs and bones within the body.

Summary

• Ultrasound waves are sound waves with frequencies higher than the limit of human hearing.

• Ultrasound can be used in medicine for pre-natal scanning, and in industry for quality control and for cleaning.

12:18 Inside the Earth

In the Earth materials module, you learned about the structure of the Earth. The drawing shows the important features.

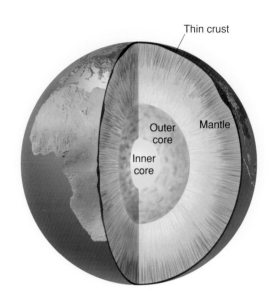

- We live on the thin, solid crust.

- The mantle is made of hot rock. It extends halfway to the centre of the Earth.

- The core is very dense, because it is made of iron and nickel. The outer core is molten (liquid). The inner core is solid.

a Which layer of the Earth is hottest? Which is coolest?

A look inside

We can't see inside the Earth, and we can't drill down as far as the mantle. So how do we know about the structure of the Earth?

The answer is that we make use of earthquakes. An earthquake sends strong vibrations (**seismic waves**) right through the Earth. These can be recorded by scientists using instruments called **seismographs**.

A seismograph produces a trace which is like a graph showing the vibrations which have travelled through the Earth. The stronger the earthquake, and the closer the seismograph is to where it happened, the greater the amplitude of the trace.

This building was built to be strong enough to withstand an earthquake. Unfortunately, that didn't stop it from falling over backwards when a quake came.

A seismograph, and the trace produced by a major earthquake.

P and S waves

There are two types of seismic wave:

- P waves (or primary waves): These are detected first, because they travel fastest. They are longitudinal waves.

- S waves (or secondary waves): Travel more slowly. They are transverse waves.

Both types of wave can travel through solid materials, but only P waves can travel through a liquid such as the molten core of the Earth.

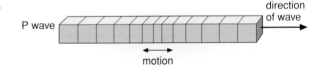

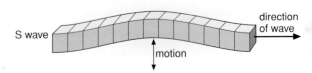

Through the Earth

In the event of an earthquake, P and S waves spread out through the Earth. Both travel along curved paths through the mantle. (Their paths are curved because they are speeding up as they go.) When they strike the surface of the core, two things happen:

◆ P waves are partly reflected, partly refracted.

◆ S waves are reflected; they cannot enter the liquid core.

Seismograph stations around the world pick up the waves. Knowing how long these have taken to reach their destination, geologists can then use their measurements to build up a picture of the inside of the Earth, in just the same way that an ultrasound scanner builds up an image of an unborn child.

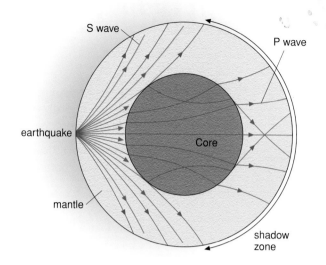

P waves change direction abruptly when they are refracted.

Questions

1 Copy the table; use the words from the list to complete it.

P waves	_____ waves	travel _____	travel through _____ and _____
S waves	_____ waves	travel _____	travel through _____ but not _____

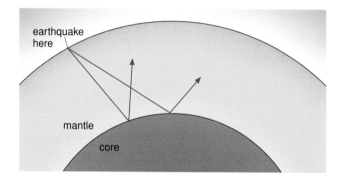

**slower   faster   solids   liquids
longitudinal   transverse**

2 The diagram shows how a shock wave travels through the Earth.

   a Copy the diagram, and mark on it two places where seismographs would detect shock waves.

   b Explain how scientists can use their findings to understand the inside of the Earth.

3 When astronauts visited the Moon, they left a seismograph. Later, a disused spacecraft was crashed onto the Moon's surface. Why do you think this was done?

4 Look at the diagram at the top of the page which shows how P and S waves travel through the Earth. Explain what 'shadow zones' are, and why they occur.

DIGGING DEEPER
At the start of 'Science Year' in 2001, over one million UK schoolchildren jumped simultaneously. The resulting vibrations were detected on seismographs around the country, including many home-made ones.

Summary
• Earthquakes produce two types of seismic waves, P and S, which can be detected using seismographs.

• By studying how seismic waves travel through the Earth, we can find out about its structure.

End of module questions

1. Jane has tied one end of a rope to a hook on the wall. She is moving the other end up and down, so that waves travel along the rope.

   The diagram shows the waves on the rope at one instant.

   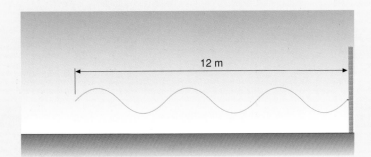

   12 m

   a Are these waves transverse or longitudinal? Give a reason to support your answer.

   b How many complete waves are there along the length of the rope?

   c What is the wavelength of the waves?

2. Sound travels as waves.

   a Does sound travel as transverse or longitudinal waves?

   b Sound waves cannot travel through a vacuum. Give an example of a wave which does not need a medium through which to travel.

   A loudspeaker produces sound waves whose frequency is 100 Hz. Their wavelength is 3 m.

   c Write down an equation which connects **wave speed**, **frequency** and **wavelength**.

   d Calculate the speed of the sound waves.

3. A ripple tank is useful for looking at waves on the surface of water. In the diagram, ripples are travelling across the water. When they pass through the gap in the barrier, they spread out into the space beyond.

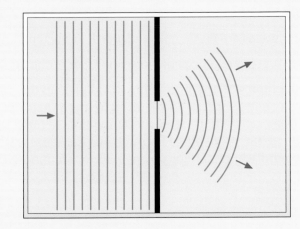

   a Is this an example of reflection, refraction or diffraction?

   b Radio signals also spread out when they pass through a gap. What does this suggest about radio signals? Give an example of a situation when this would be useful.

4. The diagram shows an infrared ray travelling down an optical fibre.

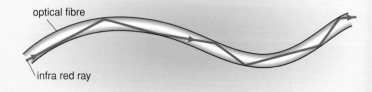

optical fibre

infra red ray

   a Copy the diagram, and mark with an X the points at which the ray undergoes total internal reflection.

   Optical fibres are often used to transmit information such as television signals, instead of cables carrying electrical signals.

   b Give two advantages of optical fibres over cables.

5 The diagram shows how a concert may be transmitted to our homes. The signal is coded as a series of pulses.

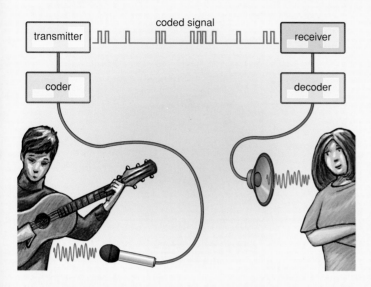

coded signal

transmitter · coder · receiver · decoder

a Is this an analogue or a digital signal?

b As analogue signals travel, their quality deteriorates. State two ways in which this can happen.

c State two advantages which digital signals have over analogue signals for transmitting information over long distances.

6 The radiation produced by radioactive substances can be hazardous. Explain in as much detail as you can how radiation can damage cells and thus lead to cancer.

7 The graph shows how the amount of radiation coming from two samples of different radioactive substances gradually decreased.

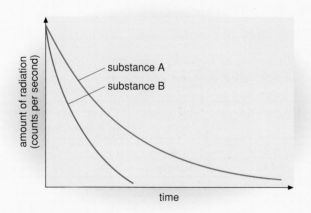

substance A
substance B

amount of radiation (counts per second)

time

a Explain what we mean by the half-life of a radioactive substance.

b From the graph, deduce which of the two substances had the longer half-life.

8 The table shows the count rate measured for a radioactive substance. The background count rate was 50 counts per second.

a Copy the table; add another row, and use it to show the values of the corrected count rate.

b What was the initial corrected count rate?

c How can you tell from the table that the substance was decaying?

d Draw a graph to represent the corrected data.

e Use your graph to work out the half-life of the radioactive substance.

Count rate in counts per second	670	560	460	390	330	280
Time in minutes	0	5	10	15	20	25

9 When a radioisotope emits radiation, it becomes an atom of a different element.

a Explain why a radioisotope which emits an alpha particle becomes an atom of a different element.

b Explain why a radioisotope which emits a beta particle becomes an atom of a different element.

10 a What particles cause the nucleus of a uranium atom to split, during nuclear fission?

b What is meant by a chain reaction?

c What can you say about the new atoms formed when a uranium atom is split?

11 An atom of a particular isotope of nitrogen contains 7 protons and 7 neutrons.

a In which part of the atom are these particles found?

b What is the nucleon number of this atom?

c How many electrons are there in a neutral atom of this isotope?

d There are other isotopes of nitrogen. How do their atoms differ from this one?

12 A geologist has been taking samples of granite rock from two different areas of the country. She finds that both have a similar composition, but one emits more radiation than the other. Explain what this suggests about the ages of the two rock samples.

13 Ultrasonic waves can be used for pre-natal scanning. They travel through different materials at different speeds.

Material	Speed in m/s
air	330
bone	3400
fat	1480
muscle	1540
saline gel	1520

When ultrasound passes from one material into another, some is reflected. The greater the difference in speeds in the two materials, the greater the amount of reflection. The drawing shows the normal arrangement for producing an ultrasound scan.

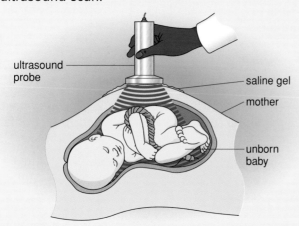

a At which of the following would reflection of ultrasound be greatest?

- where saline gel meets fat
- where muscle meets fat
- where air meets muscle

b Explain why the saline gel is important for getting a good picture. (Refer to the data in the table above.)

14 a The following sentences describe Rutherford and Marsden's experiment which allowed them to develop a new model of the atom. Complete the sentences by filling the gaps.

Rutherford and Marsden directed _____ radiation on to a thin _____ foil.

To their surprise, a small proportion of the radiation was _____.

They guessed that this radiation had been repelled by the _____ charge of the atomic nucleus.

They were able to reject the old _____ _____ model of the atom.

b Give one reason why their new model of the atom very quickly became widely accepted.

15 The diagram shows ripples in a ripple tank (viewed from above).

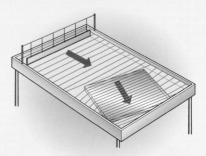

a On the right, the ripples are travelling more slowly. Why have they slowed down?

b What do we call the change in direction of ripples which can happen when they change speed?

c Draw a diagram to show how a ray of light changes direction when it travels from air into glass. How does this relate to the diagram of ripples shown above?

d A ray of light usually bends when it travels from air into glass. Under what circumstances does it not bend?

16 A teacher is showing the class the properties of radiation coming from a radioactive substance.

- She measures the radiation coming directly from the source.
- Then she repeats her measurements with various materials placed between the source and the detector.
- Finally she removes the source and measures the level of background radiation.

The table shows the results.

What type of radiation did the source give out? Explain your answer as fully as you can.

Absorber	Thickness	Count rate (counts in 1 minute)
none		470
paper	0.5 mm	472
aluminium	5 mm	120
lead	3 cm	114
background		119

Module 2: Humans as organisms

Material included in paper 1

Breaking down food

Most of the foods you eat are made from large, insoluble molecules. These have to be broken down into small, soluble molecules which can dissolve in your blood and be carried around your body.

Your digestive system produces enzymes which breakdown large, insoluble molecules into small, soluble molecules. Each type of food needs a particular enzyme to break it down.

- Carbohydrase enzymes breakdown carbohydrates into sugars.

- Protease enzymes breakdown proteins into amino acids.

- Lipase enzymes breakdown fats into fatty acids and glycerol.

In addition to these enzymes bile is released from your liver. Bile breaks down fats into tiny fat droplets. This process is called emulsification.

Getting food into the body

Molecules of digested food are small enough to be absorbed through your gut wall. The wall of your small intestine is very efficient in absorbing food because:

- It contains thousands of tiny folds called villi which create a very large surface area.

- Each villus contains many blood capillaries to transport absorbed food.

- Each villus is very thin so that food molecules can easily reach the bloodstream.

Releasing and using energy

Your body is always using energy to:

- Build large molecules from smaller ones so that you can grow and repair damaged cells.

- Make muscles contract so that you can move.

- Keep your body temperature steady.

This energy comes from glucose in your blood – glucose is your body's main fuel.

Glucose and oxygen react together in the mitochondria of body cells to release energy. This process is aerobic respiration and is summarised as:

$$\text{glucose} + \text{oxygen} \rightarrow \frac{\text{carbon}}{\text{dioxide}} + \text{water (+energy)}$$

Sometimes your body cannot get enough oxygen. When this happens glucose is broken down without using oxygen. This process called anaerobic respiration produces lactic acid as a waste product. Anaerobic respiration is summarised as:

$$\text{Glucose} \rightarrow \text{lactic acid (+ energy)}$$

Recap questions

 a Explain why the digestive system produces enzymes.

b The diagram shows an experiment on digestion. Cellophane tubing allows small molecules to pass through but not large molecules.

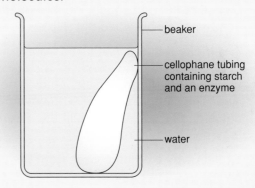

The experiment was left for 30 minutes. The water and the contents of the cellophane tubing were then tested for starch and for sugar. The results are shown in the table.

	Result of starch test	Result of sugar test
Water from beaker	negative	positive
Contents of cellophane tubing	positive	positive

Explain the results shown in the table.

2 A student breathed out into an empty breathing bag 5 times.

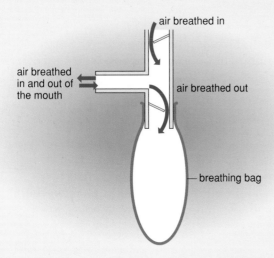

air breathed in

air breathed in and out of the mouth

air breathed out

breathing bag

a After the student had breathed out 5 times, the volume of air in the bag was 2500 cm^3.

The student then used an exercise machine. While she was exercising, she again breathed out 5 times into the bag. This time the volume of air in the bag was 8000 cm^3.

Calculate the percentage increase in the volume of air breathed out.

b A sample of blood was taken from the student before and after the exercise. The sample taken before the exercise contained no lactic acid. The sample taken after the exercise contained lactic acid. Explain the difference between the two results.

c Explain why oxygen passes from the air in the alveoli into the blood.

3 **a** Which part of the blood transports most of the:

i oxygen

ii carbon dioxide?

The graph shows how the circulation of blood changes between rest and exercise.

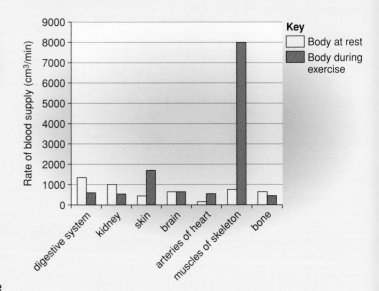

b **i** Calculate the percentage change in the rate of blood supply to the whole body.

Explain the advantage to the body of the changes in blood supply to:

• the muscles of the skeleton

• the skin

• the digestive system.

ii How does the rate of blood flow change during exercise in the digestive system?

iii How does the rate of blood flow change during exercise in the arteries of the heart?

iv During exercise, explain how the change in the rate of blood supply to the muscles attached to the skeleton helps the body.

Material included in paper 1

Starch (a carbohydrate), proteins and fats are insoluble. They are broken down into insoluble substances so that they can be absorbed into the bloodstream in the wall of the small intestine. In the large intestine much of the water is absorbed into the bloodstream. The indigestible food which remains makes up the bulk of the faeces. Faeces leave the body via the anus.

The breathing system takes air into and out of the body so that oxygen from the air can diffuse into the bloodstream and carbon dioxide can pass out of the bloodstream into the air.

During vigorous exercise, muscle cells may be short of oxygen. They can then obtain energy from glucose by anaerobic respiration (respiration which does not use oxygen).

The waste product from this process is lactic acid. The body then needs oxygen to break down this lactic acid. The oxygen that is needed is called an oxygen debt.

Blood consists of a fluid called plasma in which are suspended white blood cells, platelets and red blood cells.

Plasma transports:

- carbon dioxide from the organs to the lungs;
- soluble products of digestion from the small intestine to other organs;
- urea from the liver to the kidneys.

Photosynthesis is summarised by the equation:

$$\text{carbon dioxide} + \text{water} + [\text{light energy}] \rightarrow \text{glucose} + \text{oxygen}$$

During photosynthesis:

- light energy is absorbed by a green substance called chlorophyll which is found in chloroplasts in some plant cells;
- this energy is used by converting carbon dioxide and water into sugar (glucose);
- oxygen is released as a by-product.

Waste products which have to be removed from the body include:

- carbon dioxide produced by respiration – most of this leaves the body via the lungs when we breathe out;
- urea produced in the liver by the breakdown of excess amino acids – this is removed by the kidneys in the urine; which is temporarily stored in the bladder.

Internal conditions which are controlled include:

- the water content of the body – water leaves the body via the lungs when we breathe out and via the skin when we sweat, and excess is lost via the kidneys in the urine;
- the ion content of the body – ions are lost via the skin when we sweat and excess ion is lost via the kidneys in urine;
- temperature – to maintain the temperature at which enzymes work best.

The kidneys help to maintain the internal environment by:

- filtering the blood;
- re-absorbing all the sugar;
- re-absorbing the dissolved ions needed by the body;
- re-absorbing as much water as the body needs;
- releasing urea, excess ions and excess water as urine.

The kidneys produce dilute urine if there is too much water in the blood or concentrated urine if there is too little water in the blood. If the water content of the blood is too low, the pituitary gland releases a hormone called ADH into the blood. This causes the kidneys to re-absorb more water and results in more concentrated urine. If the water content of the blood is too high, less ADH is released into the blood. Less water is re-absorbed in the kidneys resulting in a more dilute urine.

Body temperature is monitored and controlled by the thermoregulatory centre in the brain. This centre has receptors sensitive to the temperature of blood flowing through the brain. Also, temperature receptors in the skin send impulses to the centre giving information about skin temperature.

If the core body temperature is too high:

- blood vessels supplying the skin capillaries dilate so that more blood flows through the capillaries and more heat is lost;
- sweat glands release more sweat which cools the body as it evaporates.

If the core temperature is too low:

- blood vessels supplying the skin capillaries constrict to reduce the flow of blood through the capillaries;
- muscles may 'shiver' – their contraction needs respiration which releases some energy as heat.

Recap questions

 1 The kidneys remove waste materials from the blood plasma.

The table shows the concentration of certain substances:

- in blood plasma entering the kidneys
- in the urine.

Substance	Concentration (%)	
	in blood plasma entering the kidneys	in urine
Protein	7	0
Salt	0.35	0.5
Glucose	0.1	0
Urea	0.03	2.0

a Explain the results for:

i the concentrations of substances in the liquid filtered by the kidneys

ii the concentrations of substances in the urine.

b Explain how ADH affects the functioning of the kidneys.

2 The graph shows the concentration of sugars in a plant leaf during a period of 24 hours.

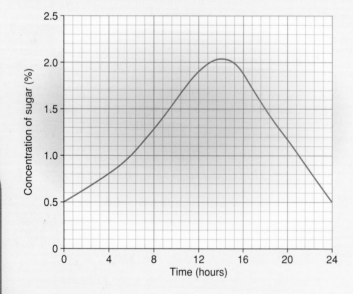

a i What was the maximum concentration of sugars in the leaf?

ii By how much did the sugar concentration change between 16 hours and 20 hours?

b Explain why the concentration of sugars rises between 0 and 14 hours.

c Explain why the concentration of sugars falls between 14 hours and 24 hours.

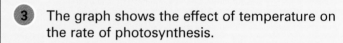 **3** The graph shows the effect of temperature on the rate of photosynthesis.

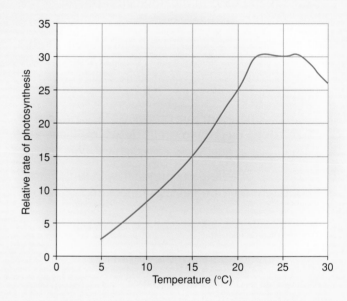

a Describe the effect of temperature on the rate of photosynthesis.

b Explain the results in terms of limiting factors.

Material included in paper 1

Where do metals fit into a table of the elements?
More than three-quarters of all elements are metals. They are found to the left and centre of the periodic table.

Groups 1 and 2 are very reactive, low density metals. Group 1 (alkali) metals such as sodium react with water, giving off hydrogen and leaving an alkaline solution of the metal hydroxide. They form colourless, water-soluble, ionic compounds with non-metals.

The transition metals, such as iron and copper, are found in the middle block of the periodic table. Like all metals these are good conductors or heat and electricity and can be easily bent or hammered into shape. Unlike the alkali metals they have high melting points (except mercury) and are hard and strong. This makes them useful as structural materials. They are less reactive and do not corrode so quickly with air and/or water. They form coloured compounds which are used in pottery glazes. The metals and their compounds are also used as catalysts.

How are metals extracted from their ores?
How a metal is obtained from its ore depends on how reactive it is. Metals can be arranged in a reactivity series, with the most reactive metals at the top. A more reactive metal can displace a less reactive metal from its compound.

How can metal compounds be made?
Metal compounds, called salts, can be made by reacting the metal hydroxide (an alkali) with an acid. Neutralisation occurs:

acid + alkai → salt + water

The salt formed depends on the metal in the alkali and the acid used.

Recap questions

Reactivity	Element
High	Potassium
	Sodium
	a
	Magnesium
	Aluminium
	b
	Iron
	Lead
	c
Low	Copper

The table shows the reactivity series of metals. Iron is made from iron ore by carbon reduction but aluminium cannot.

a Name a metal that could displace iron from iron sulphate solution.

b Non-metals can fit into this series. Where should carbon fit into this table (a,b or c)

c Lead slowly reacts with acid to give a salt and hydrogen gas. Copper never does this. Where should hydrogen fit into this table (a,b or c)

d Sodium is made by the electrolysis of molten sodium chloride. Explain why it cannot be made by carbon reduction.

e Iron could be made by electrolysing molten iron oxide. Instead it is made by heating iron oxide with coke (carbon) in a blast furnace. Suggest why this method is used instead of electrolysis.

f Iron can also be made by reacting iron oxide with aluminium in a thermit reaction. Suggest why this method of iron production is not used commercially.

2 Sodium reacts with water:

sodium + water → sodium hydroxide + hydrogen

$$Na + H_2O \rightarrow NaOH + H_2$$

a Balance this equation and add state symbols.

b What would happen if you put pH paper in the water after this reaction?

c What type of reaction is this?

d Explain why sodium metal cannot be produced by the electrolysis of salt solution.

e Lithium fizzes in water. What gas do you think is given off?

f What is the name of the alkali that forms in the water?

g Write word and balanced symbolic equations for this reaction.

3 a What is the name of the block of metals that wedges in between calcium (Z=20) and gallium (Z=31)?

b Normally the properties of the elements changes dramatically as you move along the same period. What is unusual about this block of metals?

c Iron (Z=26) is a hard magnetic metal with a high melting point which forms coloured compounds. Nickel (Z=28) is a hard magnetic metal with a high melting point which forms coloured compounds. Predict the properties of cobalt (Z=27).

4 Look again at the reactivity series shown in Q1. Zinc fits in just above iron and below carbon.

a Zinc occurs naturally as zinc sulphide ore. The first stage of zinc production is to roast this ore in air, forming zinc oxide and sulphur dioxide. Write a word equation for this reaction. (What gas in air is reacting?)

b Zinc oxide (ZnO) is then heated with coke (carbon) to extract the metal. What gas is formed?

c Write word and balanced symbolic equations for this reaction.

d Why isn't electrolysis used to get the zinc?

e Zinc dissolves in sulphuric acid to give zinc sulphate. A gas is given off. What is the gas?

f This gas comes from the acid. Why is zinc able to 'push it out' of the acid?

g Write word and balanced symbolic equations for this reaction.

h How could you get crystals of zinc sulphate from this reaction?

6 What salt (if any) would you get if you reacted:

a Hydrochloric acid (HCl) and magnesium oxide (MgO).

b Hydrochloric acid and magnesium metal.

c Sulphuric acid (H_2SO_4) and copper oxide (CuO).

d Sulphuric acid and copper metal.

e Nitric acid (HNO_3) and zinc carbonate ($ZnCO_3$).

f Nitric acid and sodium hydroxide (NaOH).

Write word and balanced symbolic equations for each reaction.

7 The flow diagram shows how various products are made from rock salt (natural sodium chloride found as beds in some sedimentary rocks).

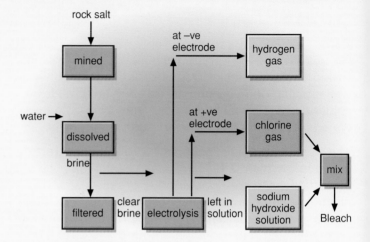

a Describe in **words** how bleach is made from rock salt.

b Use your knowledge of the reactivity series to explain why hydrogen gas forms at the negative electrode rather than sodium metal.

c Describe in simple terms how you could get metallic sodium from sodium chloride.

8 The table below shows the properties of some common metals.

Metal	Density (gcm^{-2})	Melting point (°C)
aluminium	2.7	660
copper	8.9	280
gold	18.9	1064
iron	7.9	1540
lead	11.3	327
mercury	13.6	-39
tungsten	19.4	3410

a Which metal is liquid at room temperature (25°C)?

b Why is tungsten used as the filament of electric light bulbs instead of aluminium?

c A lead weight is dropped into mercury. Does it float or sink? Explain why.

d A gold ring is dropped into mercury. Does it float or sink? Explain why.

e You can melt copper wire in a roaring Bunsen burner flame, but not iron wire. Suggest the temperature reached by a roaring flame.

f Use the periodic table to find which of these metals are not transition metals.

Module 3 – Environment

The photographs show some of the concerns that people have about the environment.

Animals can live almost anywhere, but we are destroying many of their habitats.

Forests are being cut down faster than they are being replaced.

We are polluting our environment.

Most of us are concerned about the environment. TV programmes about natural history bring animals and plants from distant parts of the world into our living rooms. But the programmes also bring news about the way we are affecting our planet. Already we are beginning to see climate changes that may bring disasters to many parts of the world. The world is not ours to use as we wish; we hold it in trust for future generations. So we must look after the Earth and its resources.

Recycling our resources is the only sustainable way forward.

This module, Environment, will help you to understand how animals and plants are adapted to live in harsh environments, and the factors that affect the sizes of their populations. You will then learn how energy from the Sun is transferred to living organisms, and how living organisms cycle natural materials. Finally, you will learn about the effects that humans have on the environment, and what we can do to preserve our world for future generations.

Climate change will make scenes like his more common.

Before you start, try these questions to check what you know about organisms and their environment.

1 List the factors that organisms need to survive.

2 What is meant by a food chain?

3 Why are green plants called producers?

4 What is a pyramid of numbers?

5 Spraying insecticides on crops may be dangerous to other organisms. Explain why.

In 1911, Sir Robert Scott led an expedition to reach the South Pole. Five of the team trekked to the Pole dragging their supplies of food and fuel on sledges. They reached the South Pole, but every member of the team died on the way back as the weather turned to blizzards and their supplies ran out.

a   What do humans need to take with them to survive in arctic conditions?

Humans are not adapted to living in very cold places like the Antarctic, but some animals have ingenious adaptations that allow them to survive in freezing climates.

The emperor penguin

Emperor penguins survive long periods in the conditions that killed Scott and his team. Penguin feathers are different from the feathers of other species of birds. At the base of each feather is a fluffy tuft of 'hairs'. These fluffy tufts overlap to form a mat that covers the whole of the penguin's body. Wind and water cannot get through this mat.

b   How do these special feathers help the penguins to survive in the Antarctic?

Emperor penguins spend the summer feeding on fish and become very fat. At end of summer, fat makes up about half of the body mass of the male penguin.

c   Give two advantages to the male penguin of having so much fat around his body.

As winter sets in and ice begins to cover the sea, pairs of penguins begin a long trek over the ice to their breeding sites on land. This trek can be as long as 150 km. The pairs of penguins mate, and then each female lays one egg. The male takes the egg from her and places it in a fold of feather-covered skin that hangs down from his abdomen.

The female then returns to the sea to feed but the male stands, keeping the egg off the ground, for 60 days until it hatches.

When there are blizzards, the penguins huddle together.

d   Explain how huddling together helps the penguins to survive blizzards.

Once hatched, the young chick stands on its father's feet, under the fold of skin to keep warm. While incubating the egg, the male loses about one third of his body mass.

e   Explain why the male lose so much body mass.

By the day after the egg has hatched, the female returns from the sea bringing food for the chick. The male now makes the long trek back to the sea to feed and replenish his fat stores.

Humans need to take all kinds of special clothing and equipment to survive in freezing conditions.

Emperor penguins are adapted to survive a very cold climate. This male is incubating an egg.

The penguins huddle together on the ice.

The musk ox

Musk oxen live in the Arctic tundra. They look a lot like bison but they have wool, like sheep. Wool traps air next to the body. Air is a poor conductor of heat.

f Explain how the coat of the musk ox helps it to survive in the Arctic.

The snowy owl

Snowy owls live in the Arctic. They feed on small mammals such as mice and lemmings. In summer, snowy owls are brownish with dark spots and stripes. In winter, they are completely white.

g What is the advantage to the snowy owl of being white in winter?

Surface area to volume ratio

As organisms increase in size, both body volume and surface area increase. But these two do not increase in the same proportion.

h Work out the volume and the surface area of a 1 mm cube. Now work out the volume and surface area of a 5 mm cube. What do you notice about the surface area and the volume of the two cubes?

How does the relationship between surface area and volume affect the rate of heat loss from animals that live in freezing conditions? Look at the photographs.

Both Weddell seals and lemmings are mammals – so they have a high, constant body temperature. Weddell seals are enormous, but you can hold a lemming in the palm of your hand.

i Which animal – a seal or a lemming – is likely to lose most heat per gram of body mass? Explain your answer.

The lemming burrows under the snow in the winter to keep warmer, but the Weddell seal can hunt all winter in ice-cold water. The seal can do this because it has a small **surface area to volume ratio**.

j Explain how the seal's body features help to reduce its surface area.

Questions

1 Sea otters do not have a thick layer of fat like seals, but they have a very thick, fine fur. Explain how this helps to keep them both warm and buoyant.

2 Arctic gulls have an interesting circulatory system in their legs: the artery supplying blood to each foot also supplies a network of capillaries that surrounds the vein ascending from the foot. Explain the advantage of this to the gull.

3 The male emperor penguin does not drink during the 60 days he is incubating the egg, but he does not dehydrate. Suggest an explanation for this.

Musk ox.

Snowy owl.

Weddell seal.

Lemming.

Summary

- Animals living in freezing climates often have white coats for **camouflage**.

- Many have a thick layer of fat under the skin for **insulation**.

- Many have thick hair or feathers to trap air, which insulates the body.

- As animals increase in size, the ratio of their surface area to their volume decreases. Small animals therefore have a greater rate of heat loss per unit of volume than large animals.

- Many animals adapted to the cold have small body parts to reduce the area through which heat is lost.

3:2 Living in hot places

The photograph shows part of the Sahara desert. You can't see any animals or plants – it is rare to see desert animals during the day. Desert animals need to have many specialised features in order to survive in difficult conditions.

a **Why do animals find it difficult to live in the desert?**

Keeping out of the sun

Not many animals can survive in deserts. Those that do come out to feed at dawn and dusk. The photographs show some of these desert animals.

b **The animals in the photographs all have a similar colour. What are the advantages of this colour to the animals?**

Most of these desert animals are small. Apart from camels, there are no animals as big as polar bears and Weddell seals.

c **Explain why it is a disadvantage to be a large animal in the desert.**

During the heat of the day, most desert animals sleep in a cool den or burrow, or under rocks and boulders.

d **If humans stay out in the hot desert sun, we can lose up to one litre of sweat per hour. Explain why sweating cools us down.**

e **The mammals in the photographs all have short hair. Why is this an advantage in the desert?**

Cooling down

Most mammals have body temperatures similar to humans – about 37 °C. Temperatures in hot deserts are often more than 40 °C and sometimes reach above 60 °C.

Instead of trying to conserve heat, like animals adapted to cold climates, many desert animals have adaptations for cooling down.

Big ears
The fennec, the jack rabbit and the bandicoot all have big ears. These ears act like the radiator in a car. A car radiator receives hot water from the car engine, gives out heat to the environment, then returns cooler water to the engine.

Large ears receive warm blood from the body, give out heat to the environment, then return cooler blood to the body.

f **Describe how the blood supply to the skin capillaries in the ears of these animals can be varied.**

g **Explain the advantage to the animal of being able to control the blood supply to these capillaries.**

The Sahara desert is one of the hottest environments in the world.

Bandicoot.

Fennec.

Caracal.

Sidewinder snake.

Jack rabbit.

Panting

Desert birds have feathers like all other birds. These feathers insulate the birds' bodies so they are as good at keeping heat out as they are at keeping it in. Even so, desert birds sometimes overheat.

Birds do not have sweat glands so they have developed other methods of cooling down. Desert owls 'pant' to keep cool. They open their mouths, and then flutter their throats to evaporate water from the lining of the mouth.

h How does this cool them down?

i What is the big disadvantage of this method of cooling down for a desert bird?

Getting water

Many desert animals never get to drink water – it is always too far away. Adult sand grouse, however, will often fly up to 40 km to a pool to collect water for their young. They have special feathers on their chest that soak up water just like a sponge. When the adult gets back to the nest the young birds suck the water from the breast feathers.

Desert animals get water in the food they eat. Most of their food contains water, particularly when the food is a juicy animal!

Kangaroo rats will not drink water even if you provide it. Their diet consists mainly of dry seeds, which do not contain any water at all. These animals manufacture their own water from the food they eat.

South African sand grouse.

Kangaroo rat.

In aerobic **respiration**, glucose from food is oxidised:

glucose + oxygen → carbon dioxide + water

Water is one of the waste products – but it is far from 'waste' for the kangaroo rat. It is its only source of water.

j The symbol equation for respiration is:

$$C_6H_{12}O_6 + 6O_2 \rightarrow 6CO_2 + 6H_2O$$

What mass of water would the kangaroo rat get by oxidising 1 g of glucose? (RAMs: C=12, H=1, O=16)

k Kangaroo rats secrete much higher amounts of ADH than humans. Explain the advantage of this to the kangaroo rat.

Questions

1 New World vultures are dark in colour. What is the disadvantage of this colouring to a desert bird?

2 These vultures have an unusual cooling method – they excrete urine onto their legs. Explain how this method will lower the bird's body temperature.

DIGGING DEEPER

A tiny fish called the pupfish survives in Salt Creek on the floor of Death Valley in California. The pools in Salt Creek reach a temperature of 45 °C in mid afternoon. What does this tell you about the enzymes in the pupfish?

In summer, so much water evaporates from the pools that the salt concentration becomes three times greater than that in sea water. The pupfish must drink this water to survive. How might the pupfish get rid of the excess salt?

Summary

- Desert animals are often active only at dawn and dusk to avoid the midday sun.

- Desert animals are usually light in colour. This helps to camouflage them and reduces the amount of heat that they absorb.

- Some desert animals have large ears. These act as radiators, increasing the surface area for losing heat.

- Many desert animals have short hair – this does not trap much heat inside the body.

Cacti

Cacti range in size from the small ones that people grow in pots on windowsills to monsters such as the one shown in the photograph. They are adapted to grow in dry places.

Look at the photograph. You will notice that the cactus has a swollen stem and no leaves.

Most cacti have swollen stems. When part of a plant becomes swollen, it is usually to store something. Cactus stems are swollen to help them store water in order to survive in very dry places.

It is not quite true to say that cacti have no leaves at all. The leaves have not been lost – they have become much reduced in size, so that they loose very little water through **evaporation**. In fact, the leaves have evolved into small spines.

a **How else will having spines instead of leaves help cacti to survive?**

b **What is the big disadvantage to cacti in reducing the size of their leaves?**

Most plants manufacture food by **photosynthesis**. Light energy is absorbed by chlorophyll and used to convert carbon dioxide into sugars. Because cacti have such small leaves, they need to use their stems to produce food.

c **Cactus stems are normally green. Why is this?**

Cacti have other adaptations that help them to survive in hot, dry conditions. Their roots are very long so that they can reach down to any water stored far beneath the surface. They also have a waxy layer on their stems to help reduce water loss.

Some cacti can grow to an enormous size.

Sand dune plants

Not all dry places are hot. Some plants are adapted for living on Britain's sand dunes. Though their adaptations are not quite as drastic as those of cacti, their problem is the same – water is hard to come by, so they must prevent too much water loss.

d **Why is the soil on sand dunes usually dry when the dunes are so close to the sea?**

Most plants have large flat leaves with **stomata** on the under surface to allow carbon dioxide to enter. Water vapour is able to diffuse out of the leaf through these stomata.

Much of the coastline of Britain consists of sand dunes.

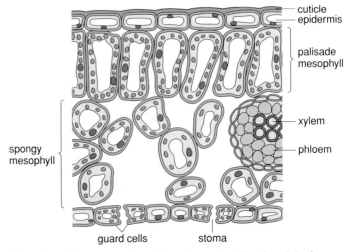
cuticle
epidermis
palisade mesophyll
xylem
phloem
spongy mesophyll
guard cells   stoma
Most plants have many stomata on the underside of each leaf.

Marram grass is a common plant on some parts of sand dunes. In wet conditions, its leaves are flat but in dry conditions its leaves roll up.

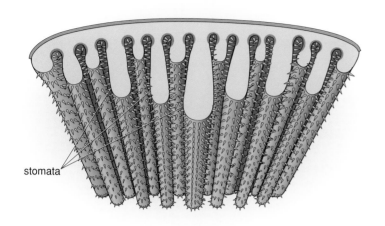

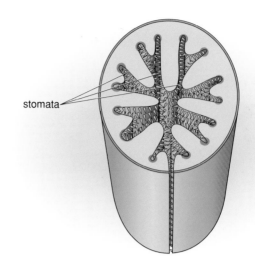

stomata

stomata

Marram grass leaves also have stomata on the underside, but the leaves roll up when there is little water available.

i Explain how rolling its leaves will help marram grass to conserve water.

Questions

1 The photograph shows a plant called a 'living-stone'. Read again about the adaptations of cacti. Then suggest four ways in which the 'living-stone' plant is adapted to living in a hot, stony desert.

The 'living-stone' plant lives in dry, stony places in hot deserts. It is about 4 cm in height.

2 Some plants produce different types of leaf in wet seasons and in dry seasons. The table shows the dimensions of the leaves of one of these plants.

Dimension	Spring leaf (wet season)	Summer leaf (dry season)
Length (mm)	30	50
Maximum width (mm)	10	1
Surface area (mm^2)	300	150
Volume (mm^3)	60	60

a Calculate the ratio of the surface area to the volume of the two types of leaf.

b Explain the advantage to the plant of producing summer leaves.

c Give one disadvantage to the plant of producing summer leaves.

Summary

Plants may be adapted to survive in dry conditions by:

- having very small leaves
- storing water in swollen stems
- being covered by a thick layer of wax
- having long roots
- rolling their leaves

3:4 Plant competition

Why weed?

Farmers and gardeners get rid of weeds by digging them up, or by using chemicals called herbicides.

Farmers spend a lot of time, money and effort getting rid of weeds from their crops. To find out why, you need to think about the factors that plants need to grow.

Factor	Why it is needed for plant growth
Warmth	Enzymes work best in warm conditions.
Light	
Carbon dioxide	
Water	
Nitrates	

a Copy and complete the table to show why a plant needs each factor to grow. The first row has been done for you.

Weeds compete with crop plants for some of these factors. Plants must adapt if they are to survive this **competition**.

b The diagram shows weeds growing in a barley field.

  i What is the advantage to the barley plants in growing taller than the weeds?

  ii What do the barley plants and the weeds compete for in the soil?

  iii How will this competition affect the barley plants?

c Look at the diagram of weeds growing in a potato field.

  i Describe the differences between the potato plants and the barley plants.

  ii There are far fewer weeds in the potato crop than in the barley crop. Use information from your answer to (i) to suggest an explanation for this.

Chemicals called **herbicides** are used to kill the weeds in the barley crop, but the weeds in the potato crop are removed by hoeing – digging them up.

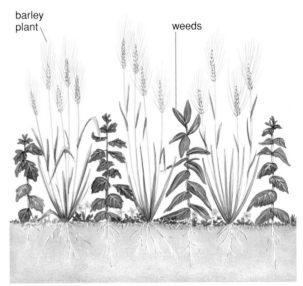

Barley is a cereal crop.

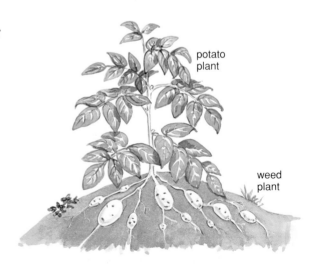

Potatoes are also grown as a food crop.

Planting seeds

Crop plants do not just compete with weeds – they compete with each other. So farmers need to know how close together they can grow crop plants so that they get the best results. Seed-planters can be programmed to sow a set number of seeds per square metre – the greater the number of seeds, the closer the plants grow to each other.

Some plants, such as cereal crops, are grown for their seeds. A farmer needs to get the highest number of seeds possible from his land. The graph shows the effect of planting different numbers of plants on the **yield** of seeds.

The seed yield of the crop depends on the number of plants grown per square metre.

d **i** What was the yield of seeds when 1000 plants were planted per m²?

  ii Copy and continue the graph to find the expected yield of seeds when 2500 plants are planted per m².

  iii How many plants would you advise the farmer to plant per m²?

  iv Explain why the yield of seeds was greater if 1000 plants were planted per m² rather than 2000 per m².

Questions

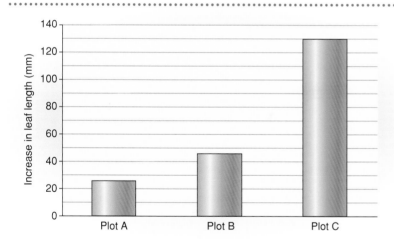

Bar chart to show how the growth of species X varied in plots A, B and C.

Scientists investigated competition between two related species of plant, X and Y. In plot A small individuals of species X were planted 10 cm from large individuals of species X. In plot B small individuals of species X were planted 10 cm from large individuals of species Y. In plot C small individuals of species X were planted at least 3 m from any other individual of X or Y. The bar chart shows the results after four weeks.

1 Describe the results of the investigation.

2 Suggest three factors that species X and Y might be competing for.

3 Which is the stronger competitor, X or Y? Explain the reason for your answer.

Summary

- Plants compete for:

  a light, which they need for photosynthesis

  b water, which they need for all their living processes

  c nitrates, which they need to make proteins

  d space in which their roots and leaves can grow.

- Plants compete with both:

  a plants of the same species

  b plants of different species.

- Competition between weeds and crop plants results in a reduction in the yield of the crop plant.

3:5 Animal competition

Animals may compete with each other for food, water and space.

a Why do animals need space?

Sea birds

In the photograph, you can see part of a cliff face. Sea birds live here. The birds catch fish in the sea.

b List the factors that these sea birds compete for.

c Which birds are likely to be more successful in competing for these factors?

Tropical squirrels

The diagram shows the outlines of three different species of squirrel. All three species live in the forest on the same island in Indonesia.

d i How much longer is the loga than the jirit?

ii What proportion of the total body length is the tail of the soksak?

The three species of squirrel live at different heights in the forest.

e i What percentage of its time does the soksak spend on the ground?

ii What percentage of its time does the loga spend at 11–15 m from the ground?

iii What percentage of its time does the jirit spend above 5 m from the ground?

iv Suggest the advantages to the three species of living at different heights in the forest.

This rock face is packed with nesting birds.

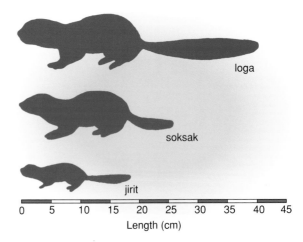

loga

soksak

jirit

Length (cm)

The loga, soksak and jirit are three species of Indonesian squirrel.

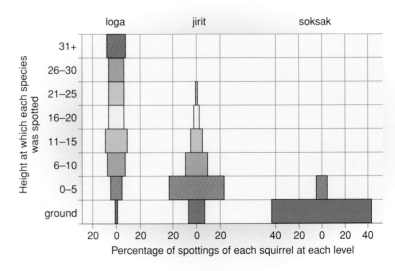

loga   jirit   soksak

Height at which each species was spotted

31+
26–30
21–25
16–20
11–15
6–10
0–5
ground

Percentage of spottings of each squirrel at each level

We can assume that the number of times a species is spotted at each level is directly related to the amount of time that species spends at that height.

Questions

Rotifers and water fleas

Rotifers and water fleas are animals that can just be seen with the naked eye. They are sold in pet shops for feeding to goldfish. Both species can be grown in flasks in the laboratory if they are given food and oxygen.

Three flasks were set up to study competition between these two animals:

- Flask X held only rotifers
- Flask Y held only water fleas
- Flask Z held both rotifers and water fleas.

Both animals feed on microscopic plants, which were added to the flasks daily. The graphs show the results of the experiment.

1 Describe what happened to the population of the rotifers:

  a when living alone (flask X)

  b when living with water fleas (flask Z).

2 Water fleas do not eat rotifers. Explain the reason for the fall in the number of rotifers after day 10 in flask Z.

3 Explain why the number of rotifers did not rise after day 16 in Flask X.

4 Describe what happened to the population of the water fleas:

  a when living alone (flask Y)

  b when living with rotifers (flask Z).

5 Suggest why the numbers of water fleas never rises as fast as the number of rotifers.

Red squirrels and grey squirrels

Read the passage.

6 Suggest ways in which the population of red squirrels could be restored.

In the 1920s, red squirrels began to be replaced by grey squirrels introduced to about 30 sites in England from eastern North America between 1876 and 1929. Red squirrels seem unable to survive in the presence of greys, but the reasons for this are not fully understood. There is no evidence that grey squirrels aggressively chase out red squirrels, or that grey squirrels brought a disease with them from America which affects red squirrels. The key as to why grey squirrels have replaced red squirrels seems to be their ability to compete for food in different types of habitat. Red squirrels live in all types of woodland habitats from pure broadleaf, to mixed broadleaf and conifer, to pure conifer. However, it is believed they prefer pure conifer forests because they can forage in them more efficiently and survive in them better than in broadleaf forests.

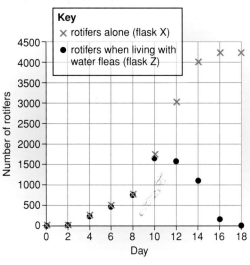

This graph shows how the numbers of rotifers in flasks X and Z changed over 18 days.

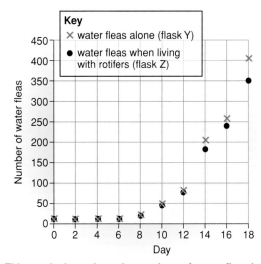

This graph shows how the numbers of water fleas in flasks Y and Z changed over 18 days.

Summary

- Animals compete with each other for:

  a food

  b water

  c space to breed.

- Animals compete with both:

  a animals of the same species

  b animals of different species.

- When animals live in the same habitat they often avoid competition for food by feeding on different types of food.

3:6 Predators and prey

Animals that kill and eat other animals are called **predators**. The animals they eat are called **prey**. In the photograph, the killer whale is the predator. The leopard seal is its prey. Predators usually have more than one type of prey.

Look at the **food web** below. The arrows in the diagram shows what feeds on what. For example, an arrow from 'leopard seals' to 'killer whales' means that the killer whale is a predator and the leopard seal is one of its prey.

a **i** Which other animals are prey for killer whales?

  ii Which animals are predators of small fish?

  iii Name an animal that is both predator and prey.

Voles and owls

Owls are predators of voles. The chart below shows how the numbers of owls and voles in a forest varied over a ten-year period.

b **i** How many voles were there in year 3?

  ii In which year was the number of owls 28?

c **i** Suggest why there was a large fall in the number of voles between years 5 and 6.

  ii Suggest why there was a large fall in the number of owls between years 6 and 7.

  iii Suggest why the number of voles rose between years 6 and 8.

This photograph shows a killer whale catching a leopard seal.

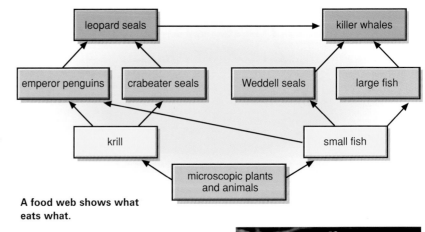

A food web shows what eats what.

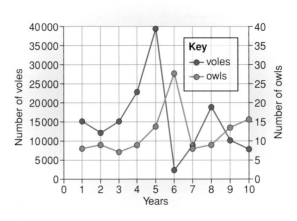

The numbers of predators and prey animals living in a habitat affect each other.

Owls are predators. Voles are among their prey species.

The populations of many predators and prey animals vary in this way – they change in a **cycle**.

Questions

Snowshoe hare and lynx

The Hudson Bay Company in Canada bought the skins of animals from fur-trappers during the nineteenth and early twentieth centuries. They kept records for over a hundred years. The graph shows estimates of the populations of two of these animals, the snowshoe hare and the lynx, over many decades.

1 What was the largest population of hares?

2 By how much did the population of lynx fall between 1885 and 1890?

3 Describe the pattern shown by the numbers of snowshoe hares.

4 Calculate the average number of years between the peaks in the population of the lynx.

5 Use information from the graph to state which animal is the predator and which is the prey. Explain the reasons for your answer.

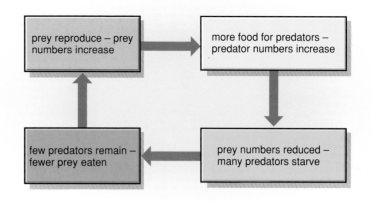

The number of predators depends on how many prey animals there are to eat. The number of prey depends on how many predators are eating them.

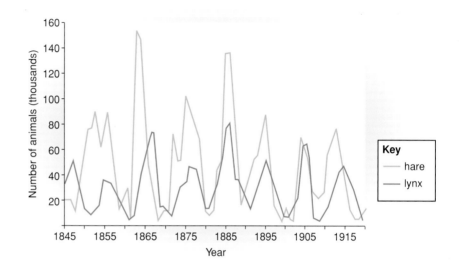

The numbers of prey animals and of predators vary together over time.

The lynx was valued for its coat in past centuries.

Summary

- Animals that eat other animals are called predators. The animals they eat are called prey.

- If the population of prey increases, more food is available for its predators so the predator population increases.

- If the population of predators increases, more food is needed so the population of prey decreases.

3:7 Populations

Deer and wolves

A farmer took 200 deer to a small, uninhabited island in 1915. There were no predators large enough to kill deer on the island.

The graph shows what happened to the population of deer.

a **i** Explain why the population of deer rose year after year until 1930.

ii Suggest two reasons for the large fall in the population of deer between 1930 and 1935.

iii The population of deer rose again until 1940 but peaked at a much lower level than before. Suggest an explanation for this.

In 1945, a pair of wolves (male and female) swam to the island. Wolves are predators of deer.

b Sketch a copy of the graph.

i On your copy, draw a line to show what might happen to the population of wolves between 1945 and 1960.

ii Then, draw a line to show what might happen to the population of deer between 1945 and 1960.

iii Explain the reasons for the shapes of the curves that you have drawn.

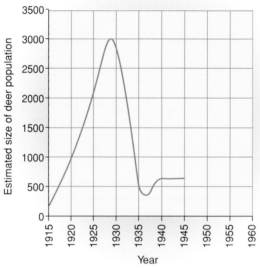

Sea shore populations

In a sea shore habitat, a disease killed a large number of the whelks.

c How might this affect the populations of:

i mussels

ii starfish?

Explain the reasons for your answers.

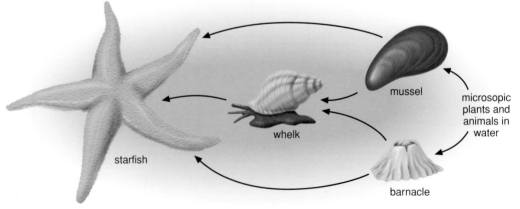

A food web for organisms on the sea shore.

Duckweed

Duckweed is a small plant that lives in ponds. In an investigation, two species of duckweed, *Lemna trisulca* and *Lemna minor*, were grown in two beakers of pond water, X and Y. Beaker X contained only *Lemna trisulca*. Beaker Y contained both *Lemna trisulca* and *Lemna minor*.

The results of the investigation are shown in the graph.

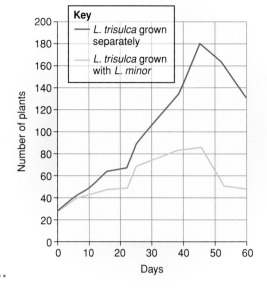

d Explain why the numbers of Lemna trisulca declined in both beakers after day 45.

e *Lemna trisulca* lives under the surface of the water. *Lemna minor* lives on the surface of the water. Suggest an explanation for the results for *Lemna trisulca* when grown with *Lemna minor*.

Questions

Read the article.

Conservationists want to re-introduce the wolf to the Highlands of Scotland. But talk of a pilot project on the Scottish island of Rhum is already causing a stir.

Rhum is a soggy, deer-infested island off the coast of Scotland. It was first suggested as a site for introducing wolves some twenty years ago. Overgrazing by the island's huge population of red deer is one of the reasons why the native pine woods cannot regenerate. So why not introduce wolves to prey on the deer and ease the pressure?

Red deer, which humans hunted to extinction during the second half of the eighteenth century, were re-introduced to the island in 1845. Since then, their numbers have been controlled by culling (selectively killing some individuals). But the culling is both labour-intensive and time-consuming.

'Wolf predation would be a far more efficient way of controlling the red deer,' says Derek Yalden, a zoologist at the University of Manchester, 'and it would be more in keeping with the objectives of a National Nature Reserve.' He estimates that the annual cull on Rhum produces over 25 000 kg of meat – enough, he says, to sustain a population of 19 wolves.

But there is more to survival than an adequate food supply. Other evidence suggests that deer and wolf populations can only coexist if there is enough space. When two pairs of wolves were introduced to Coronation Island in Alaska in 1960 the experiment ended in spectacular failure. The wolf population grew to 13 in four years and deer numbers declined drastically. By 1968, only one wolf survived. The island had supported a large population of deer but the area of the island was only 73 square kilometres. The Alaska Department of Fish and Game concluded that Coronation Island was too small to support both deer and wolves. Yet at about 100 square kilometres, Rhum is not significantly larger.

Summary

The size of a population may be affected by:

- available food
- competition for food
- competition for light
- predation or grazing
- disease.

1 Explain why the deer on Rhum need to be culled.

2 Explain why introducing wolves might be a good way of culling deer on Rhum.

3 Introducing wolves onto Coronation Island was not successful. Suggest an explanation for this.

3:8 Energy flow

The new oil wells

One hectare of the sugarcane crop shown in the photograph can produce enough fuel to drive a car round the world twice! And this fuel produces practically no pollution.

How can we get fuel from plants?

Farmers plant small pieces of sugarcane stem. Nine months later they can harvest up to 190 tonnes of sugarcane per hectare. From these crops, 75 million tonnes of sugar are produced each year. In countries like Brazil some of the sugarcane is fermented to produce ethanol. Many cars there have engines designed to run on pure ethanol.

The sugarcane crop produces a large mass of living material, and this living material contains a lot of energy.

The mass of the sugarcane crop is known as its **biomass**. Your mass is also biomass – as is the mass of all living organisms. It is called biomass because it has come from processes in living organisms. Plants are called **producers** because they produce all the biomass on Earth. They do this via a process called photosynthesis.

In Maintenance of Life you learned the equation for photosynthesis.

a Complete the equation for photosynthesis:

carbon dioxide + _____ (+ light energy) → sugar + _____

Plants use some of the energy from sunlight to convert carbon dioxide and water into sugars. This reaction has produced the countless millions of tonnes of living matter that exist on Earth. It has also produced the oxygen in the atmosphere that all living organisms use in respiration.

However, plants can only use a small proportion of the energy in sunlight.

b Scientists measured the amount of sunlight energy that was used by plants in an area of Britain. In one year, 7 000 000 kilojoules of sunlight energy reached each square metre of the area. Of this, only 90 000 kilojoules were used in photosynthesis. Calculate the proportion of sunlight energy that was used by the plants.

Food chains

When animals eat plants, they obtain biomass from the plant biomass. When one animal eats another animal, it obtains biomass from that animal. In the moorland **food chain** shown, the mouse obtains biomass when it eats the blackberries, and the kestrel obtains biomass when it eats the mouse.

Sugarcane is powerful stuff!

A moorland food chain.

The biomass contains carbohydrates that can be oxidised during respiration to release energy. So the mouse obtains energy from the blackberries and the kestrel obtains energy from the mouse.

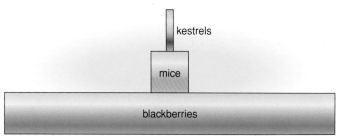

A pyramid of numbers.

Pyramid of biomass

In an area of moorland, there are many blackberry plants, a smaller number of mice, and very few kestrels. At Key Stage 3, you learned to represent this information as a **pyramid of numbers**.

We can measure the biomass of the organisms in a food chain, but this only makes sense if we measure the biomass per unit area of the habitat. So we usually express biomass in grams per square metre (g/m^2).

Some calculations of biomass from the moorland food chain are shown in the table. We can draw these to scale in a pyramid. This pyramid is called a **pyramid of biomass**.

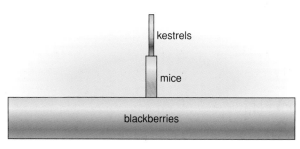

A pyramid of biomass.

c The diagram shows a rough drawing of a pyramid of biomass. Use the data in table to draw the pyramid of biomass to scale. Use a horizontal scale of $2 \text{ mm} = 5 \text{ g/m}^2$.

d Describe what happens to the biomass at each stage in the food chain.

e What proportion of the biomass of the blackberries is transferred to the kestrel?

Organism	Biomass (g/m² of moorland)
blackberries	500
mice	1
kestrels	0.1

Questions

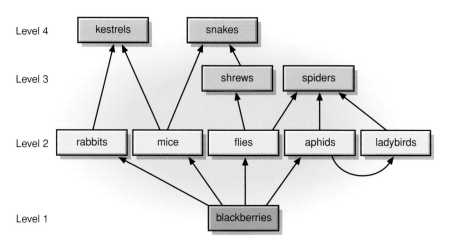

1 Name the producer in the moorland food web shown above.

2 Which level, 1 to 4, would have:

a the greatest total biomass

b the smallest total biomass?

3 Draw and label the pyramids of biomass you would expect for the food chains:

a blackberries → flies → shrews → snakes

b blackberries → aphids → ladybirds → spiders

Summary

- The energy that green plants trap from sunlight is the source of energy for all living organisms.

- The biomass at each stage in a food chain is less than it was in the previous stage.

- The biomass at each stage in a food chain can be drawn to scale as a pyramid of biomass.

3:9 Food factories

What do the photographs have in common? They all show ways of producing protein food for humans. But what people eat depends on where they live and what they can afford. To most people in the world, meat is a luxury they cannot afford.

Here you will learn why meat is so expensive compared with plant foods.

Chickens

When you eat plant foods, all the material and energy from the plant goes directly into your body. If that same plant food was fed to an animal, and then that animal was killed and eaten, not all of the original material and energy in the plant would be passed to your body.

This is because the animal, while it was alive, used up a lot of the energy and passed much of the plant material out of its body in faeces – so relatively little of the plant biomass got incorporated into the animal's biomass. This is why rearing animals is not a very efficient way of producing food.

The diagram shows how much of the energy we supply in food to a free-range chicken is transferred to human food.

a **i** Calculate the proportion of energy in the cereal fed to the chicken that is transferred to human food.

   ii Out of every 100 g of cereal we feed to chickens, how much is *not* transferred to human food?

Of each 1000 kJ in the chicken's food, 115 kJ passes out of the body in the faeces. Much of this energy is in the form of fibre from the cereal. This is because the fibre consists of cellulose. Most animals cannot produce enzymes to digest **cellulose**, so fibre goes in through the mouth and out through the anus.

Of every 1000 kJ in the chicken's food, 575 kJ – more than half – is lost as heat and movement. This energy comes from respiration.

b Copy and complete the equation for aerobic respiration.

glucose + oxygen → _____ + water (+ energy)

People produce food in many different ways.

| 575 kJ lost as movement and heat |
| 165 kJ in chicken meat |
| 1000 kJ in food |
| 145 kJ in egg |
| 115 kJ lost in faeces |

Chickens are usually fed on cereals.

Some of the energy from respiration is used in movement, but most of it is used to maintain the body temperature of the chicken at constant at 40 °C. For most of the year the air temperature in this country is less than 20 °C, so the chicken is constantly losing heat to the outside air.

c Chickens have fluffy down feathers next to their bodies. Suggest how these down feathers reduce the rate of heat loss from the chicken.

If chickens cannot move, they don't waste so much energy.

Efficient food production

Mammals keep their bodies at a constant temperature of about 37 °C, so much of the energy in the food that cattle, pigs and sheep take in is lost as heat to the air.

Modern farming methods, such as rearing chickens or calves in cages inside warm buildings, increase the efficiency of transferring energy from cereal to human food. Less heat is lost via movement because this is restricted by the cage. Less heat is lost to the air since the air is kept warm.

It now takes only 3.6 kg of cereal food to produce 2.0 kg of body mass in chickens – but, even so, almost half of the cereal food still does not reach humans if we use it to feed chickens first.

However, the methods shown in the photographs are now considered to be cruel and have been, or are being, phased out in many parts of the world.

If calves are kept indoors in warm surroundings, they lose less energy to the air.

Fresh fruit

Until the last century, tropical fruits could only be obtained in Britain by growing them here in heated greenhouses. If we tried to import them, they went bad before they arrived.

Bananas are picked well before they are ripe.

Bananas are picked while they are still green. They are then placed in containers where the atmosphere is carefully manipulated so that the bananas are just ripening when they arrive here. Manipulating the atmosphere involves adding ethylene, which acts as a plant hormone to control ripening. The oxygen concentration is usually raised and the carbon dioxide concentration raised to slow down ripening.

Summary

- At each stage in a food chain, less energy and material are contained in the biomass of the organisms.

- Energy is lost via faeces, and also by movement and as heat.

- This means that it is more efficient to produce food by growing crops rather than by rearing animals.

- The efficiency of food production can be increased by limiting the movement of animals and keeping them in a warm environment.

- Hormones are used to regulate ripening of fruit both on the plant and during transit.

Questions

1 An area of ground equal to five football pitches will support 24 people if wheat is grown on it, but only 2 people if cattle are reared on it. Explain why this is so, as fully as you can.

2 Wrapping apples in polythene slows down the rate at which they soften and go yellow. Suggest an explanation for this.

3 Give some pros and cons of raising animals for food.

3:10 Getting rid of faeces

Some of you may have been to scout or guide camp and used pit latrines. After using the latrine, you throw some soil over the faeces. This is not just to remove the smell, or to keep the flies off! Covering the faeces with soil helps them to decompose.

A pit latrine is a real outdoor loo – not much more than a hole in the ground!

Soil microbes

Faeces in the soil are broken down by **microbes**. These include bacteria, fungi and single-celled organisms. Bacteria and fungi digest faeces and other waste products, by producing digestive enzymes. The enzymes pass out of the microbe's body and onto the waste materials, which they break down into soluble compounds. These soluble compounds are then absorbed into the body of the microbe. Soil microbes obtain much of their food from waste materials such as faeces. The breakdown of waste materials by microbes is known as **decay**.

a All the material in faeces is broken down by microbes. Which enzyme must they produce that is not produced by most animals?

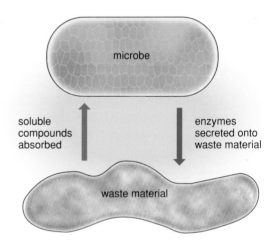

Soil microbes feed on other animals' waste.

Sewage works

The residents of a British city will produce thousands of tons of faeces in a year. The faeces are flushed down toilets and sent to a sewage works. Here, there is far too much faeces to bury, as happens in a pit latrine. So, another method is used to break down the faeces – but it uses similar microbes to those found in soil. The sewage is run into large tanks through which air is bubbled.

In the activated sludge tank, microbes quickly break down waste material.

The microbes in the tank digest 80% of the waste material within a few hours. The oxygen in the air speeds up the activity of the microbes.

b Which process that occurs in the microbes uses oxygen?

Biological filters

There is still some waste material in the sewage after it leaves the sludge tank, so the next stage is to filter it. The sewage is allowed to trickle through filter beds. The stones in the filter bed are coated with a layer of microbes, which digest the remaining waste materials. Clean water then runs into rivers or the sea.

The filter bed leaves the water clean enough to flow back into rivers.

Muck-spreading

Faeces from cows on a farm are not dumped. They are spread on the fields as a 'natural' fertiliser. The faeces are broken down by soil microbes. Protein in the faeces is converted into nitrates by some of these microbes. Plants need nitrates to grow.

c **What do plants make out of sugars and nitrates?**

Farmers need to use fertilisers because they harvest crops. These crops have taken nitrates out of the soil. Farmers must replace the nitrates if they want a good crop next year. They can do this in two ways. They can buy chemical fertilisers or they can use animal faeces. Using animal faeces is known as **organic farming** because the fertiliser has come from living creatures, not chemical factories.

d **Suggest the advantages and disadvantages of using natural and artificial fertilisers.**

Compost heaps

Microbes break down dead organisms as well as waste materials. In autumn, in a garden, many plants lose their leaves. These leaves contain nutrients that can be recycled by soil microbes.

Many gardeners collect all the dead leaves and use them to make **compost.** Compost contains nutrients such as nitrates, so it acts as a natural fertiliser when it is spread on the garden.

The diagram shows one way of making compost. Layers of leaves are put in a large container. A layer of soil is placed between each layer of leaves. The sides of the container are perforated to allow air to circulate through the container. A lid keeps the rain off. The microbes in the soil digest the leaves to form compost.

Decay conditions

Decay occurs most quickly if conditions are moist, warm and there is a good supply of oxygen.

e **Explain why each of these factors increases the rate of decay.**

Questions

Squares of tree leaves, 20 mm across, were placed into bags made with mesh of different sizes. The bags were buried in soil for three months. The diagram shows the results.

1 Copy each square onto graph paper. Calculate the mean percentage of leaf square decomposed at each mesh size.

2 Suggest an explanation for the results.

As waste materials decay, valuable nutrients are released.

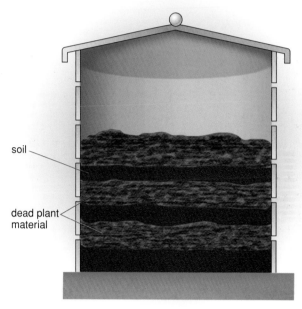

soil

dead plant material

The formation of compost is another example of decay.

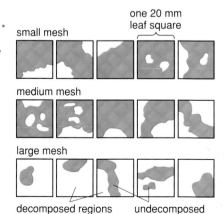

one 20 mm leaf square

small mesh

medium mesh

large mesh

decomposed regions of leaf square

undecomposed regions of square

Summary

- Materials decay because they are broken down by microbes.
- Materials are digested by enzymes that pass out of the bodies of the microbes.
- Microbes digest materials fast in warm, moist conditions with a good supply of oxygen.
- Microbes are used to decay sewage.
- Microbes are used to decay dead plants to produce compost.
- The decay process releases nutrients that plants need for growth.

Carbon cycle

This is the Amazon rainforest in South America.

Plants

The photograph shows a tropical rainforest. It exchanges thousands of tonnes of carbon dioxide with the atmosphere every year. There are two processes involved in this exchange – photosynthesis and respiration. Photosynthesis uses carbon dioxide from the atmosphere. Respiration adds carbon dioxide to the atmosphere.

a Does a forest increase the amount of carbon dioxide in the atmosphere over a year, or decrease it? Explain the reason for your answer.

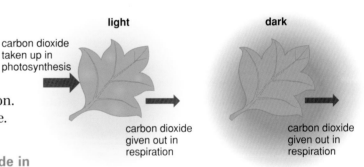

Overall, green leaves take up carbon dioxide during daylight, and give out carbon dioxide at night.

Animals

Herbivores eat plants. They digest the leaves into sugars, amino acids, fatty acids and glycerol. All these compounds contain carbon. The carbon compounds are then made into the proteins and fats that form the cells of the animal's body. If a carnivore eats a herbivore, the carbon compounds in the herbivore are converted into carbon compounds in the carnivore.

All animals respire. Some of their food is converted into sugars, which can be respired. The carbon in the sugars returns to the atmosphere as carbon dioxide.

b Explain why animals decrease in mass when they respire.

Decay organisms

When organisms die, small animals and microbes feed on their bodies. The carbon compounds in the dead organisms become carbon compounds in the bodies of these small organisms. When the small organisms respire, some of the carbon compounds from their food are converted into carbon dioxide.

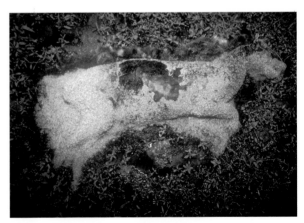

When living things die, carbon compounds in their tissues are taken up by decay organisms.

Putting it all together

Now we can group plants, animals and microbes into one cycle – the **carbon cycle**.

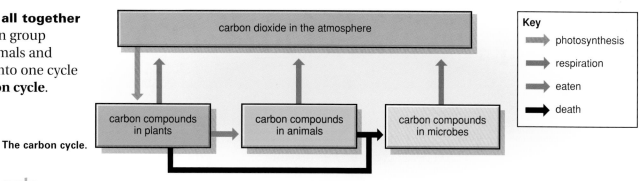

The carbon cycle.

Summary

• Plants produce carbon compounds from carbon dioxide, by photosynthesis.

• Animals obtain carbon compounds by eating plants or other animals.

• Both animals and plants return carbon dioxide to the atmosphere during respiration.

• When animals and plants die, microbes obtain carbon compounds from their bodies.

• Microbes respire, releasing carbon dioxide into the atmosphere.

• The movement of carbon compounds from the atmosphere into organisms and back again is called the carbon cycle.

• Plants use nitrates to produce proteins.

• The proteins in dead animals and plants are converted into ammonium compounds by putrefying bacteria.

• Ammonium compounds are converted into nitrates by nitrifying bacteria.

• The movement of nitrogen compounds from the soil into organisms and back again is called the nitrogen cycle.

Nitrogen cycle

Plants

All living organisms need proteins to grow. Plants can make their own proteins if they are supplied with nitrates. Proteins are nitrogen-containing compounds.

Plants obtain nitrates from the soil. In the wild, nitrates are released when faeces or dead organisms are broken down by microbes. On farms, harvesting crops removes nitrogen compounds. So the farmer has to replace these by spreading manure or chemical fertiliser.

Farmers must replace the nitrates in the soil if they are to keep producing crops year after year.

Animals

When herbivores eat plants, or carnivores eat other animals, some of the nitrogen-containing compounds in the food become part of proteins in the consuming animal.

Decay organisms

Two kinds of bacteria are involved in producing nitrates from the bodies of dead animals and plants.

Putrefying bacteria (and some fungi) break down nitrogen-containing compounds from the dead bodies of plants and animals. They convert these compounds into ammonium compounds.

Nitrifying bacteria then convert the ammonium compounds into nitrates.

Putting it all together

Now we can group plants, animals and microbes into one cycle – the **nitrogen cycle**.

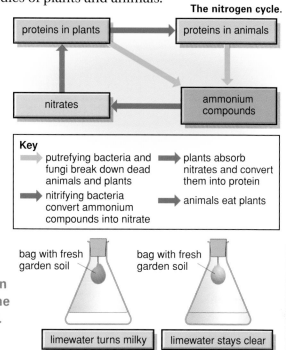

The nitrogen cycle.

Questions

1 The diagram shows the result of an experiment on soil organisms. Explain the results of the experiment.

2 A lion eats an impala. Describe how the nitrogen in the protein in the impala's body eventually becomes part of proteins in grass.

The photograph shows some spectators at the Olympic Games in Sydney, Australia, in 2000. About 100 000 people were there, from every country in the world. How many people do you think there are in the world? In the millennium year, 2000, there were about six billion. This is an enormous number, but what is more worrying is that the number is increasing rapidly.

a   i Look at the graph showing estimates of world population. Describe the pattern shown in the graph.

   ii Copy the graph. Use it to estimate the population in 3000 AD.

Six thousand years ago, the population of the world was about 0.2 billion. People lived in small groups, and most of the world was unaffected by human activities.

As the population increases, raw materials are rapidly being used up. Some of these resources, such as fossil fuels, are **non-renewable**. This means that once we have used them, no more can be made, so eventually supplies will run out.

As we use these raw materials, a great deal of waste is produced. Much of this waste causes pollution.

Using resources

The table shows how some of the world's resources are used by the industrialised world (European countries, USA and Japan, for example), and the developing world (poor countries in Africa and Asia, for example).

b   i Suggest why industrialised countries consume so much of the world's energy resources.

   ii Suggest why industrialised countries consume so much of the chemical production.

c   i Look at the graph on the opposite page showing differences in population growth rates. Describe the trends shown by the graph.

   ii In 2000, what proportion of the population lived in developing countries?

   iii Suggest reasons for the different population growth rates in industrialised regions and developing regions.

About 100 000 people came to watch the men's 100 m final at the 2000 Olympic Games, when Maurice Greene won the gold medal.

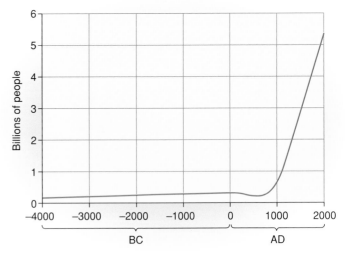

Estimates of world population from 4000 BC to 2000 AD.

Industrialised world	Developing world
25% of world population	75% of world population
uses 80% of total energy	uses 20% of total energy
each person uses 250–1000 litres of water per day	each person uses 20–40 litres of water per day
40% of this water is used in industry	93% of this water is used in agriculture
consumes 85% of chemical production	consumes 15% of chemical production
consumes 90% of cars	consumes 10% of cars
has 87% of world trade	has 13% of world trade
not affected by famine	100 million people affected by famine

Producing waste

The chart below shows the amount of municipal waste and industrial waste that needs to be got rid of each year, per person, in different parts of the world. Municipal waste includes sewage and what goes in your dustbin.

d **i** Describe the patterns shown in the chart.

ii Suggest why North American countries produce much more municipal waste than developing countries.

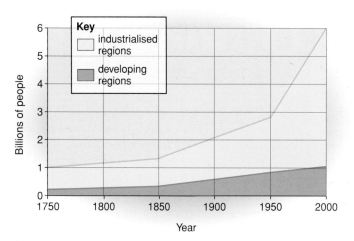

Differences in population growth rates in industrialised and developing regions, between 1750 and 2000.

Questions

The world is in danger of running out of resources. People in industrialised countries and developing countries might have very different ideas about how to solve the problem.

Look at the cartoon.

1 What is the solution proposed by the man from the industrialised country?

2 What is the solution proposed by the man from the developing country?

3 What do you think is the solution to the problem?

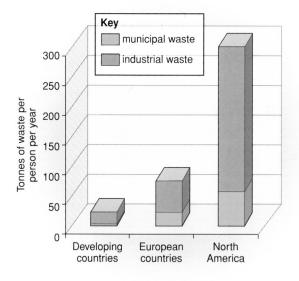

Getting rid of waste is a real problem – the more waste, the bigger the problem!

Graphic by Clive Offey in The New Internationalist

We all have to work together to conserve and share out the world's resources fairly.

Summary

- The human population is rising rapidly.

- Raw materials, including non-renewable energy resources, are rapidly being used up.

- More waste is being produced.

- Unless waste is properly handled, more pollution will be caused.

Homes

The photograph shows a familiar sight – land being swallowed up for new houses. Every year, we have to build more homes to house the increasing numbers of people in the world. Before building began, this land provided habitats for animals and plants. Every new home built for humans reduces the land available for animals and plants.

The photograph shows a huge quarry, which provides the materials to build the houses. So, extracting raw materials from the Earth also reduces the amount of land available for animals and plants.

The new houses have to be supplied with electricity – so the demand for electricity goes up. Many parts of the world cannot afford to import fossil fuels to produce electricity – so they build dams for hydroelectric schemes. More habitats for animals and plants are lost.

The inhabitants of each new house will produce rubbish. The town council has to get rid of this rubbish. Most of the rubbish is dumped. Still more habitats are lost to animals and plants.

Cities are growing faster than the population as a whole. In 1950, only 29 people in every 100 in the world lived in cities. By 2000, the number of people living in cities had trebled. Now, 85% of the increase in population takes place in cities.

Cities import most of their food, fuel, building materials and water, whereas rural communities are often almost self-sufficient. Cities also produce much more waste per head of population than rural communities.

The more humans there are in the world, the less room there is for other animals and plants.

It is not just houses that use up land.

A huge area of land was flooded when this hydroelectric dam was built in Glen Canyon.

a   i   In England, the number of new houses being built is increasing much more rapidly than the number of people in the population. Suggest why this is happening.

   ii List the reasons why building new houses reduces the space available for plants and animals to live.

Farms

The increase in population means that we need more food. To grow more food, more land is now used for agriculture. There are now very few parts of Britain where there is no agriculture at all.

Using farms for agriculture reduces the number of habitats for wild animals and plants.

The more people there are, the more rubbish they make.

Fertilisers and pesticides

Farms have other impacts on wildlife. Besides destroying the habitats of many kinds of animals and plants, many farms use chemicals that also affect them.

Farmers use **herbicides** to kill weeds in their crops. If these herbicides reach wild plants they will kill them too. Many of these wild plants provide food for animals such as butterflies. If we kill the wild plants the butterflies have nothing to feed on so they die too. The numbers of most kinds of butterflies in this country have drastically declined over the last 50 years as farmers have used more herbicides. If herbicides are washed by rain into streams and ponds they kill the plants growing there.

Farmers used **pesticides** mainly to kill animals that eat their crops. Most pesticides are used to kill insects. These pesticides also kill harmless insects that are food for birds. The populations of many kinds of birds have decreased over the last 50 years as farmers have increased the use of pesticides. If pesticides are washed by rain into streams and ponds they kill the animals living there.

Farmers use **fertilisers** to increase the yield of their crops. If fertilisers are washed into streams or ponds, they increase the growth of plants living there.

Eutrophication

Run-off of excess fertilisers can have catastrophic effects on animals and plants living in rivers, lakes and ponds. The fertilisers are absorbed by aquatic plants, causing a rapid increase in their growth. The water often becomes overcrowded with plants. This means that only those plants with enough leaves growing near the surface of the water will receive sufficient light for photosynthesis. The plants that are unsuccessful in competition for light will die.

Microbes living in the water decay the dead plants. As the number of dead plants increases, so does the number of microbes that feed on them. The microbes use up oxygen in respiration. This means there is less oxygen available in the water for other organisms, which leads to suffocation of aquatic animals.

The whole process is known as **eutrophication**. It is summarised in the flowchart.

Allowing sewage to enter water has the same effect as allowing fertilisers to enter, but for a slightly different reason. The sewage provides food for the microbes directly. So these microbes increase in number and their respiration removes oxygen from the water.

Questions

1 Give the differences between fertilisers, pesticides and herbicides.

2 Describe and explain the effects of farming on the environment.

Eutrophication can occur when fertilisers get into natural waters.

Healthy balance of plants and animals.

Fertiliser run-off causes large increase in number of plants.

Competition for light results in death of plants. Increase in numbers of microbes causes oxygen depletion via respiration.

Summary

- Humans reduce the amount of land available for other animals and plants by building, quarrying, farming and dumping waste.

- Farms also affect living organisms by the use of pesticides, herbicides and fertilisers.

- Fertiliser run-off causes excess growth of aquatic plants.

- Competition for light results in the death of plants.

- Increasing numbers of microbes feed on the dead plants.

- Their respiration depletes the oxygen in the water, leaving less for other aquatic wildlife.

- This process is called eutrophication.

3:14 Acid rain

Power stations

Coal is burned to release energy. The main element in coal is carbon. During burning, this is oxidised to form carbon dioxide.

carbon + oxygen → carbon dioxide (+ energy)

Carbon dioxide dissolves in rainwater and makes it slightly acid.

Most kinds of coal also contain sulphur. When sulphur burns it is oxidised, and forms sulphur dioxide.

sulphur + oxygen → sulphur dioxide

Sulphur dioxide dissolves in rainwater and makes it more acid.

Acid rain has a pH of 4 or less. It has very damaging effects on the environment.

It is very difficult and expensive to remove sulphur dioxide from power station smoke, so in recent years a large number of coal-fired power stations in Britain have been replaced by stations that burn natural gas. Natural gas contains very little sulphur so little sulphur dioxide is produced when it burns.

a Some coal-fired power stations have 'scrubbers' to remove sulphur dioxide. The smoke is passed over a chemical. What type of chemical do you think this is? Give a reason for your answer.

A coal-burning power station. Large heaps of stored coal can be seen in the background.

Cars

Cars also burn fossil fuels – petrol or diesel. Some types of petrol contain sulphur, so sulphur dioxide is emitted in the exhaust fumes. Low-sulphur petrol and diesel are now available from fuel stations to reduce the amount of sulphur dioxide emitted.

Power stations and cars also produce nitrogen oxides. These oxides dissolve in rainwater too and make it more acid. Many cars are now fitted with catalytic converters that reduce the amounts of nitrogen oxides in the exhaust fumes.

Damage to trees

The photograph shows trees in the mountains of Norway that have been damaged by acid rain. One of the first signs of damage by acid rain is a condition called 'crown-loss'. The young leaves – those near the top of the tree – are killed by the acid rain.

b Suggest why young leaves are killed by acid rain but older ones are not.

Crown-loss is not the only damage caused by acid rain. The acid affects the covering of the older leaves. This makes it easier for disease organisms to attack the tree.

Acid rain damages and kills trees.

The young root hairs of the trees are damaged when acid rainwater gets into the soil.

c Suggest the effect on the tree of having damaged root hairs.

healthy tree   young leaves killed by acid rain   root hairs killed by acid rain – tree dies

Acid rain damages the roots of trees, as well as the leaves.

Effect on freshwater organisms

When acid rain runs into streams and lakes, it makes the water more acid. As the water gets more acid, fewer animals and plants can survive. (Remember that pH 5 is ten times more acid than pH 6.) The bar chart shows how the pH of water affects which animals live in it. All the animals listed, except snails, are fish.

d i Which fish tolerates acid water the best?

ii What is the lowest pH in which snails live?

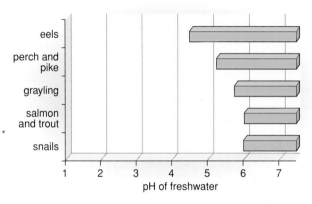

Different organisms are able to live in different ranges of pH.

Questions

Look at the map.

1 If you looked at 1000 trees in Norway, how many would you expect to be damaged by acid rain?

2 Use an atlas to find the name of the country that has the smallest percentage of trees damaged by acid rain.

3 Ireland has a lower percentage of trees damaged by acid rain than Britain. Suggest an explanation for this.

4 Norway emits very little sulphur dioxide and nitrogen oxides into the atmosphere, but 26% of its trees are damaged by acid rain. Suggest an explanation for this.

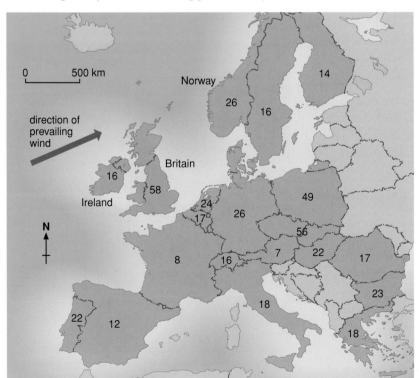

The percentage of trees damaged by acid rain in European countries.

Summary
- Burning fossil fuels, such as coal and oil, releases sulphur dioxide into the atmosphere.
- Nitrogen oxides are also released when fossil fuels are burned.
- Sulphur dioxide and nitrogen oxides dissolve in rainwater and make it more acid.
- Acid rain kills the young leaves of trees and may kill the root hairs. If the water in lakes and rivers becomes too acid, plants and animals cannot survive.

The Earth's atmosphere is slowly warming up. The warming is caused by 'the greenhouse effect' – so called because the process is similar to the way in which a greenhouse warms up.

Earth's atmosphere is warming up because of an increase in the proportions of 'greenhouse gases' it contains. These gases are produced both by natural processes and by human activities.

Without the natural greenhouse gases, the temperature of the Earth would be 33 °C colder than it is at the moment. So most living things would not survive without the greenhouse effect!

But human activities are causing the concentrations of greenhouse gases in the atmosphere to rise above natural levels, and that is causing a great deal of concern.

Global warming.

Greenhouse gases

The pie chart shows how much each gas contributes to the greenhouse effect. By far the biggest contributor is carbon dioxide.

Carbon dioxide

When you studied the carbon cycle (page 136), you learned that plants remove carbon dioxide from the atmosphere during photosynthesis, and most living organisms pass carbon dioxide back to the atmosphere when they respire. These two processes balanced each other for thousands of years. But in the last few centuries humans have interfered with this balance in two major ways.

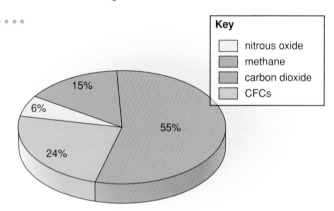

Key
- nitrous oxide
- methane
- carbon dioxide
- CFCs

15%
6%
55%
24%

Four main gases cause the greenhouse effect.

1 There has been a massive increase in the combustion of fossil fuels both by industry and by use of motor vehicles. This is increasing the amount of carbon dioxide in the atmosphere.

2 Large areas of forest have been cleared both to produce timber and to clear land for agriculture. When trees are cut down, only the trunk is kept. The branches are burned. This combustion releases carbon dioxide into the atmosphere. The roots of the trees die, and are decomposed.

a **Explain how decay of tree roots increases the carbon dioxide concentration of the atmosphere.**

Cutting down trees also means that the amount of photosynthesis going on in the world is reduced. Trees take in millions of tonnes of carbon dioxide every year. Most of this is converted into the cells that form wood. We say that the carbon dioxide is 'locked up' in the wood. Many trees live for a hundred years or more, so the carbon dioxide remains 'locked up' for a long time.

Carbon dioxide is responsible for just over half of the total greenhouse effect. You also need to learn about one of the other major greenhouse gases – methane.

The carbon locked away in the biomass of the forest is released suddenly into the atmosphere when trees are felled and burned.

Methane

Methane is a gas produced by certain types of microbes that can live where there is very little oxygen. They produce this gas when they break down organic materials. Many of these microbes are involved in the decay process.

Rice fields are under water for long periods, so there is very little oxygen in the soil. Bacteria in these soils produce a lot of methane.

Cows have a four-chambered stomach. Microbes live in these chambers and digest parts of the cow's food. Because there is very little oxygen in the cow's stomach, these microbes produce methane.

As the world's population has increased, so has the total area of rice fields and the number of cattle, to provide food for all the people. So, there has been an increase in the amount of methane in the atmosphere.

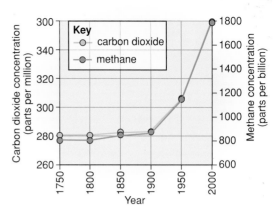

Concentrations of carbon dioxide and methane in the atmosphere since 1750.

b **i** Describe the patterns shown by the graph.

   ii Which of the two greenhouse gases has shown the greater increase in concentration over the last 250 years?

Effects of greenhouse gases

The increased concentrations of greenhouse gases are causing the temperature of the atmosphere to rise, slowly but surely. The Earth is warmed by radiation from the Sun. It, in turn, produces infra-red radiation. Greenhouse gases absorb this radiation and re-radiate some of it back to Earth.

The temperature rise will cause changes to climates around the world – some places will become wetter, others drier. The climate changes will change the areas where crops can be grown.

The warming of the atmosphere is causing melting of the polar icecaps. This will cause sea levels to rise. Some low-lying pieces of land will become flooded.

radiation from Sun passes through atmosphere and warms surface of Earth

greenhouse gases re-radiate some infra-red rays back to Earth

warm Earth emits infra-red radiation

Gases in the atmosphere re-radiate infra-red back to the Earth, just as the glass traps heat in a greenhouse.

Question

Look at the cartoon. Explain why people in the two hemispheres of the Earth might have different views about how to reduce levels of greenhouse gases.

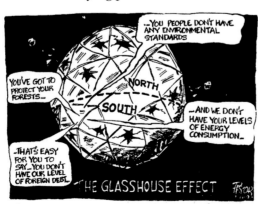

People who live in glass houses shouldn't throw stones.

Summary

- Increased combustion of fossil fuels has increased the amount of carbon dioxide in the atmosphere.

- Large scale deforestation has increased the release of carbon dioxide to the atmosphere by combustion and decay. It has also reduced the rate at which carbon dioxide is 'locked up' as wood.

- Increased numbers of cattle and rice fields have increased the amount of methane released into the atmosphere.

- Increasing levels of carbon dioxide and methane may be causing an increase in the 'greenhouse effect'.

- An increase in the Earth's temperature may cause climate changes and a rise in sea level.

- Greenhouse gases absorb infra-red radiation from the Earth and re-radiate it back, causing global warming.

3:16 Sustainable development

Every year a famine occurs somewhere in the world. Television news programmes often show us pictures of people squatting on the edges of cities in developing countries. All of us would like to see a better standard of living for the whole of the world's population. But we must not compromise the needs of future generations to improve our quality of life.

Improving quality of life without compromising future generations is known as **sustainable development**. This involves protecting the environment and using natural resources wisely.

Famine occurs when food is not in the right place at the right time.

What is going wrong?

In the last few pages, we have seen that:

◆ the world population is rising too fast

◆ forests are being destroyed

◆ natural resources are being used up

◆ pollution is affecting land, sea and water

◆ climates are changing.

Millions of people in the world live in very poor conditions.

What can we do about it?

Birth rate

Raising living standards and health care standards reduces the rate of population growth. The table shows data for some developing countries. The infant mortality rate in England is 9 per 1000 births.

Country	Birth rate per 1000 of population	Infant mortality rate per 1000 births	People with access to health care (%)	Females who can read (%)
Sierra Leone	48.1	146	36	11
Nigeria	46.6	99	67	40
Bangladesh	40.6	111	74	22
Thailand	20.0	28	59	91
Sri Lanka	20.7	25	90	84

People tend to have more children in poor regions.

a What is the general relationship between:

i the birth rate and the infant mortality rate

ii the birth rate and access to health services

iii the birth rate and the percentage of women who can read?

b Use the data to suggest how the birth rate in developing countries could be reduced.

Nearly half the children around here die before they are grown up; I am going to have several children so that even if some die, I will still be left with some.

Energy use

c Look at the diagram showing energy use in different countries. Bangladesh is a developing country. Explain why the USA uses so much more energy than Bangladesh.

Most energy used in industrialised countries comes from non-renewable energy resources. So industrialised countries are using up non-renewable energy resources far more quickly than developing countries.

d Suggest ways in which people in industrialised countries can reduce the amount of energy used.

At a recent conference, industrialised countries set themselves a target of using **renewable** energy sources to supply at least 10% of their energy needs.

e From your year 10 work on Energy, list the different types of renewable energy sources.

Renewable energy resources do not use up fossil fuels and they do not produce pollution. But they can have an impact on the environment.

f Describe the impact on the environment of:

　i using a tidal barrage to generate electricity

　ii using a wind farm to generate electricity.

Recycling

One way of conserving precious natural resources is to recycle them. We can all contribute to this by using recycling bins. Many local councils now provide households with two bins – one for rubbish that can be recycled and one for waste that cannot be recycled.

g How does recycling each of the following save natural resources?

　i newspaper

　ii bottles

　iii aluminium cans

Increasing food production

Over one billion people do not get enough food to eat. At least 400 million get less than 80% of the food they need to keep them active and healthy – so they do not grow correctly and they are more liable to catch diseases.

There is more than enough food in the world to feed everyone. Grain production has outstripped population growth in recent years. (In Europe we are now even paying farmers to *stop* growing food!) But much of this food is in the wrong place.

India is a production success story. Planting new strains of cereal crops helped it to double its production of wheat between 1965 and 1972. It even exported its surplus to neighbouring countries.

But half the hungry people in the world live in India. These people cannot afford to buy wheat.

h What is the best long-term solution to providing food for people who cannot afford to buy it?

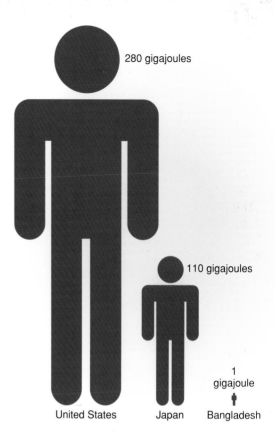

280 gigajoules

110 gigajoules

1 gigajoule

United States　　Japan　　Bangladesh

The amount of energy used per head of population, per year, in different countries (1 gigajoule = 1 000 000 000 J).

Recycling materials helps to conserve natural resources.

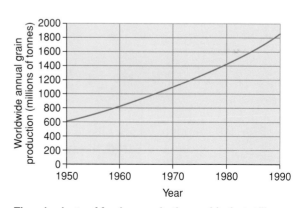

There is plenty of food grown in the world – but still people starve.

End of module questions

1 The photograph shows a seal pup.

Use information from the photograph to explain two ways in which the seal pup is adapted for survival in the Arctic.

2 The photograph shows an elephant. It is very hot and the elephant has covered itself with mud. It is flapping its ears.

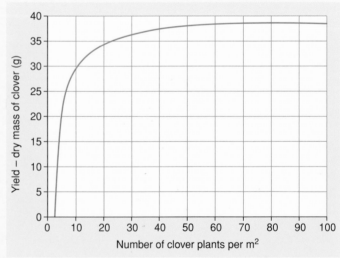

2.1 Elephants have very large ears. They have no natural predators. Suggest how having large ears helps elephants to survive in a hot climate.

2.2 Suggest how the mud helps to keep the elephant cool.

3 The drawing shows a plant that lives in hot deserts.

Explain how each of the following helps the plant to survive:

3.1 the thick waxy coat on the leaves

3.2 the sharp prickles

sharp prickles

thick coat of wax on leaves

4 Clover is a plant that grows in grassland. Clover plants were grown in plots of soil. The graph shows how the yield of clover was affected by the number of clover plants sown in each plot.

4.1 Describe the effect of the number of clover plants per m² on the yield of clover.

4.2 Give *two* factors for which clover plants compete.

4.3 Explain why each of these factors is needed for plant growth.

5 The diagram shows a food web for a lake.

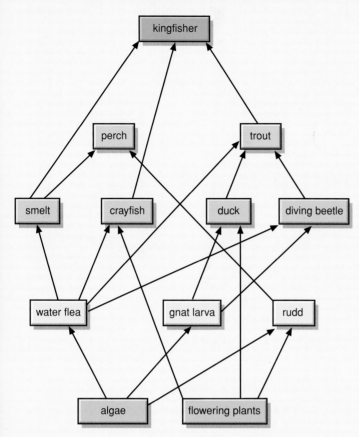

5.1 Name *one* animal that is eaten by crayfish.

5.2 Name *two* predators of gnat larvae.

Anglers begin fishing in the lake. They catch large numbers of trout.

5.3 How might this affect the populations of water fleas and smelt? Explain your answer in each case.

6 The table shows the results of a ten-year study of the populations of owls and voles in a forest.

Year	Number of voles (to the nearest thousand)	Number of owls
1	15 000	8
2	12 000	9
3	15 000	7
4	23 000	9
5	40 000	14
6	2 000	28
7	9 000	8
8	19 000	9
9	10 000	14
10	8 000	16

6.1 Plot the data on a grid similar to the one below.

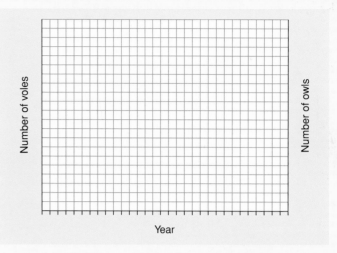

6.2 How is the number of owls related to the number of voles?

6.3 Suggest *three* reasons for the large fall in the number of voles between years 5 and 6.

7 The diagram shows a food web from a moor.

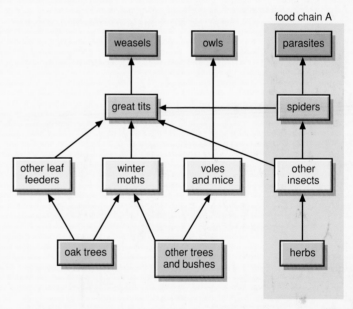

7.1 Name two producers in this food web.

7.2 Draw a pyramid of biomass for food chain A.

7.3 Explain why the total biomass decreases at each stage in a food chain.

8 The diagram shows what happens to the energy in the grass eaten by a bullock from 1 m² of grazing land.

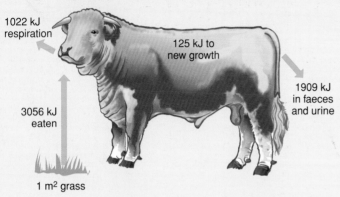

1022 kJ respiration

125 kJ to new growth

1909 kJ in faeces and urine

3056 kJ eaten

1 m² grass

8.1 Calculate the amount of energy lost via respiration.

8.2 Calculate the proportion of the energy in the grass that was transferred to new growth in the bullock.

8.3 Explain why it is more efficient to produce food by growing crops rather than by rearing animals.

8.4 Explain how the efficiency of producing food by rearing animals can be improved.

9 A gardener decides to build a compost heap in the garden.

9.1 Why is compost useful to the gardener?

9.2 What type of organism breaks down dead plant material into compost?

9.3 Describe how these organisms break down dead plant material.

9.4 List the conditions needed for fast breakdown of compost.

10 The diagram shows the carbon cycle. Describe the processes occurring at A, B, C and D.

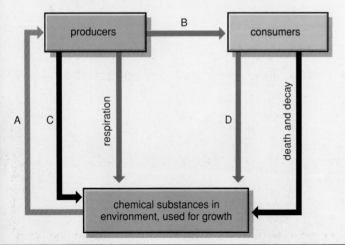

producers

B

consumers

respiration

A   C

D

death and decay

chemical substances in environment, used for growth

11 The diagram shows a simplified diagram of the nitrogen cycle.

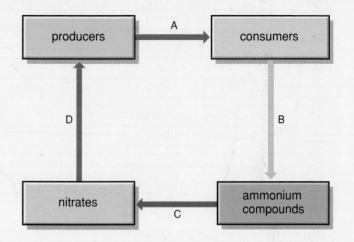

producers

A

consumers

D

B

nitrates

C

ammonium compounds

11.1 In stage A, plant proteins become animal proteins. Explain how this happens.

11.2 How are ammonium compounds produced in stage B?

11.3 How are nitrates produced in stage C?

11.4 How do plants make proteins from nitrates in stage D?

12 **12.1** Describe how acid rain is produced.

The graph shows how the pH of water in lakes affects the number of species of some of the animals that live there.

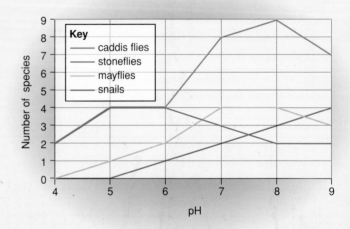

Key
— caddis flies
— stoneflies
— mayflies
— snails

Number of species

pH

12.2 Describe the effect of acid rain on the number of species of the four types of animal.

12.3 Describe the effects of acid rain on plants.

Module 7 – Patterns of chemical change

We rely on chemical reactions to turn raw materials into the many useful materials we use everyday. To make these reactions work on an industrial scale, we need to understand more about:

◆ reaction rates and how to alter them – why are some reactions too slow whilst other are dangerously fast?

◆ catalysts and enzymes – how can these be used to make reactions more efficient?

◆ reacting masses – how much of each reactant do we need and how much product will it make?

◆ energy changes – why do some reactions need vast amounts of energy put into them, whilst others give energy out?

◆ reversible reactions – why do some reactions go to completion, whilst others seem to 'stick'?

In this module you learn to understand these problems in terms of colliding particles and the breaking and making of chemical bonds.

Before you start, check what you remember about the patterns of chemical change.

1 Imagine you have mixed some acid and alkali in a test-tube. How could you tell a chemical reaction had occurred just by holding the test-tube?

2 Natural gas burns in air to give carbon dioxide and water. What else do you get from this reaction? (Think: why do we burn gas?)

3 Plants make food using two simple chemicals: carbon dioxide and water. This reaction takes energy in. What provides the energy for this reaction?

4 Your digestive system is full of enzymes. What do they help to do?

7:1 Rates of reaction

How fast?

You already have some idea about **reaction rates** from Module 5. For example, you saw that the reactivity series of metals could be found by looking at how quickly different metals react with acid.

a Which metal reacts faster with sulphuric acid, iron or magnesium?

Some reactions are very fast indeed, but others are very slow.

◆ In a car engine, the petrol/air mixture reacts in an almost instantaneous explosion.

◆ The steel body of the car may take many years to react with air and water and turn to rust.

b What makes the petrol/air mixture reaction start?

Controlling reaction rates is very important in the chemical industry.

◆ If a reaction takes place too quickly, it might get out of control and cause an explosion.

◆ If a reaction runs too slowly, this will make the process very inefficient and will raise production costs.

c Imagine you are cooking a cake. What would happen to the cake if the reactions went too fast?

Reaction rates need to be controlled. But before you can control reactions rates, you need to be able to measure them.

Measuring reaction rates

To find how fast a reaction is going, you need to be able to time something. In the case of a metal reacting with an acid, you can time how long it takes for the metal to disappear completely.

In an experiment, you would need to:

◆ react samples of different metals in acid;

◆ use a large amount of acid to make sure that all the metal reacts;

◆ use the same amount of each metal in order to make it a fair test;

◆ use the same amount of acid in each case to make it a fair test.

The longer it takes for the reaction to occur, the slower the reaction is.

To find the speed (or rate) of the reaction, you can divide the amount of metal reacted (in grams) by the time the reaction took (in seconds). This would give you a reaction rate in grams per second.

d Which of the metals shows the highest rate of reaction? What is the rate of reaction in grams per second?

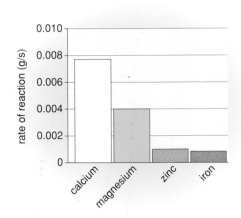

Metal (0.1 g)	Time taken to react completely (s)
calcium	13
magnesium	24
zinc	90
iron	120

What can you measure?

To time a reaction, you need to measure either:

♦ the loss of the reacting chemicals (**reactants**); or

♦ the increase in the **products** of the reaction.

For example, consider the simple reaction between a metal and an acid:

reactants		products
magnesium +	sulphuric acid	→ magnesium sulphate + hydrogen
Mg +	H_2SO_4	→ $MgSO_4$ + H_2

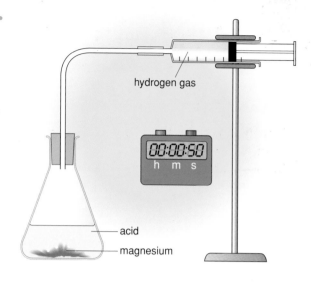

hydrogen gas

acid
magnesium

You can measure how long it takes for one of the reactants, for example the magnesium, to be used up in the reaction. But this reaction also produces bubbles of hydrogen gas.

Measuring the volume of a gas

You can measure how fast a gas is produced by using a **gas syringe**. As the gas is formed, it forces the barrel of the syringe back against atmospheric pressure. This gives a true volume for the particular temperature and pressure.

Using this method you can find how long it takes to produce a particular volume of gas. You can then work out the rate of reaction in terms of cm^3 of gas per second.

e How is the rate of reaction shown here changing with time?

Alternatively, you can take readings every few seconds and plot a graph of the volume of hydrogen formed against the time. Graphs like this clearly show that the reaction slows down as it approaches the '**end-point**'. This is because the reactants get 'used up'.

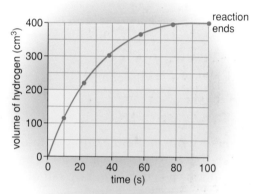

time to produce 200 cm^3 of hydrogen is 20 seconds

rate = $\frac{200}{20}$ = 10 cm^3/s

Questions

1 Suggest a simple way to detect the end-point of the following reactions.

  a Magnesium ribbon burning in air.

  b Sodium carbonate reacting with a citric acid solution.

2 Limestone reacts with acid, producing carbon dioxide gas. These results show the volume of gas produced over time.

Time (s)	0	30	60	90	120	150	180	210
Volume (cm^3)	0	45	84	115	135	150	155	158

  a Plot a volume/time graph.

  b What is the rate of gas production over the first 30 seconds?

  c How much gas was produced between 30 and 60 seconds? What was the rate of gas production in that time?

  d Explain this pattern of changing rate of reaction.

Summary

• Different reactions can run at very different rates.

• In industry it is very important to control the rate of reaction.

• You can follow the rate of a reaction either by measuring how fast a reactant is used up, or by measuring how fast a product is formed.

7:2 Speeding things up

Controlling the rate of a reaction is very important in industry. If you can speed up a reaction, you can usually keep the costs of the reaction down. There are many ways of speeding up reactions.

Before a chemical reaction can take place, the particles of the reacting chemicals have to meet and collide with each other. Anything you can do that makes the particles collide more often will speed up the reaction.

Two ways of doing this would be:

◆ increasing the **surface area** of a solid;

◆ increasing the **concentration** of a solution.

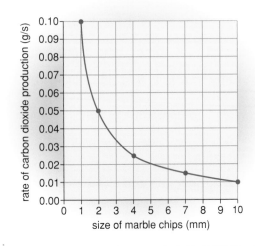

Investigating surface area

Marble chips are a natural form of calcium carbonate. Calcium carbonate reacts with hydrochloric acid, giving off carbon dioxide gas.

$$\text{calcium carbonate} + \text{hydrochloric acid} \rightarrow \text{calcium chloride} + \text{water} + \text{carbon dioxide}$$

$$CaCO_3 + 2HCl \rightarrow CaCl_2 + H_2O + CO_2$$

One large lump of marble dropped into a beaker fizzes steadily. But use the same amount of marble in powdered form and the reaction foams up out of the beaker.

a What does the difference between the two reactions show about the rate of reaction?

Acid particles can only collide with the carbonate particles when the carbonate particles are exposed on the surface of a piece of marble. Breaking up a solid exposes more and more of the surface area and so makes the reaction go faster.

b Why does chewing your food well help you to digest it?

1 cube of 4 cm   = 8 cubes of 2 cm   = 64 cubes of 1 cm

volume = 64 cm³

...but the total surface area =

$1 \times 6 \times 16 = \textbf{96 cm}^2$ $8 \times 6 \times 4 = \textbf{192 cm}^2$ $64 \times 6 \times 1 = \textbf{384 cm}^2$

Smaller cubes; larger surface area.

Following the reaction

Carbon dioxide is produced when calcium carbonate reacts with acid. If the reaction takes place in an open beaker, the carbon dioxide escapes into the air. If the reaction is carried out on a balance, the total mass remaining in the beaker will go down as the carbon dioxide escapes.

If you measure how much mass is lost in a given time, you can work out the rate of the reaction.

The graph shows that the reaction rate speeds up when you use smaller marble chips.

c What is the mass loss per second for the 2 mm chips?

rate of carbon dioxide production (g/s) — size of marble chips (mm)

Investigating concentration

The reaction between calcium carbonate and acid can be used to show how the reaction rate changes as you change the concentration of the acid. You can do this very simply by dropping calcium carbonate into beakers of acid of different concentrations. You should not be surprised to find that a stronger acid gives a faster reaction. What is the explanation?

d Sketch the shape of the graph you would expect if you plotted rate of reaction against concentration of acid.

Remember, before two particles can react, they must meet! If the acid is at a low concentration, the acid particles will be widely spread in the water. The number of collisions between them and calcium carbonate particles will be limited. At higher concentrations, however, the chance of a collision between the acid particles and the calcium carbonate particles is increased.

acid particles

marble chip

low concentration
slow reaction

meet and react

marble chip

higher concentration
faster reaction

Pressure, too

In reactions involving gases, the pressure is equivalent to concentration. All else being equal, the greater the pressure, the greater the number of particles of a gas in a given space. The closer the particles are together, the more chance they have of colliding with another. If you double the pressure, you will double the rate of reaction.

Graphs drawn for rate against concentration and rate against pressure look very similar.

rate of reaction

concentration or pressure

Questions

1 Why is it that delicate carvings on churches seem to suffer more from the effects of acid rain than large blocks made from the same stone?

2 Explain why breaking up a solid increases the surface area and so speeds up any chemical reaction.

3 Here is the data from a marble/acid experiment.

Time (s)	0	20	40	60	80	100
Mass (g) (including beaker)	323.97	323.35	323.03	322.88	322.80	322.76

a Copy the table and add an extra row for mass lost since the start of the experiment.

b Plot a graph of mass loss (y axis) against time (x axis).

c What is the initial rate of reaction over the first 20 s?

d On your graph, sketch the lines you would expect if you:
(i) doubled the concentration of the acid or
(ii) halved the concentration of the acid.

Summary

• It is often important to be able to speed up reactions in industry.

• Particles must meet before they can react.

• Reactions can be speeded up by breaking up any solids and so increasing the surface area.

• Reactions can be speeded up by increasing the concentration of solutions or the pressure in gases.

If you think a reaction is going too slowly, the first thing you would probably do would be to heat it up.

It is a common experience in chemistry that heating a reaction makes the reaction go faster. Two examples of chemical reactions in the home illustrate this:

◆ meat cooks faster in a hotter oven;

◆ you keep milk cool in the fridge to stop it going 'off'.

It is surprising just how much an increase in temperature affects the rate of reaction. The 'rule of thumb' for most reactions is that the rate will double for every 10 °C or so rise in temperature.

a These bottles of milk are the same age. Which was left in a warm room, and which was left in the fridge?

Which bottle of milk would you like to drink?

Following a reaction

Sodium thiosulphate is a chemical used in photography. If you mix a clear solution of sodium thiosulphate with hydrochloric acid, a reaction occurs. Sulphur is one of the products of the reaction; the sulphur is produced as a creamy-yellow **precipitate**.

$$Na_2S_2O_3 \; + \; 2HCl \; \rightarrow \; 2NaCl \; + \; SO_2 \; + \; S \; + \; H_2O$$

sodium thiosulphate   sulphur

The precipitate does not start to form immediately, but begins to appear after a short time. The mixture turns cloudy as the precipitate forms. It is difficult to tell precisely when this reaction has stopped. One method you can use is to time how long it takes for a pencil cross to disappear when viewed through the liquid.

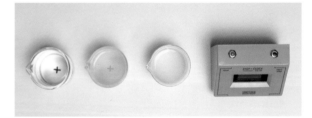
Going, going, gone! The thiosulphate/acid reaction turns the solution cloudy.

Seeing the pattern

You can carry this experiment out several times at different temperatures. All you need to do is to heat the thiosulphate solution to a higher temperature each time, before adding a fixed amount of acid. Then you can measure the reaction temperature with a thermometer once the reactants have been mixed and the stop clock started.

b Why is it important to use the same amount of acid in each experiment?

If you plot the time taken for the cross to disappear against the temperature, you can clearly see how increasing the temperature speeds up the reaction.

c Use the graph to work out how much the temperature needs to be raised in order to make the reaction happen in half the time.

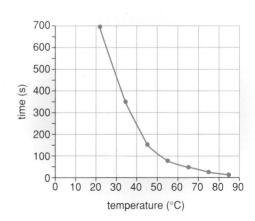

A graph of rate against temperature

From looking at a rate/temperature graph you might expect all industrial reactions to be run at as high a temperature as possible. High temperatures are often used but there are limits. For example, the products may themselves break down if heated too much.

Cost is also important. You need a lot of energy to reach very high temperatures, and energy costs money. Industrial chemists are always on the lookout for the most cost-effective ways to run their chemical reactions. (This is discussed in the next couple of pages.)

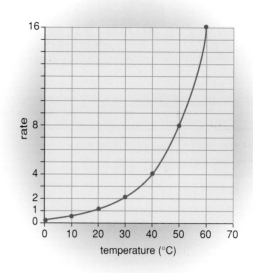

Why is temperature important?

To understand why temperature is important, you need to think about what is happening to the particles.

You have seen that reactions take place when reactant particles collide. Without a collision, the reactants cannot possibly 'change partners' in a chemical reaction.

A collision on its own is not enough. If it were, most chemical reactions would be almost instantaneous. The particles must also collide with enough energy to make a reaction happen. This energy is needed to break the existing bonds so that the particles are free to make new bonds.

d Gas burning in air is a chemical reaction. Why doesn't a Bunsen burner light as soon as you turn on the gas?

The minimum collision energy required for any given reaction to take place is called its **activation energy**. At any given temperature, collisions of many different types will occur, from a maximum energy 'head-on' collision to gentler glancing blows. But temperature will also have an effect, as the higher the temperature, the higher the average speed of the particles.

The faster a particle, the more kinetic energy it has and so the more chance it has of reaching the activation energy threshold in a collision.

If the temperature is raised, the average speed increases, so a larger proportion of the collisions transfer sufficient energy for the particles to react.

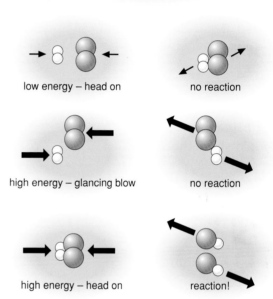

low energy – head on   no reaction

high energy – glancing blow   no reaction

high energy – head on   reaction!

You need the right kind of collision before you get a reaction.

Questions

1 Photographers use 'developer' solution to bring out the image in their photographs. If the film is left in the developer too long, the photos will be very dark because the chemical reaction will have gone too far. If a film takes 5 minutes to develop in solution at room temperature, what would happen if it was left for 5 minutes in a solution made with hot water?

2 Hydrogen gas and bromine gas react when heated.

$$H_2 + Br_2 \rightarrow 2HBr$$

Explain what happens in terms of colliding particles.

Summary

- The rate of a chemical reaction increases if the temperature increases.

- Particles must collide with enough energy to break their bonds if they are to react.

- The amount of energy needed in a reaction is called the activation energy.

- Raising the temperature means that more collisions of particles reach the activation energy.

7:4 Catalysts and enzymes

Everlasting activity!

Hydrogen peroxide is an unstable compound made of hydrogen and oxygen. Left on its own, it will slowly break down into water and oxygen gas.

hydrogen peroxide → water + oxygen

If you drop some manganese dioxide into hydrogen peroxide, the hydrogen peroxide starts to fizz rapidly as oxygen is given off. Nothing particularly surprising in that, you might think – just another chemical reaction in progress.

The only thing is that the manganese dioxide has not been changed. If you filter the mixture after the reaction you can get the same amount of manganese dioxide back – and use it again and again!

a Look at these diagrams. Now explain how you could show that manganese dioxide is not taking part directly in this reaction.

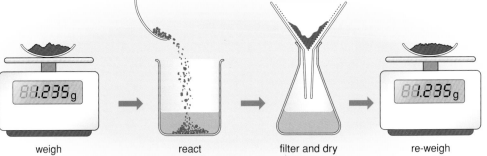

weigh   react   filter and dry   re-weigh

Manganese dioxide speeds up the breakdown of hydrogen peroxide, but remains unchanged itself.

What is happening?

The reaction that occurs is the breakdown of hydrogen peroxide to water and oxygen, which would have occurred slowly on its own.

The manganese dioxide has speeded up this reaction without itself being altered. It has acted as a **catalyst**.

$$2H_2O_2(l) \xrightarrow{\text{MnO}_2 \text{ catalyst}} 2H_2O(l) + O_2(g)$$

Catalysts work by reducing the activation energy that is needed for a chemical reaction to occur. The reaction takes place on the surface of the catalyst. This is why the catalyst has to be finely divided, so it has the biggest possible surface area. You also need to find the right catalyst for the reaction you are trying to speed up.

For the breakdown of hydrogen peroxide, iron oxide or copper oxide will work too, but manganese dioxide gives the fastest reaction.

b How could you compare the effectiveness of different metal oxides as catalysts for this reaction?

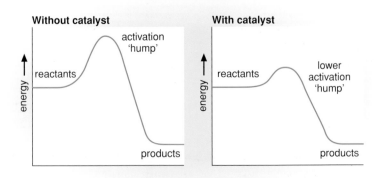

Catalysts lower the activation energy needed to get a reaction going.

Catalysts at work

Catalysts are very important in industry, as they allow reactions to take place more efficiently and at lower temperatures. This, of course, saves money!

Transition metals or their oxides are often used as catalysts.

◆ Iron is used in the production of ammonia by the Haber process (see page 176).

◆ Nickel is used to turn oils into fats to make margarine.

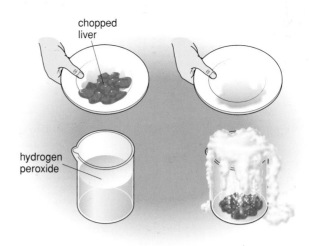

Enzymes

If you added a drop of blood or some chopped liver to hydrogen peroxide the effect is even more dramatic than adding manganese dioxide. This is because of the presence of a biological, protein-based catalyst called catalase.

These biological catalysts are called **enzymes**. Their action can be very powerful. Most life processes, for example digestion and respiration, depend on enzyme action.

Chopped liver catalysis in action!

So what's different?

With a catalyst, the rate of reaction also increases as the temperature increases, doubling for every 10 °C or so increase in temperature.

From 0 °C up to about 40 °C, enzymes behave in a similar way. But their action starts to tail off rapidly by 45 °C. By about 60 °C most enzymes have stopped working altogether.

c   In what ways are enzymes similar to other catalysts? In what ways are they different?

Enzymes are different because they are proteins. Like the proteins in food, enzymes break down (become cooked!) at higher temperatures. It should not surprise you that the best temperature for enzyme action corresponds closely to your body temperature.

d   Why is it that enzyme action drops away so rapidly above 45 °C?

Enzymes are also affected by pH. The enzymes that help to digest the food in your stomach work best at very low pH – which helps to explain why your stomach is full of hydrochloric acid. Other enzymes work best at different pH levels.

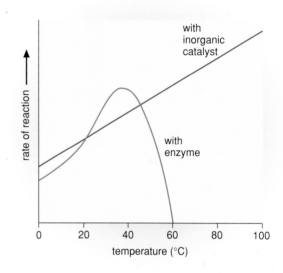

Enzyme action peaks at 37 °C – that's body temperature.

Questions

1 Chemicals such as magnesium destroy hydrogen peroxide by reacting with the 'extra' oxygen:

$$H_2O_2 + Mg \rightarrow H_2O + MgO$$

   How is this different from catalysis?

2 Suggest a reason why your body temperature is maintained at 37 °C.

Summary

• Catalysts speed up chemical reactions without being used up themselves.

• Transition metals are often used as catalysts. They are very important in industry.

• Enzymes are biological catalysts that work best at warm rather than hot conditions.

7:5 Traditional uses of enzymes

All living cells use enzyme-controlled chemical reactions to make new materials. Some of these processes have been turned to human advantage for centuries.

Brewing

Sugars are energy foods that you use as fuels. You react glucose with the oxygen you breathe to make carbon dioxide, water and the energy you need for life.

Some organisms, such as **yeast** (a simple fungi), are able to use their enzymes to get energy from sugars without needing oxygen. This process is called **fermentation**.

If living yeast cells are put into a sugary solution and kept at about 37 °C, they start to grow and divide rapidly. The sugar is turned into alcohol and lots of carbon dioxide is produced, which is allowed to escape.

$$\text{sugar} \xrightarrow[\text{yeast enzymes}]{\text{fermentation}} \text{alcohol} + \text{carbon dioxide}$$

Fermentation has been used for centuries to make alcoholic drinks such as beer and wine.

a Beer is made from barley mash. As barley seeds germinate, the starch in the seeds turns to sugar. How does this happen?

Many traditional festivals celebrate the importance of enzyme-based chemistry.

Baking

The same enzyme-based reaction is also used in breadmaking. Yeast and a little sugar are mixed with water and flour to give an elastic dough. Fermentation begins but in this case the carbon dioxide is trapped and cannot escape. It forms tiny bubbles within the dough which get larger and larger, making the dough 'rise'. This makes light-textured bread when it is baked.

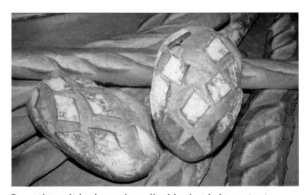

Sometimes it is the carbon dioxide that is important.

Testing for carbon dioxide

Carbon dioxide is a colourless gas that has no smell. Carbon dioxide also puts out a burning splint. If you want to be sure that a gas is carbon dioxide, you should use the limewater test.

Limewater is a clear solution of calcium hydroxide. When you react it with carbon dioxide, you get insoluble calcium carbonate, which forms a milky white precipitate: it is the calcium carbonate that turns the solution 'milky'.

$$\begin{array}{ccccccc} \text{calcium} & + & \text{carbon} & \rightarrow & \text{calcium} & + & \text{water} \\ \text{hydroxide} & & \text{dioxide} & & \text{carbonate} & & \end{array}$$

$$Ca(OH)_2(aq) + CO_2(g) \rightarrow CaCO_3(s) + H_2O(l)$$

You can easily try the carbon dioxide test by breathing out through limewater.

b Describe a simple way in which you could test the gas given off by fermenting fruit juice to see if it was carbon dioxide.

Cheese and yoghurt

Some bacteria get their energy from the sugar in milk (**lactose**). These bacteria produce **lactic acid** rather than alcohol. The lactic acid makes the milk curdle to form cheese or yoghurt. You can buy some yoghurts that still contain the live bacteria.

If you want to make your own yoghurt, all you need to do is mix a little of a 'live' yoghurt into some milk and leave the mixture in a warm place. The bacteria will grow rapidly and their enzymes will get to work on the milk – providing the bacteria with food and energy and you with an endless supply of yoghurt.

c What would be the best temperature to 'grow' your own yoghurt?

Stopping enzyme action

Not all enzyme action is useful. Unwanted bacteria cause our food to decay – the bacteria use enzymes to break the food down. Cooking stops this by killing the bacteria and destroying the enzymes. But cooking also changes the food itself.

d What other methods are used to kill bacteria in food?

A 'gentler' way to keep food longer without it going bad is to keep it cool. Below about 40 °C, enzymes behave in a similar way to other catalysts. Their reaction rates halve for every 10 °C drop in temperature. Cooling food reduces the rate at which bacteria can both feed and breed – so cold food stays 'fresh' for longer.

Questions

1 Alcohol can be used to sterilise wounds. Why do you think that it is not possible to get more than a relatively weak solution of alcohol (5–12%) by brewing?

2 Why is bread left to 'rise' in a warm place for some time before baking? What would the best temperature be?

3 Milk curdles into solid curds and watery whey as the bacteria get to work. What would you expect the pH of whey to be? 5, 7 or 9?

4 Fresh milk will last 8 days in the fridge (5 °C).

  a Approximately how long would you expect fresh milk to last at room temperature (25 °C)?

  b How long would fresh milk last on a very hot summer's day (35 °C)?

  c Pasteurised milk is milk that has been heated to just over 60 °C. Why does this last longer than unpasteurised milk?

DIGGING DEEPER
People eat 'live' yoghurt to encourage the special bacteria to grow in their stomachs and intestines. These 'good' bacteria help to stop other bacteria getting established and causing food poisoning.

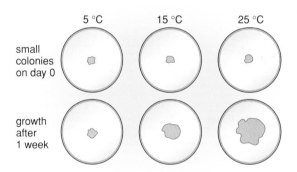

Bacteria cultured on agar grow at a much slower rate if kept chilled.

Summary

• Living cells use chemical reactions to produce new materials.

• Yeast cells convert sugar into carbon dioxide and alcohol.

• This process is called fermentation and is used to brew beer and make bread rise.

• A simple laboratory test for carbon dioxide is that it turns limewater milky.

• Bacteria turn milk into yoghurt.

7:6 Enzymes at work

The use of enzyme technology has steadily increased over recent years. This is because new uses for enzymes have been discovered.

Baby foods

The production of commercial baby foods is now very big business. At first, baby foods were simply meals that had been mashed up for small people without teeth. But very young babies can have difficulty digesting 'adult' foods, even in this form.

To overcome this problem, many baby foods are now 'pre-digested' using the enzyme **protease**. Protease starts the breakdown of the proteins in the food before the food is put in the jar. This means that young babies can digest the food more easily.

a **Prot**ease breaks down **prot**eins. What food group do you think is broken down by the enzyme **carbohydr**ase?

'Biological' washing powders

Many stubborn stains on clothing are caused by proteins, fats and oils. These stains are not easily soluble in water. Traditional soap powders use soaps or detergents to help to loosen the stains and lift them free from the fabric.

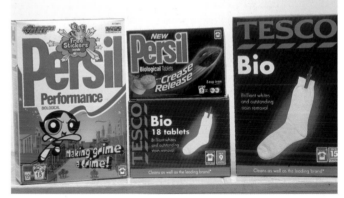

A different approach is to use special enzymes that help to break up the stains before removing them.

◆ Protease is again used to break up proteins.

◆ **Lipase** is used to break up fats and oils (fats and oils are called **lipids**).

b Some people do not like to use enzyme-rich washing powders in case they get the enzymes on their skin. Why might they be concerned about this?

Glucose

The sugar you have in your sugar bowl is called **sucrose**. This very sweet sugar is only found in sugar beet or sugar cane, which can make it relatively expensive.

The carbohydrate **starch** is much more common in nature and is produced in vast quantities in corn, for example. Starch can be easily and inexpensively harvested and converted to the sugar **glucose** using the enzyme **carbohydrase**.

c Many sports drinks contain glucose. Why might athletes need extra glucose?

A ready source of starch.

Fructose syrup

The glucose syrup produced from corn starch is not usually used directly in food. The problem is that glucose is not as sweet as sucrose so you would need to use more of it to get the same sweetening effect. This makes it very undesirable in slimming foods, for example.

d Why do people on diets want to reduce the amount of sugar they eat?

Fortunately another enzyme, called **isomerase**, can be used to convert glucose into another sugar, called **fructose**. Fructose is even sweeter than sucrose, and so is used in smaller amounts.

Effective industrial use of enzymes

Enzymes work best at relatively low temperatures and ordinary pressures, so they are very useful for many industrial processes.

Without enzymes, many chemical reactions might need to be run at very high temperatures or pressures. This would mean expensive equipment is needed, as well as leading to high energy costs.

But using enzymes can also lead to problems. Because enzymes are proteins, they can be broken down quite easily. They are usually water-soluble, and so get mixed up with the products of the reaction. Often the enzymes cannot be easily recovered. This means that the reaction has to take place in big vats, and all the enzymes must be replaced every time a new **batch** is started.

Ideally, industrial reactions should be run as **continuous processes** as this reduces costs. For this to be possible, enzymes have to be **stabilised** so that they remain active for long periods. They must also be **immobilised** so that the reactants can be passed over them continuously.

e Describe the differences between batch and continuous processes. Why are batch processes more expensive?

Enzymes may be immobilised by trapping them in some way. They may be 'stuck' onto a carrier such as alginate beads or trapped between the molecular strands of a polymer.

Questions

1 Suggest a type of enzyme which could be used to:

   a remove an oil stain from a carpet;

   b make glucose from carbohydrate in bread;

   c remove bloodstains from a shirt.

2 Some enzymes that have been immobilised onto carrier beads are still used in batch processes. They are kept in the vat of reactants until the yield of the product is high enough. How does immobilisation help to keep the costs down even in cases such as this?

These foods have a low sugar content – so fructose will be used instead of glucose.

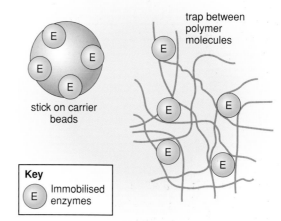

trap between polymer molecules

stick on carrier beads

Key

E Immobilised enzymes

Summary

- In industry, enzymes are used to make reactions work at normal temperatures and pressures, which saves money.

- Enzymes are used in biological washing powders to digest stains, to pre-digest baby food and to make glucose and fructose syrups from corn starch.

- For an industrial enzyme reaction to work effectively, the enzyme must be stabilised and immobilised, so that a continuous process may be used.

Relative atomic mass

Atoms are so very small that it is difficult to talk about their tiny masses all the time. Instead, their masses are usually just compared to each other.

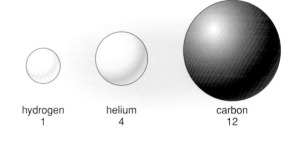

hydrogen 1   helium 4   carbon 12

◆ Hydrogen, the smallest atom, is 1 on this scale.

◆ A helium atom has four times the mass of a hydrogen atom, so it is 4.

◆ A carbon atom has twelve times the mass of a hydrogen atom, so it is 12, and so on.

4 is the **relative atomic mass** (A_r) for helium. Relative atomic masses have been calculated for all elements. You can look them up in tables or find them on the periodic table in the data sheets at the back of this book.

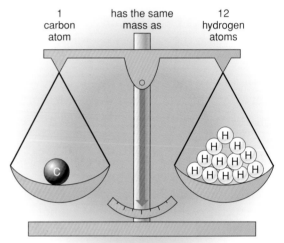

1 carbon atom   has the same mass as   12 hydrogen atoms

a Find the relative atomic masses for fluorine (F), silicon (Si), iron (Fe) and lead (Pb).

Formula mass

Molecules are also very small, so it makes sense to compare their masses on the same scale as for atoms.

If you know the formula of a compound, you can find its **formula mass** (M_r) by adding up the relative atomic masses of all the atoms that make up the compound.

Some examples should help.

Water

  formula: H_2O (A_r H = 1, O = 16)

  formula mass (M_r) = $(2 \times 1) + 16 = 18$

Methane

  formula: CH_4 (A_r H = 1, C = 12)

  formula mass (M_r) = $12 + (4 \times 1) = 16$

Carbon dioxide

  formula: CO_2 (A_r C = 12, O = 16)

  formula mass (M_r) = $12 + (2 \times 16) = 44$

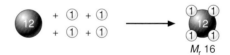

Calcium carbonate

  formula: $CaCO_3$ (A_r Ca = 40, C = 12, O = 16)

  formula mass (M_r) = $40 + 12 + (3 \times 16) = 100$

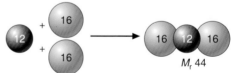

b Calculate the formula mass (M_r) for:

◆ aluminium oxide, Al_2O_3 (Al = 27, O = 16)

◆ sodium nitrate, $NaNO_3$ (Na = 23, N = 14, O = 16)

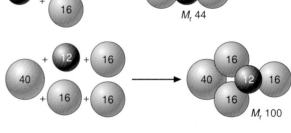

Finding how much reacts?

How do we know what the formula of a compound is?

The first step is to measure carefully the masses of elements that combine to form that compound. This can be done easily for magnesium oxide, as shown in the diagram.

c Draw a simple flow chart for this process, briefly describing each step in turn.

d Using the values on the balance, calculate the relative masses of magnesium and oxygen that have combined. What simple ratio Mg:O does this give?

It doesn't matter how many times you repeat this experiment, or where you get the magnesium from: the ratio of the masses of magnesium and oxygen that have combined to form magnesium oxide always stays the same.

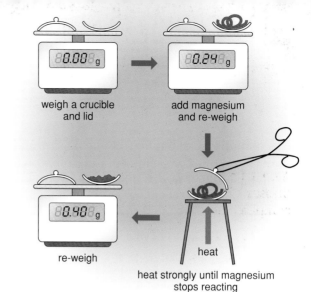

weigh a crucible and lid → add magnesium and re-weigh

re-weigh ← heat / heat strongly until magnesium stops reacting

Magnesium burns in air to give magnesium oxide.

So what's the formula?

This still doesn't tell you what the formula of magnesium oxide actually is. It could be Mg_2O, or MgO or MgO_2, for example. You now need to use your understanding of formula mass to find out which is correct, by calculating the Mg:O mass ratio you would expect to get for each possible formula:

Possible formulae

Mg_2O: M_r would be 64
Mg:O ratio would be $(2 \times 24):16 = 48:16 = 3:1$

MgO: M_r would be 40
Mg:O ratio would be $24:16 = 3:2$

MgO_2: M_r would be 56
Mg:O ratio would be $24:(2 \times 16) = 24:32 = 3:4$

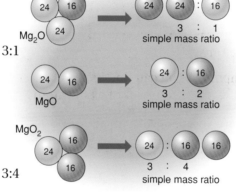

If you compare these 'theoretically possible' ratios to the ratio found by experiment, you will see that the formula must be MgO, giving the simple 3:2 ratio.

The formula found by experiment in this way is called the **empirical formula**.

Questions

1 What is the sulphur:oxygen ratio in:

a sulphur dioxide (SO_2)

b sulphur trioxide (SO_3)
(S = 32, O = 16)

2 By experiment, it is found that the copper/sulphur mass ratio in copper sulphide is 2:1. (Cu = 64, S = 32)

Is the formula of copper sulphide Cu_2S, CuS or CuS_2?

Summary

• The atoms of different elements have different masses.

• The masses of the atoms may be compared by their relative atomic mass (A_r).

• The relative formula mass (M_r) of a compound can be found by adding up the relative atomic masses of the atoms.

• You can find the empirical formula of a compound if you know the mass ratios of the combining atoms.

Calculations using relative atomic masses and relative formula masses can be very useful. For example, you can find the percentage of metal in different metal ores. This information is important for mining and metal refining companies. It helps people to answer questions about the ores they are using.

Case study 1: Which ore to use?

Both **haematite** (Fe_2O_3) and **pyrite** (FeS_2) can be used as iron ores. Which one gives the most iron per tonne of ore? The percentage of iron in each compound can be easily calculated from the A_r and M_r values. (Fe = 56, O = 16)

Haematite is Fe_2O_3

$M_r = (2 \times 56) + (3 \times 16) = 160$

amount of iron $= (2 \times 56) = 112$

percentage of iron $= \dfrac{112}{160} \times 100 = 70\%$

Pyrite is FeS_2

$M_r = 56 + (2 \times 32) = 120$

amount of iron $= 56$

percentage of iron $= \dfrac{56}{120} \times 100 = 47\%$

A sample of haematite.

A sample of pyrite.

a Pyrite is called Fools' Gold. It is worthless compared to gold, but how does it compare to haematite as an iron ore?

b How many kilograms of iron could you get from 1 tonne (1000 kg) of haematite?

Case study 2: Quicklime from limestone

Quicklime (calcium oxide) is used as a fertiliser. It neutralises acid soils and improves the texture of the soil. Quicklime is made by heating limestone in a kiln. Limestone is made of calcium carbonate, which breaks down and gives off carbon dioxide when heated.

$$\text{calcium carbonate} \xrightarrow{\text{heat}} \text{calcium oxide} + \text{carbon dioxide}$$
$$CaCO_3 \longrightarrow CaO + CO_2$$

But how much quicklime do you get from limestone?
(Ca = 40, C = 12, O = 16)

M_r of $CaCO_3 = 40 + 12 + (3 \times 16) = 100$

M_r of $CaO = 40 + 16 = 56$

Percentage of CaO in $CaCO_3 = \dfrac{56}{100} \times 100 = 56\%$

c How many kilograms of quicklime could you get from 1 tonne of limestone?

From limestone...   ...to quicklime.

Finding reacting masses

You can also use A_r and M_r values to calculate the quantities required for industrial or laboratory reactions. This makes for efficient use of reactants, but may also be crucial to ensure that a reaction runs smoothly.

Case study 3: The perfect thermit

In the thermit reaction, aluminium is used to displace iron from iron(III) oxide. When it works well, this is a spectacularly exothermic reaction, producing nearly white-hot molten iron. This reaction is still used to weld iron railway lines together in position on the tracks.

A thermit reaction.

The thermit reaction can be spectacular in the laboratory, too. But it is a notoriously difficult reaction to 'get right' and often just fizzles out. To be sure of success, you need the correct proportions of iron(III) oxide and aluminium.

The iron(III) oxide to aluminium ratio can again be found by calculation. (Fe = 56, O = 16, Al = 27)

The word equation is:

iron(III) oxide + aluminium → aluminium oxide + iron

Step 1: Write out the balanced equation

$$Fe_2O_3 \quad + \quad 2Al \quad \rightarrow \quad Al_2O_3 \quad + \quad 2Fe$$

Step 2: Calculate the M_r values for the reactants

$(2 \times 56 + 3 \times 16) + (2 \times 27)$

Step 3: Work out the ratio of iron(III) oxide to aluminium

160:54 (which is approximately 3:1 by mass)

d **How many grams of aluminium powder would you need to mix with 8 g of iron(III) oxide to give a perfect thermit?**

Questions

1 **What is the percentage of lead in galena? Galena is lead sulphide, PbS. (Pb = 207, S = 32)**

2 **What is the percentage of aluminium in bauxite? Bauxite is aluminium oxide, Al_2O_3. (Al = 27, O = 16)**

3 **What mass of carbon dioxide is given off if 1 kg of limestone is roasted until it has completely broken down?**

4 **What mass of carbon dioxide is given off if 1 kg of limestone is completely dissolved in hydrochloric acid? If you think you know the answer without further calculation, you need to explain why you think this.**

5 **Iron and sulphur react to give iron sulphide:**

$$Fe + S \rightarrow FeS$$

Calculate the simple ratio of iron and sulphur by mass that is needed for this reaction to work perfectly. (Fe = 56, S = 32)

Summary

- If you know the formula of a compound you can calculate the percentage of each element in it by mass.

- If you know the balanced chemical equation for a reaction, you can work out the proportions of each reactant that are needed by mass.

Introducing the mole

When you write an equation, you are describing the reaction between one set of particles. But the equation would also be true if you were to double the number of each type of particle present, or treble them, or multiply them by ten, or a hundred, or a million – or any number you chose to use. The relative proportions in the equation would still remain constant. And, of course, in the actual reaction, countless billions of particles will be involved.

The reason that formula mass calculations work is that if you scale the A_r and M_r figures up to grams, the ratio of particles remains the same. To put it another way, if you take the M_r of any particle and weigh out that number of grams of the substance (the formula mass in grams), you will always have the same number of particles. This number is very large indeed. It comes out at approximately 6×10^{23} or six hundred thousand million million million!

This number is used to define a standard unit of particles – the **mole**. You can have a mole of atoms, of molecules or of ions, even a mole of electrons. Whatever it is, if you have 6×10^{23} of them, you have a mole. In its simplest form, you have one mole of a substance if you have the atomic (or formula) mass of the substance in grams. But the mole can take on many other guises.

a How many particles are there in 9 g of water?

b How many moles are there in 10 g of calcium carbonate?

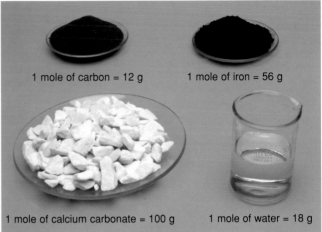

1 mole of carbon = 12 g

1 mole of iron = 56 g

1 mole of calcium carbonate = 100 g

1 mole of water = 18 g

600 000 000 000 000 000 000 000

Working with gases

If you are looking at reactions between solids or pure liquids (not solutions), you can easily find the mass of each reactant by weighing the solid or liquid. If you are looking at the way gases react then weighing gases is not so easy.

With gases, it is easier to measure the volume. But how does the volume of a gas link up with the idea of moles?

Fortunately it has been found that, at the same temperature and pressure, the same volume of gas contains the same number of particles. So 1 dm^3 (1 litre) of methane, for example, has the same number of particles as 1 dm^3 of oxygen, or 1 dm^3 of chlorine, and so on.

Similarly, for gases, if you have the same number of particles (all else being equal), you will have the same volume of each gas. Thus 1 mole of any gas will have the same volume. This volume is roughly 24 litres at room temperature and pressure.

c What is the volume of 3.2 g of oxygen (O_2 molecules) at room temperature and pressure?

It is not easy to find the mass of a gas...

80.008 g

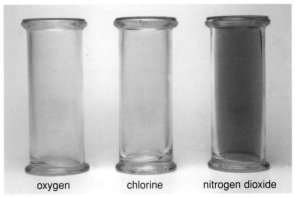

oxygen   chlorine   nitrogen dioxide

There are the same number of molecules in each gas jar.

Case study 1: Making water

Water is formed when hydrogen is burnt in oxygen. What gas volumes would you need to get the perfect reaction?

The word equation is:	hydrogen + oxygen → water
The balanced equation is	$2H_2 + O_2 \rightarrow 2H_2O$
The number of reacting particles is	2 + 1
Scale up to moles	2 moles + 1 mole
Convert to molar volumes	48 litres + 24 litres
The volume ratio is	2:1

d **What volume of hydrogen would you need to react with 5 litres of oxygen?**

Case study 2: Limestone and acid

What volume of carbon dioxide will you get if you dissolve a fixed amount of limestone in acid? You don't even need to have the full equation to work this out, or even worry about which acid you are using. You can just use the part of the equation that deals with limestone and carbon dioxide.

The word equation is

limestone (+ acid) → carbon dioxide (+ salt + water)

The part of the equation you need is	$CaCO_3 \rightarrow CO_2$
The number of particles is	1 → 1
The number of moles is	1 mole → 1 mole

The M_r of 1 mole of calcium carbonate is $40 + 12 + (3 \times 12) = 100$ g

1 mole of carbon dioxide occupies 24 litres. So 100 g of calcium carbonate produces 24 litres of carbon dioxide.

e **Jazira wanted to carry out an experiment to measure the rate of reaction between magnesium ribbon and hydrochloric acid.**

   $Mg + 2HCl \rightarrow MgCl_2 + H_2$

   He wanted to collect the gas in a 100 ml gas syringe. What mass of Mg ($A_r = 24$) would give exactly 100 ml of hydrogen at the end of the reaction?

   Hint: Work out the volume of H_2 you would get from 1 mole of Mg, and then scale it down.

Questions

1 **Hydrogen and chlorine react in sunlight to give hydrogen chloride gas:**

   $H_2 + Cl_2 \rightarrow 2HCl$

   What volume of hydrogen chloride gas would you get from 1 litre of hydrogen (measured at room temperature and pressure)?

Summary

- The mole is a handy idea for thinking about reacting masses and volumes.

- There are roughly 6×10^{23} particles in 1 mole.

- The formula mass in grams is 1 mole.

- 1 mole of gas at room temperature and pressure has a volume of 24 litres.

- If you are given the balanced equation for 'mixed' reactions, you can compare the masses of solids with the volume of gases produced.

- You don't always need the full equations – as long as you know how many particles are reacting or forming.

7:10 Energy changes

Give it out

It is not always easy to tell when a chemical reaction has occurred. For example, if you mix cold, dilute hydrochloric acid with some cold sodium hydroxide solution, you will not see any obvious change. Two colourless liquids just mix to form another colourless liquid. But if you hold the test-tube you will *feel* that something has happened. The test-tube will have got warmer!

a   How else could you tell that a reaction had occurred?

Chemical changes are often accompanied by changes in temperature. This is because energy is transferred to or from the surroundings. In this case, heat energy has been given out during a neutralisation reaction. Chemical reactions that give out heat energy like this are called **exothermic** reactions.

The neutralisation reaction is:

acid + alkali → salt + water + **energy**

For example

$HCl + NaOH \rightarrow NaCl + H_2O + \textbf{energy}$

Many chemical reactions are exothermic like this. Reactions that start as soon as the reactants are mixed are usually exothermic. The reaction of metals with acids is exothermic.

metal + acid → salt + hydrogen + **energy**

$Mg + H_2SO_4 \rightarrow MgSO_4 + H_2 + \textbf{energy}$

b   Name two other metals that would react in this way.

c   Describe another exothermic reaction you have met.

Combustion reactions

The combustion reaction of a fuel, such as methane, is also strongly exothermic. In fact, when you burn a fuel, you are not usually bothered about the chemical products of the reaction. It is only the heat energy output that you're after!

fuel + oxygen → waste gases + **energy**

For example

$CH_4 + 2O_2 \rightarrow CO_2 + 2H_2O + \textbf{energy}$

There is a difference between a neutralisation reaction and a combustion reaction. The difference is that fuels need a kick-start of energy before the reaction begins. This is true for most chemical reactions.

d   What problems might it cause if fuels did not need a kick-start of energy before they reacted?

You could follow the rise in temperature during neutralisation with a temperature sensor connected to a computer.

Calcium and magnesium both fizz in acid. The test-tubes will get hot.

calcium   magnesium

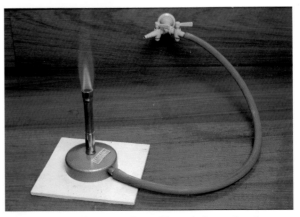

Fuels need a kick-start to burn. Then their combustion reactions are strongly exothermic.

Breaking bonds

The reason that most reactions need a 'kick-start' of energy to get them going is really quite simple. You need to break some of the existing bonds in the reactants before new bonds can form in the products – and it takes energy to break bonds!

e Where does the energy needed to break bonds come from once an exothermic reaction has started?

Energy profiles

Hydrogen is another fuel that reacts with oxygen in an exothermic reaction. Once again the hydrogen and oxygen molecules need a kick-start of energy to break some of the existing bonds before they will combine to form water.

f Write a balanced chemical equation for this reaction.

Perhaps an analogy will help? Consider a boulder lying in a hollow on a hillside. The boulder has stored, gravitational potential energy. If it were on a simple slope it would roll to the bottom of the valley, changing its stored energy to kinetic energy as it rolled. Because the boulder is in a hollow, however, work must first be done on it (more energy must be put in) in order to push it up and over the lip of the hollow. Only then would it be free to move. Once it came to a halt, the excess energy would be converted to heat energy.

Similarly, molecules of hydrogen and oxygen contain stored chemical energy. As elements they have higher energy levels overall than water molecules. Given the chance, the reaction would 'roll down' the energy slope, giving out its energy as the new bonds formed. But first it needs the 'kick-start' of energy to break the bonds and push it up over the energy lip. The energy needed to do this is called the **activation energy**. This has been discussed before – see page 157.

g What effect do catalysts and enzymes have on the height of the 'activation energy lip'?

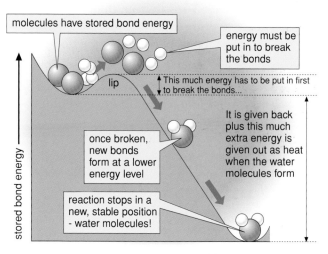

boulder at high level but in a hollow

boulder must first be pushed up slope

lip

This much energy has to be put in first

It is given back as boulder rolls over lip...

plus this much energy is given out as heat when the boulder stops

boulder will run down slope on its own once over the lip

boulder stops at lower stable position

potential energy

molecules have stored bond energy

energy must be put in to break the bonds

lip

This much energy has to be put in first to break the bonds...

It is given back plus this much extra energy is given out as heat when the water molecules form

once broken, new bonds form at a lower energy level

reaction stops in a new, stable position - water molecules!

stored bond energy

Questions

1 Sparklers are made from iron filings glued to a wire. They can be hard to light but, once alight, burn fiercely forming iron oxide.

  a Write a word equation for this reaction.

  b What else is produced during this reaction? (What type of reaction is this?)

  c Draw a simple energy profile diagram for this reaction. Is the 'activation energy lip' high or low?

Summary

- Exothermic reactions give out energy to the surroundings.

- Even exothermic reactions need an initial input of energy to break bonds and get the reaction started.

- This is called the activation energy.

7:11 More energy changes

Going down

You can make a pleasant summer drink by adding a spoonful of baking soda to a glass of lemon juice. When you do this a chemical reaction occurs:

$$\text{sodium hydrogencarbonate} + \text{citric acid} \rightarrow \text{sodium citrate} + \text{carbon dioxide} + \text{water}$$

(baking soda) (lemon juice)

a **What would you see happening that suggests a chemical reaction was occurring?**

If you were holding the glass as you stirred in the baking soda, you would also feel a change in temperature. A temperature change is another indication that a chemical reaction is happening. But in this case, the temperature goes down!

Take it in

Reactions that take energy in from their surroundings are called **endothermic** reactions. It is fairly rare for endothermic reactions to 'go on their own' like the one discussed above. You usually need to pump energy into them to make them work.

For example, the production of hydrogen and oxygen by the electrolysis of water is an endothermic reaction.

water + **electrical energy** $\rightarrow$ hydrogen + oxygen

b **The hydrogen atoms and oxygen atoms in water are held together by strong bonds. What is the electrical energy doing in the electrolysis of water?**

One of the most important endothermic reactions of all is **photosynthesis**. Plants use the energy from sunlight to build complex chemicals such as glucose, starting from carbon dioxide and water.

Making and breaking bonds

It seems fairly obvious that you will need to use energy to break something apart. This is true of the bonds that hold chemical compounds together, so any situation where chemical bonds are being broken will be endothermic. You will have to put energy into the reaction.

What may seem less obvious is that when bonds re-form, you get the energy back again. So bond making is an exothermic process.

c **You can apply the same rules to melting ice and freezing water. Which process is exothermic and which is endothermic?**

No ice is needed for this summer drink!

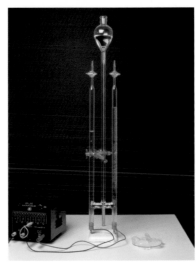

You need to break bonds to electrolyse water into hydrogen and oxygen, so this reaction is endothermic.

You are re-making bonds when you burn hydrogen to make water; overall this reaction is exothermic.

Both together

In most chemical reactions, some of the existing bonds have to be broken first before new bonds can form in the products. That is why reactions usually need the activation energy 'kick-start'.

In exothermic reactions, the energy you have to put in to break the original bonds is less than the energy you get back out when the new bonds form. This gives an energy profile where the reactants are 'up the slope' and the products are down in the 'valley'. The bigger the 'height' difference between the reactants and products, the more energy is given out and so the more exothermic the reaction is.

In endothermic reactions, the reactants are down in the 'valley' and so have to be pushed 'up the slope' to make the reaction work. The bigger the vertical height, the more energy is taken in and so the more endothermic the reaction is.

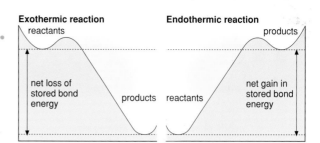

d Look at these energy profiles (R = reactants, P = products).

Which reaction is endothermic?

Which reaction is the most exothermic?

Which exothermic reaction has the higher activation energy?

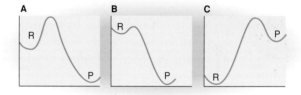

Energy by the bond

By studying a range of reactions, the amount of energy needed to make or break any bond has been established. This amount of energy is called the **bond energy**. You can use bond energies to predict whether any given reaction will be endothermic or exothermic.

For example, consider the reaction that takes place when hydrogen burns in air.

Bond	Energy
H–H	436
C–C	348
C–H	412
O=O	496
C=O	743
H–O	463

Some bond energies in kJ per mole.

     reactants   products

$$2H_2 + O_2 \rightarrow 2H_2O$$

energy to break $2 \times (H–H) + (O=O) = 2 \times 436 + 496 = 1368$ kJ in

energy to make $4 \times (O–H) = 4 \times 463 = 1852$ kJ out

The overall energy change = $1852 - 1368 = 484$ kJ out

This means that the reaction is exothermic.

Questions

1 How much energy is given out when you burn 1 mole of methane (16 g)?

$$CH_4 + 2O_2 \rightarrow CO_2 + 2H_2O$$

Step 1: How many C–H and O=O bonds have to be broken?

Step 2: How many kJ of energy are needed to do this?

Step 3: How many O–H and C=O bonds are formed?

Step 4: How many kJ of energy will be given out?

Step 5: What is the difference between the kJ values in steps 4 and 2?

Summary

- Energy has to be put in to break bonds.

- Energy is given out when bonds re-form.

- Exothermic reactions give out more energy overall than they take in.

- Endothermic reactions take in more energy overall than they give out.

- You can calculate the energy change in a reaction if you know the bond energies.

7:12 Reversible reactions

So far you have looked at chemical reactions as one-way processes.

reactants → products

For example, if you burn wood you get carbon dioxide and water. You cannot easily get the wood and oxygen back again.

But you also know many reversible processes. Water turns to ice if cooled, but melts back to water when heated. This happens in some chemical reactions, too.

You should be familiar with blue copper sulphate. It has water molecules chemically bound into its crystal structure. These water molecules can be driven off by heating, leaving a white powder called **anhydrous** copper sulphate. But if water is added to this white powder, the water recombines with the copper sulphate and the blue colour reappears. This **reversible reaction** is a chemical test for water.

Most chemical reactions are 'one way'...

... but some are reversible.

$$\text{hydrated copper sulphate} \underset{\text{water added}}{\overset{\substack{\text{water driven} \\ \text{off by heat}}}{\rightleftharpoons}} \text{anhydrous copper sulphate} + \text{water}$$

(blue)   (white)

a 'Anhydrous' means 'without water'. What do you think 'hydrated' means?

Heat it/cool it!

If you heat ammonium chloride, it turns directly from a solid to a gas. It **sublimes**. It then reappears as a white solid at the cool end of the tube. This is not just a physical change. Instead, it is another reversible chemical change.

$$\text{ammonium chloride} \underset{\text{cool}}{\overset{\text{heat}}{\rightleftharpoons}} \text{hydrogen chloride} + \text{ammonia}$$

(white solid)   (colourless gases)

$$NH_4Cl(s) \rightleftharpoons HCl(g) + NH_3(g)$$

The link between this reaction and the 'water test' is temperature. Heating drives the reaction to the right, but the reaction reverses as it cools down.

The reaction from left to right is endothermic, as energy has to be put in to make it work, but the reverse reaction is exothermic. In fact, the amount of energy transferred in this reaction is the same either way – it is just taken in in one direction and given back out in the other.

b Explain why the mixture gets hot when you perform the 'water test' with anhydrous copper sulphate.

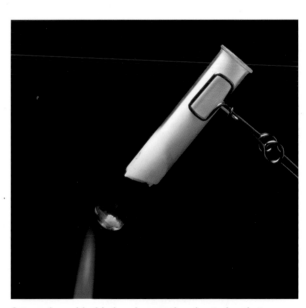

Ammonium chloride breaks up when heated, only to re-form at the cool end of the tube.

Forward and back reactions

You can think of reversible reactions in terms of the **forward reaction** and the **back reaction**.

$$A + B \xrightleftharpoons[\text{back reaction}]{\text{forward reaction}} C + D$$

If you pass steam over heated iron, the iron is oxidised to iron oxide and the steam is reduced. This is the forward reaction.

But if the hydrogen produced is now pushed back over the hot iron oxide, the reaction is reversed and the iron oxide is reduced. This is the back reaction.

$$\text{iron} + \text{steam} \xrightleftharpoons[\text{back reaction}]{\text{forward reaction}} \text{iron oxide} + \text{hydrogen}$$

c Describe the 'sublimation' of ammonium chloride in terms of the forward and back reactions.

Open and closed systems

The iron/steam experiment only works, reaching one end-point or the other, because one of the products is removed from the reaction site each time. The reaction is taking place in an **open system**.

But if iron and steam were heated in a **closed system** (such as in a sealed, pressure-proof container), the reaction would stick part-way, with all four molecules present. It would reach **equilibrium**. Equilibrium is shown in equations by the symbol $\rightleftharpoons$.

$$3Fe + 4H_2O \rightleftharpoons Fe_3O_4 + 4H_2$$

You might think that the reaction has stopped at equilibrium, but that is not the case. Some iron and steam particles are still reacting to give iron oxide and hydrogen, but they are compensated for by other iron oxide and hydrogen particles reacting to give iron and steam again!

d In a big department store, people are constantly travelling up and down the escalators, yet the number of people on each floor remains about the same. Use this as an analogy to explain how chemical equilibrium works.

Questions

1 Calcium carbonate ($CaCO_3$) decomposes when heated to give calcium oxide (quicklime, CaO) and carbon dioxide (CO_2).

a Write this as a balanced chemical equation.

b Is this reaction exothermic or endothermic? How do you know?

c In a closed system, a back reaction also occurs. Is this exothermic or endothermic?

d Why does this reaction go to completion when heated in an open tube? What would happen in a closed container?

Steam passed over hot iron: iron oxide forms if hydrogen is removed.

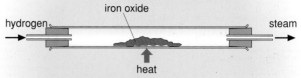

Hydrogen passed over iron oxide: iron is re-formed if the steam is removed.

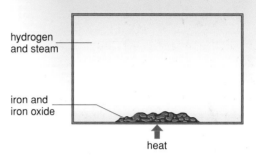

All four particles exist in a closed system.

Summary

- Some chemical reactions are reversible.

- If a reversible reaction is exothermic in one direction it is endothermic in the opposite direction. The same amount of energy is transferred in each case.

- The reversible reaction with anhydrous copper sulphate can be used as a test for water.

- When a reversible reaction occurs in a closed system, an equilibrium is reached – the reactions occur at exactly the same rate in both directions.

Ammonia for fertilisers

Plants need nitrogen to grow well. Unfortunately, plants cannot use the vast amounts of nitrogen in the atmosphere directly. However, nitrogen can be made to react with hydrogen to form ammonia. Then ammonia can be used to make nitrogen-providing **fertilisers** for plants.

$$\text{nitrogen} + \text{hydrogen} \xrightleftharpoons[\text{back reaction}]{\text{forward reaction}} \text{ammonia}$$

$$N_2 + 3H_2 \rightleftharpoons 2NH_3$$

Unfortunately, this reaction is very slow and is also reversible. Some of the ammonia that does form breaks down to form nitrogen and hydrogen again. The first attempts to make ammonia in this way gave just a few percent of ammonia. Something had to be done to increase the percentage yield of ammonia before this process could be used commercially.

a 100 years ago people became concerned that the population in Europe was growing very fast. Why do you think this sparked an interest in this 'ammonia' reaction?

Fritz Haber – the father of fertilisers.

What controls the yield?

Changing temperature

Heating increases the rate at which reactions occur. However, heating can also affect the balance point if the reaction is reversible. If you heat the mixture, the endothermic reaction will be encouraged as this will absorb the extra heat energy.

Unfortunately, here it is the back reaction that is endothermic. So heating the mixture will make the reaction go faster but will decrease the yield.

Changing pressure

The pressure of a gas depends on the number of particles there are in a set volume. In this reaction four particles (one N_2 and three H_2) produce two ammonia particles in the forward reaction. If the volume remains the same, the forward reaction will lead to a reduction in pressure because there are fewer particles.

If the pressure is increased, the balance point of the reaction shifts in the direction that will try to cancel out the increase in pressure. This reaction will shift in the direction of the forward reaction, just as is needed.

b From the evidence above, what do you think would be the best conditions for this reaction: high or low temperature? high or low pressure?

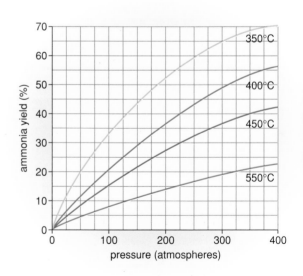

How the yield varies with temperature and pressure.

The Haber process

The basic theory would suggest that ammonia should be made at low temperature and very high pressure to give the highest possible yield. But this is not satisfactory as the reaction would be far too slow and the equipment needed far too expensive!

The solution to the problem was finally worked out 100 years ago by Fritz Haber. In the **Haber process,** the reaction is run at moderately high pressure, but also at a moderately high temperature to make it go faster. Even so, an iron catalyst is needed to speed things up further.

This is by no means a perfect solution in terms of yield, but Haber came up with a final trick. Ammonia boils at only –33 °C. He realised that ammonia could be cooled and liquefied easily and so removed from the system. The unreacted gases could then be recycled in a continuous process, eventually achieving total conversion.

c   A typical Haber plant may run at 450 °C and 200 atmospheres pressure. What is the percentage yield?

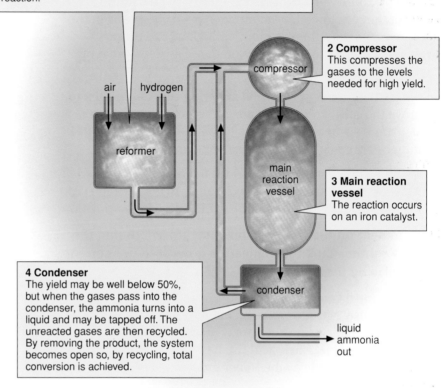

1 Reformer
Hydrogen (usually made on-site from natural gas) is heated and mixed with air. The oxygen in the air reacts with some of the hydrogen to produce water. This may seem wasteful, but by removing the oxygen in this way, the remaining air is virtually pure nitrogen. This is cheaper than producing the nitrogen by fractional distillation.

Also, if exactly the right amount of air is added, the resultant mix gives the 3:1 ratio of hydrogen to nitrogen needed by the Haber reaction.

2 Compressor
This compresses the gases to the levels needed for high yield.

3 Main reaction vessel
The reaction occurs on an iron catalyst.

4 Condenser
The yield may be well below 50%, but when the gases pass into the condenser, the ammonia turns into a liquid and may be tapped off. The unreacted gases are then recycled. By removing the product, the system becomes open so, by recycling, total conversion is achieved.

Questions

1 In 1918 Fritz Haber earned a Nobel Prize for his method of ammonia production.

   a Other chemists could have predicted the conditions that would have given the best yield in this reaction. What stopped them from making ammonia commercially?

   b Describe in your own words how Haber overcame these problems.

2 Look at the Haber process graph. What is the yield under 250 atmospheres pressure at:

   a 350 °C

   b 450 °C?

3 In a reversible reaction, three reactant particles react to form two product particles. The forward reaction is exothermic. What effect on the percentage yield of products would you have if you:

   a raised the temperature

   b raised the pressure?

Summary

• In reversible reactions the percentage yield can by changed by changing the temperature and pressure.

• Ammonia is made from nitrogen and hydrogen by the Haber process.

• A catalyst is used to speed up the reaction, but the yield is still low.

• The ammonia is removed by cooling the mixture and the gases are recycled.

7:14 More about fertilisers

The importance of fertilisers

Plants need nitrogen in order to make proteins and grow. Plants are unable to use the nitrogen that makes up 80% of the air. Instead, they are forced to get nitrogen from chemicals in the soil. Unfortunately, there is rarely enough usable nitrogen available naturally to grow crops on the scale demanded by modern farming.

In the past, farmers used natural materials rich in nitrogen to improve the soil – animal manure and vegetable compost. Today, some farmers are trying to go back to this method of farming, as 'organic' food becomes popular.

Most farmers throughout the world still have to use industrially produced fertilisers. They need to, in order to get the high crop yields that are essential to feed the world's growing population.

a Comment on the rate of population growth during the 20th century. Link the population growth to our current reliance on fertilisers.

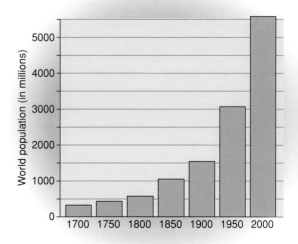

The world's population has increased hugely since 1700.

Fertilisers must contain nitrogen in a form that the plants can take in and use. Nitrogen as an element (N_2) is not suitable. Compounds made using ammonia (NH_3) and nitric acid (HNO_3) are suitable. Nitric acid can be made by oxidising some of the ammonia made by the Haber process.

Nitric acid

The production of nitric acid is a two-stage process. In the first stage the ammonia and oxygen are passed over a hot platinum catalyst. The ammonia is oxidised to nitrogen monoxide.

b What is the other oxidation product of ammonia? Write the word equation.

The nitrogen monoxide is cooled and mixed with more oxygen. The nitrogen monoxide/oxygen mixture is then passed up a tower against a steady trickle of water. Nitric acid forms and runs out at the base. This is the second stage.

c Write this second reaction out as a word equation.

d What is the purpose of the heat exchanger in this industrial process?

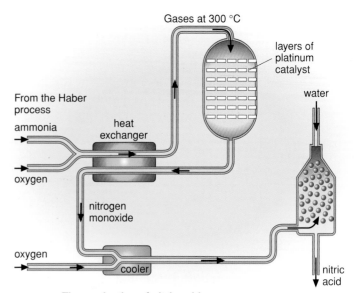

The production of nitric acid.

Ammonium nitrate fertiliser

One of the most commonly used 'nitrogen' fertilisers is ammonium nitrate (NH_4NO_3). Ammonium nitrate is made by dissolving ammonia in water and then combining the ammonium hydroxide with nitric acid in a neutralisation reaction.

ammonia + water → ammonium hydroxide

$$NH_3 + H_2O \rightarrow NH_4OH$$

ammonium hydroxide + nitric acid → ammonium nitrate + water

$$NH_4OH + HNO_3 \rightarrow NH_4NO_3 + H_2O$$

The ammonium nitrate solution is then evaporated to give ammonium nitrate crystals.

e Ammonium nitrate carries a 'double dose' of nitrogen – in both the 'ammonium' and 'nitrate' parts. But what is the percentage of nitrogen in ammonium nitrate by mass? (N = 14, H = 1, O = 16)

Nitrate problems

Manufactured fertilisers have worked wonders on crop production. Yields have gone up and food is cheap. But there are problems.

If fertilisers wash into rivers, they can upset the natural balance and make algae grow out of control. These 'algal blooms' end up by poisoning the fish in the river.

Another serious problem can be caused by nitrate fertilisers getting into drinking water. This occurred recently in East Anglia, where vast fields of wheat are heavily sprayed with fertiliser to keep the crop yields high.

The problem is that the nitrates are converted to nitrites (the NO_2^- ion). Nitrites can react with the iron in your blood. (The iron is part of your haemoglobin.) This reduces the blood's ability to carry oxygen. In its extreme form it causes 'blue baby syndrome', in which a baby turns blue due to lack of oxygen.

f East Anglia also has a problem with its lakes and rivers. Many parts of the Norfolk Broads are now covered by thick algal growths that have killed the fish. What might have caused this?

These fish are dead or dying because of lack of oxygen in the water caused by an algal bloom.

Questions

1 Draw a flow chart for the production of ammonium nitrate, starting with the nitrogen and hydrogen used for the Haber process.

2 a Fertiliser is expensive so you need to know what return you will get for your money. The table shows crop yields of wheat per hectare of land, compared with the amount of fertiliser used. Plot these figures as a scatter graph.

Kilogram of fertiliser added	0	50	100	150	200	250
Tonnes of grain grown	4.9	6.0	7.1	8.2	8.1	7.4

b What is the maximum amount of fertiliser to add to avoid waste?

Summary

- Many farmers use nitrogen fertilisers to increase their crop yields.

- These fertilisers are made from ammonia and nitric acid.

- Nitric acid is made by the catalytic oxidation of ammonia.

- Fertilisers can cause problems if they get into lakes or drinking water.

End of module questions

1 Alan put a beaker containing 200 cm³ of 1 M hydrochloric acid and a watch glass with 1 g of limestone chips onto an electric balance. He then zeroed the display on the balance. After this he tipped the limestone into the acid, placed the watch glass back on the balance next to the beaker, and noted the readings on the scale every 20 seconds.

Here are his results:

Time (seconds)	20	40	60	80	100	120	140	160	180
Balance reading (g)	−0.12	−0.23	−0.33	−0.40	−0.43	−0.44	−0.44	−0.44	−0.44

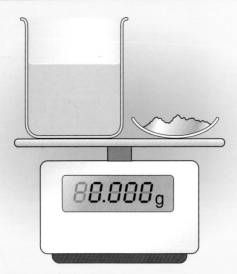

a Alan held some limewater over the beaker and it turned milky. What gas was given off?

b Copy and complete this word equation:

calcium carbonate + hydrochloric acid → calcium chloride + _____

c Explain why the reading on the balance scale dropped below zero.

d Plot a graph of Alan's results. Put the time along the x-axis and the mass loss in grams along the y-axis.

e What would Alan have *seen* happening during the first minute or so?

f Suggest *two* ways in which Alan would have known that the reaction was finished after 2 minutes.

g Alan repeated the experiment exactly, except he used 1 g of powdered limestone instead of limestone chips. Explain how this experiment would have looked different from the first one.

h On your graph from part **d**, sketch what you think the graph line for part **g** would have looked like.

i Explain your answer to part **h**.

2 The chart shows the main processes involved in the manufacture of ammonia:

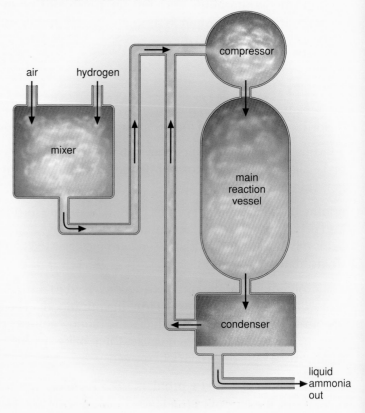

nitrogen + hydrogen ⇌ ammonia

a Why doesn't all the nitrogen and hydrogen turn to ammonia in the main reaction vessel?

b How is the ammonia removed from the system so that the unused nitrogen and hydrogen may be recycled?

c What is the source of the nitrogen for this reaction?

d Calculate the percentage by mass of nitrogen in ammonia, NH_3 (relative atomic masses are N = 14, H = 1).

3 Magnesium ribbon reacts with hydrochloric acid.

a Balance the symbolic equation for this reaction.

$$Mg + HCl \rightarrow MgCl_2 + H_2$$

b The graph shows the volume of gas given off against time when 0.1 g of magnesium ribbon is dissolved in an excess of 1 M hydrochloric acid.

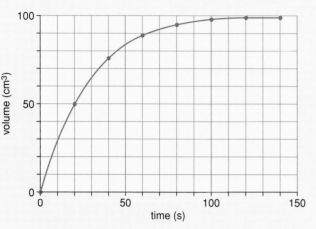

What is the maximum volume of gas you would expect to get if you dissolved 0.1 g of magnesium ribbon in an excess of 2 M hydrochloric acid (i.e. an acid that is twice as strong)?

c Copy the graph above onto graph paper. Draw a graph on the same axes to show what you would expect to happen if you dissolved 0.1 g of magnesium ribbon in an excess of 2 M hydrochloric acid, as in part **b**.

d Give one other way in which this reaction could be made to go faster.

4 Quicklime is made by heating limestone (calcium carbonate) in a kiln:

$$CaCO_3 \rightarrow CaO + CO_2$$

In one quarry it was estimated that 1000 000 tonnes (1000 000 000 kg) of limestone had been dug out and converted to quicklime in this way over the years.

a Calculate the mass of carbon dioxide that would be produced if 100 g of calcium carbonate was converted to quicklime in this way (relative atomic masses are Ca = 40, C = 12, O = 16).

b What is this as a percentage of the limestone?

c What mass of carbon dioxide gas has therefore been produced from this quarry over the years (from all 1000 000 tonnes of limestone)?

d The relative molecular mass of a gas has a volume of 24 litres at room temperature. What volume of carbon dioxide gas has therefore been produced from this quarry over the years (from all 1000 000 tonnes, which is 1000 000 000 000 g of limestone).

5 The balanced equation for the reaction of hydrogen and chlorine is shown using structural formulae.

$$H—H + Cl—Cl \rightarrow 2H—Cl$$

The bond energies involved (in kJ/mole) are: H—H = 436, Cl—Cl = 242, H—Cl = 431.

a Copy and complete this table:

Bond type	Reactants		Products	
	number broken	energy needed to break bond(s)	number formed	energy given out when bond(s) form
H—H				
Cl—Cl				
H—Cl				
	total energy in:		total energy out:	

b Is this reaction exothermic or endothermic?

c What is the net transfer of energy?

d This reaction needs a small kick-start of energy to get it going (sunlight, for example). Draw the likely energy profile for this reaction.

6 A student is investigating the way hydrogen peroxide breaks down when manganese dioxide powder is added.

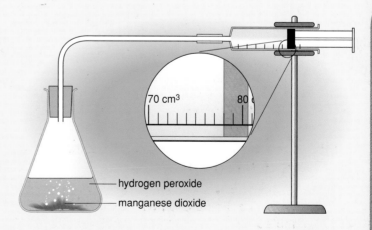

hydrogen peroxide

manganese dioxide

a What is the volume of gas that has been collected?

b In this reaction the hydrogen peroxide breaks down to form water and the gas that is being collected. What is the gas?

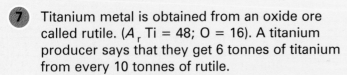

hydrogen peroxide → water + ———
    (H_2O_2)   (H_2O)

c Write the equation from part **b** as a balanced chemical equation.

d What would happen if you plunged a glowing splint into a tube of this gas?

e The manganese dioxide is acting as a catalyst in this reaction. Explain what a catalyst does.

f How many grams of oxygen would you get from 68 g of pure hydrogen peroxide? Explain your working.

g What would the volume of this amount of gas be at atmospheric pressure and room temperature?

7 Titanium metal is obtained from an oxide ore called rutile. (A_r Ti = 48; O = 16). A titanium producer says that they get 6 tonnes of titanium from every 10 tonnes of rutile.

a What is the percentage of titanium in rutile?

b What is the mass ratio Ti:O in rutile?

c From this, calculate the empirical formula for rutile. (Hint: You may wish to calculate the theoretical ratios Ti:O for some possible formulae such as Ti_2O, TiO and TiO_2.)

d The titanium producer also says that rutile forms just 1% of the ore-bearing sands that they have to process initially. How much titanium could they get from 1 tonne of the ore-bearing sand?

8 Bloggs and Co. are setting up a business to make chemical Z. When the solid chemical X is heated it decomposes to give two gases, Y and Z. This forward reaction is endothermic. Gas Y dissolves in water, but gas Z does not. The reaction is shown by the equation:

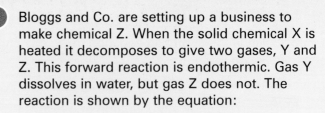

X ⇌ Y + Z

a What does the symbol ⇌ tell you about this reaction?

b The chief chemist of the company has said that this reaction is likely to reach an **equilibrium** with a 50% **yield** of Z at 300 °C. Explain the terms equilibrium and yield.

c Mr Bloggs wants to get a better yield than this and thinks that changing the temperature will help. Should he raise or lower the temperature to do this? Explain your answer.

d Mr Bloggs has also heard that high pressure is used to increase the yield in the Haber process. Would it help in this case? Explain your answer.

e Suggest a way in which the unwanted product Y could be removed from product mixture to give pure Z.

Module 11 – Forces

For thousands of years, people have looked up at the night sky and watched the movement of the stars and planets across the sky. Physicists and astronomers such as Galileo, Newton and Einstein discovered how, by understanding forces, we could make sense of what we see in space, as well as how things move here on Earth. They showed that the same ideas about forces and motion work for giant stars and for the movement of everyday objects such as falling stones and moving cars.

In this module, you will find out about how forces can affect the way things move. Gravity is a very important force, and you will find out about how gravity governs how things move here on Earth and in space, as well as the life and death of stars, and even of the Universe itself.

In this photo, taken by the New Technology Telescope in Chile, clouds of gas are seen deep in space. They are pulled together by gravity. Where the clouds become hot and dense, new stars can be seen forming.

Before you start this module, check that you can recall the answers to the following questions about movement, forces and space:

1 What two quantities do you need to know if you are going to measure the speed of an object as it moves between two points?

2 How would you calculate the object's speed from these two quantities?

3 What is the name of the force which always acts opposite to the direction in which an object is moving?

4 How does the spinning of the Earth give rise to night and day?

5 For what purposes are satellites sent into orbit around the Earth?

Forces affect the way things move. You cannot see forces, but you can see how they change an object's speed.

You can easily predict who will win this race. Everyone has to travel the same distance, but the racing driver will get to the finishing line first.

The table shows how long each competitor took to travel 1000 m.

Competitor	Time taken (s)
runner	200
cyclist	100
racing driver	25

a Work out each competitor's speed. (Remember to include your units.)

Plotting graphs

Here is a description of a bus journey. 'The bus left my stop and took 30 s to travel 250 m to the next stop. It waited there for 10 s while the passengers got off. Then it took 50 s to travel 500 m to the bus station.'

We can show this information in two ways: as a table, and as a **distance–time graph**. The table and the graph show the same information.

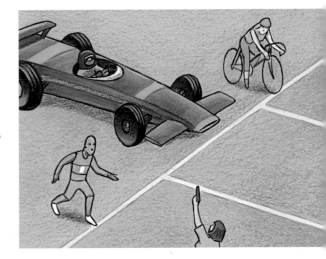

Distance travelled (m)	0	250	250	750
Time taken (s)	0	30	40	90

b Look at the graph. Explain why the middle section of the graph is horizontal, and why the last section of the graph is steepest.

c How would the slope of the graph change if the bus was travelling very slowly in heavy traffic?

d Use the graph to find out how far the bus had travelled 60 s after setting off.

Speed from slope

The steeper the slope of a distance–time graph, the greater the object's speed. You can use the slope of the graph to calculate the speed of the bus:

Speed = slope (gradient) of distance–time graph

This graph shows the last section of the graph for the bus's journey. To find its speed:

◆ choose two points on the graph;

◆ draw a right-angled triangle under the graph, from the two points;

◆ work out the lengths of the two sides of the triangle.

(The vertical side of the triangle tells you how far the bus travelled; the horizontal side tells you the time taken.)

Now calculate the speed:

Speed = distance travelled/time taken = 500 m/50 s = 10 m/s

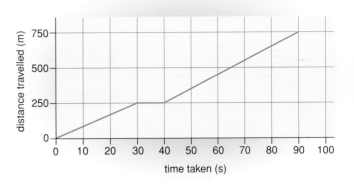

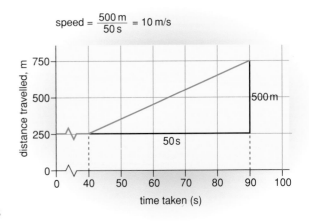

$$\text{speed} = \frac{500\,\text{m}}{50\,\text{s}} = 10\,\text{m/s}$$

Speed and velocity

Often we simply say how fast something is moving – its **speed**. Sometimes it is important to know the direction in which an object is moving. If we give speed and direction, we call this its **velocity** – for example, 'The ball rolled towards the goal at 5 m/s.'

Questions

1 The graphs represent the motion of four different objects.

   a Which graph is for a stationary object?

   b Put the other three objects in order, from slowest to fastest.

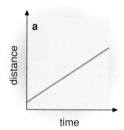
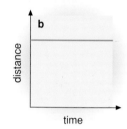
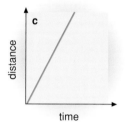
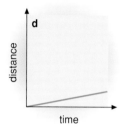

2 a Draw a distance–time graph to represent this motion:

   'I cycled 200 m along the road in 20 s. It took me 25 s to travel the next 200 m. Then I stopped for 20 s.'

   b From the graph, work out the cyclist's speed during each section of the ride.

3 The table shows how far a train has travelled along its route during part of its journey.

Distance travelled (m)	200	280	360	440	520
Time taken (s)	10	12	14	16	18

   a Draw a distance–time graph to show this data.

   b Was the train running at a steady speed? How can you tell?

   c From the graph, work out the train's speed.

4 What *two* things must you know in order to tell the velocity of something?

Summary

- A distance–time graph can show us how an object is moving.

- The steeper the graph, the greater the object's speed.

- Velocity means speed in a given direction.

- The gradient of a distance–time graph tells us the object's speed.

11.2 Speeding up

Some cars are advertised like this: '0 to 60 miles per hour in 8.0 seconds!' This tells you how good it is at speeding up. If the train was advertised like this, it might say: '0 to 180 miles per hour in 10 minutes!'

The train can go much faster than the car, but it takes much longer to get up speed. *Speeding up* is known as *accelerating*. If the train accelerated like the car, all of the passengers would be in danger of falling over as it set off.

People accelerate, too. At the beginning of a race, you accelerate away from the starting line. If someone is catching up behind you, you might accelerate in order to keep your lead.

a When might a bus accelerate?

Velocity–time graphs

Here is a **velocity–time graph**. It shows how the velocity of a train changes as it leaves a station. Take care! This is not the same as a distance–time graph. Always check the labels on the axes. A velocity–time graph has:

- ◆ time taken on the horizontal axis;
- ◆ velocity on the vertical axis.

b Which axis is the same as for a distance–time graph? Which is different?

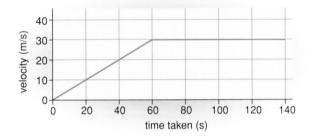

The graph for the train is in two parts.

At first, it is speeding up at a steady rate. It has constant acceleration. The graph is a straight line, sloping upwards. The steeper the slope, the greater the acceleration.

When it has reached top speed, the train no longer accelerates. It has constant velocity. The graph is a horizontal straight line.

c From the graph, find the train's velocity after 20 s. What is its greatest velocity?

How far?

We can use the velocity–time graph to find out how far the train travels. You need to find the area under the graph. It is easiest to divide the area into two parts, a triangle and a rectangle.

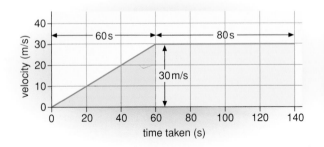

Area of triangle = $\frac{1}{2}$ base × height = $\frac{1}{2}$ × 60 s × 30 m/s = 900 m

Area of rectangle = base × height = 80 s × 30 m/s = 2400 m

Total distance travelled = 900 m + 2400 m = 3300 m

d How far did the train travel while its velocity was constant?

e How far did it travel while its acceleration was constant?

Spy in the cab

A lorry driver does a lot of driving in a day. The lorry speeds up and slows down. Its speed is recorded by an instrument called a tachograph.

The tachograph makes a graph to show the lorry's speed. The line on the graph goes up and down as the lorry's speed changes.

Questions

1 A car is moving along a road at 10 m/s. When it leaves the town, it speeds up. After 8 s it is moving at 22 m/s.

  a What is the car's average speed during the time it is accelerating?

  b How far did it travel during this time?

2 The graph shows how the velocity of a lorry changed as it travelled along the road.

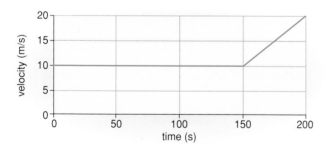

  a How fast was the lorry moving at first?

  b After how long did it start to accelerate?

  c How far did the lorry travel at constant velocity?

  d How far did the lorry travel altogether?

3 A tachograph chart shows how a lorry's speed has changed during its journey.

  a What does the graph look like when the lorry has been travelling at a steady speed?

  b Police can check the chart. How can they tell if the driver stopped for a rest?

  c Why do you think that drivers sometimes call it 'the spy in the cab'?

Summary

- A velocity–time graph can show us if an object's velocity is changing.

- The steeper the graph, the more rapidly the object's velocity is changing – the more it is accelerating.

- The area under a velocity –time graph tells us how far the object has moved.

11:3 Acceleration

The trolley in the photo is running down a ramp. As it moves, it picks up speed. It is accelerating.

The students are using two light gates to measure the trolley's acceleration.

◆ Light gate 1 measures its velocity near the top of the slope, where it is going slowly.

◆ Light gate 2 measures its velocity near the foot of the slope, where it is moving faster.

The computer uses this information to work out the trolley's acceleration.

a **If the students tilted the ramp so that it was steeper, would the trolley's acceleration increase or decrease?**

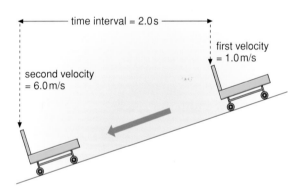

Calculating acceleration

The computer needs three pieces of information to work out the trolley's acceleration: two measurements of velocity, and the time interval between them. It gets this information from the light gates. The worked example shows how it calculates the acceleration.

Worked example 1

Step 1 Calculate the change in velocity by finding the difference between the two velocity measurements.

Change in velocity = 6.0 m/s – 1.0 m/s = 5.0 m/s

Step 2 Divide by the time taken for this change.

$$\text{Acceleration} = \frac{5.0 \, \text{m/s}}{2.0 \, \text{s}} = 2.5 \, \text{m/s}^2$$

time interval = 2.0 s

first velocity = 1.0 m/s

second velocity = 6.0 m/s

How quickly is the trolley's velocity changing?

The meaning of acceleration

Imagine you are at the start of a 100 m sprint race. If you are to win, you want to get up to speed as quickly as possible. You want your acceleration to be high. 'Acceleration' means 'how quickly your velocity changes'. A better way to say this is:

The acceleration of an object is the rate at which its velocity changes.

From the worked example above, you can see how to write this as an equation:

$$\text{Acceleration} = \frac{\text{change in velocity}}{\text{time taken for change}}$$

Sprinters have to accelerate as much as they can at the start of a race.

Acceleration is measured in m/s² (metres per second squared). An acceleration of 1 m/s^2 means that your velocity is changing by 1 m/s every second.

b If your acceleration is 10 m/s², by how much does your velocity change in 1 s? And in 2 s?

Worked example 2

If you were running at a steady speed of 6 m/s and decided to speed up, 2 s later your velocity may have increased to 9 m/s. What is your acceleration? (The graph shows the same information.)

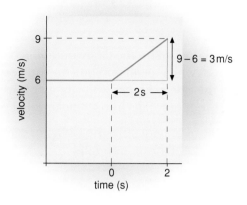

Step 1 Calculate the change in your velocity.

Change in velocity = 9 m/s – 6 m/s = 3 m/s

Step 2 Divide by the time taken.

$$\text{Acceleration} = \frac{\text{change in velocity}}{\text{time taken}} = \frac{3 \text{ m/s}}{2 \text{ s}} = 1.5 \text{ m/s}^2$$

Using the graph

Look at the graph which accompanies Worked example 2. You should be able to see another way to find the acceleration:

Acceleration = gradient of the velocity–time graph

Drawing the triangle to find the gradient (slope) of the line gives us:

◆ change in velocity (the vertical side of the triangle);

◆ time taken (the horizontal side of the triangle).

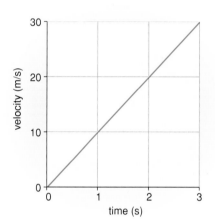

c The graph on the right shows how the velocity of a falling stone increases. Use the gradient of the graph to find the stone's acceleration.

Questions

1 An old car can accelerate from 0 m/s to 20 m/s in 10 s. What is its acceleration?

2 A stone falls with an acceleration of 10 m/s². By how much will its velocity increase in 5 s?

3 The table shows how the velocity of a car changes at the start of a short trip.

Velocity (m/s)	0	5	10	15	15	15
Time (s)	0	2	4	6	8	10

a Draw a velocity–time graph to represent the car's motion.

b Use your graph to find the car's acceleration during the first 6 s of its journey.

c How far does the car travel during the first 10 s of its journey?

Summary

• An object's acceleration is the rate at which its velocity is changing.

• Acceleration = $\dfrac{\text{change in velocity}}{\text{time taken}}$.

• Acceleration is measured in m/s².

• The gradient of a velocity–time graph tells us the object's acceleration.

If you take a ride on the Oblivion rollercoaster at Alton Towers, the forces which push and pull on you keep changing. At the end of the ride, your car waits for 4 s above a vertical drop. Then it suddenly falls into a smoke-filled pit.

The force of gravity pulls the Oblivion car downwards. The car goes faster and faster as it falls.

Mass and weight

The Earth's gravity pulls on every object on its surface, and on every object below and above the surface. It pulls straight downwards, towards the centre of the Earth. If you move away from the Earth into space, gravity gets weaker as you are further from the mass of the Earth.

The force of the Earth's gravity on you is called your **weight**. Because weight is a force, it is measured in **newtons** (N). What people usually call the *weight* of something is really its *mass*.

a Gravity is a force which pulls things downwards. Name a force which slows things down when they are moving. What units is this force measured in?

Far out in space, a long way from the Earth or any other object, you would be completely weightless. There's nothing there to pull on you. But that doesn't mean you have completely disappeared! Your weight is zero, but your mass is just the same as on Earth. You're made of just as many kilograms of atoms and molecules, whether you're on Earth or in space. It's just that there is no gravity pulling on you.

If your mass is 60 kg, it stays the same wherever you are. Your weight changes because gravity is stronger in some places than others.

The strength of gravity

You can measure the weight of something using a newtonmeter.

The Earth's gravity pulls on each kilogram on the Earth's surface with a force of about 10 N. If you know the mass of something (in kg), you can work out its weight:

Weight on Earth (N) = mass (kg) × 10 N/kg

In other words, multiply the mass by 10 and change the units to newtons.

b What will be the weight of a child on the surface of the Earth if his mass is 50 kg?

Two newtonmeters are being used here to measure the weight of a brick and of a person.

Falling

Look at the photograph. Gravity makes the ball fall. The multiflash photograph shows that it goes faster and faster as it falls. Gravity makes things accelerate as they fall.

It's easier to see this if you roll a ball down a slope. The ball speeds up as it rolls down towards the bottom.

c How can you tell from the photograph that the ball is accelerating as it falls?

A ball accelerates as it falls. Its position is shown at intervals of one-tenth of a second.

Questions

1 Work out the weight (in newtons, N) of each of the following things, on the Earth's surface:

   a a 1 kg book

   b a 50 kg person

   c a 500 kg car.

2 Because it is much smaller than the Earth, the Moon's gravity is weaker than the Earth's. The Moon pulls with a force of 1.6 N on each kg of an object's mass. Calculate the weight on the Moon of each object in Question 1.

3 a Explain why your *weight* gets less when you go to the Moon.

   b Explain why your *mass* stays the same if you go to the Moon.

4 A spacecraft travels from the Earth to the Moon. There is a point on its journey where the pull of the Earth's gravity is cancelled out by the pull of the Moon's gravity. Explain why this is, and draw a diagram to show where this happens.

5 A boy weighs himself in the lab, using a newtonmeter. He finds that his weight is 520 N. What is his mass?

DIGGING DEEPER
If you go on a rollercoaster ride, you may experience some sudden accelerations. The greatest acceleration is not when you are falling under gravity, but when you suddenly change direction.

Summary

- Weight is the force of the Earth's gravity pulling on an object.

- Close to the Earth's surface,

  weight (N) = mass (kg) × 10 N/kg

- Gravity makes things accelerate as they fall.

11:5 Balanced forces

When you are sitting comfortably in your chair, there are two forces acting on you:

- the force of gravity (your weight) is pulling downwards on you;

- the chair is pushing upwards on you.

These two forces are balanced, and you stay on the chair. Without the upward push of the chair, you would descend through the floor.

Now, if your chair turns out to be an ejector seat, it may give you an extra large upward push. There is an unbalanced force on you – more force upwards than downwards. The unbalanced force makes you fly upwards.

a **Look at the drawing showing two balanced forces. What can you say about the sizes of these two forces?**

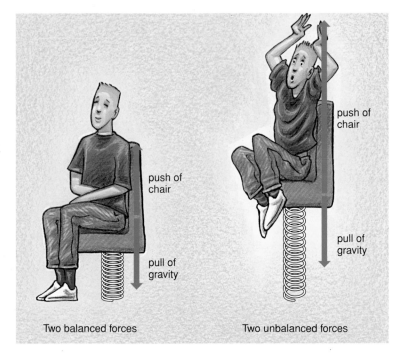

push of chair

pull of gravity

push of chair

pull of gravity

Two balanced forces

Two unbalanced forces

Balanced and unbalanced

We can represent forces by arrows. The arrow shows the direction of the force. The size of the force is given in newtons (N).

b **Explain how to calculate the size of the unbalanced force. How can you tell which direction it acts in?**

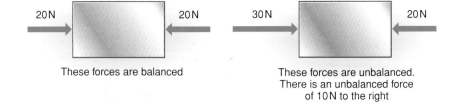

20 N   20 N

These forces are balanced

30 N   20 N

These forces are unbalanced. There is an unbalanced force of 10 N to the right

The effects of balanced forces

You can see that an object will not start to move if the forces on it are balanced. It is more surprising to find that a moving object will continue to move at a steady speed when the forces on it are balanced.

- The force of the engine is trying to make the car speed up.

- The force of air resistance is trying to slow the car down.

These two effects cancel out, so the car doesn't speed up or slow down.

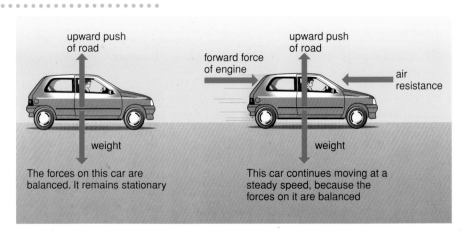

upward push of road

weight

The forces on this car are balanced. It remains stationary

upward push of road

forward force of engine

air resistance

weight

This car continues moving at a steady speed, because the forces on it are balanced

c The parachutist in the picture is falling at a steady speed. What forces are acting on her? Are they balanced or unbalanced?

Push meets shove

The car in the photo has crashed into a lamppost. The car exerted a force on the lamppost, and the lamppost exerted a force on the car. The two forces were equal in size but opposite in direction. Unfortunately, the lamppost was stronger than the car, and so the car was more badly damaged than the lamppost.

You can feel the forces two objects exert on each other by holding two magnets close together, so that they repel each other. You can feel one magnet being pushed to the right while the other is pushed to the left. The two magnetic forces are equal in size but opposite in direction.

Whenever two objects interact, the forces they exert on each other are equal and opposite.

Take care! These forces don't cancel each other out. They act on different objects (e.g. the car and the lamppost), so they do not balance out.

d If you held the magnets so that they attracted each other, what would you feel? What could you say about the forces they exert on each other?

Questions

1 Imagine you are riding on the Oblivion rollercoaster shown in the photo on page 190.

    a When you are waiting to drop, are the forces on you balanced or unbalanced?

    b Are they balanced or unbalanced as you start to drop?

2 The car in the picture is travelling at a steady speed. Four forces act on it: its weight, the upward push of the road, the forward push of its engine, and the backward push of air resistance.

    a Draw a diagram to show these forces.

    b Name two pairs of forces acting on the car which are equal in size to each other but opposite in direction.

    c Are the forces on the car balanced or unbalanced?

3 When you sit on a chair, you push downwards on the chair, and it pushes up on you.

    a What can you say about the sizes of these forces?

    b What can you say about their directions?

DIGGING DEEPER
You cannot pull yourself up by your shoelaces because of the equal and opposite forces betwen two interacting objects. The harder you pull upwards on your shoelace, the harder it pulls downwards on your hand.

Summary
- Balanced forces do not affect an object's motion. It will remain stationary, or continue to move at a steady speed in a straight line.

- When two bodies interact, they exert equal and opposite forces on each other.

11:6 Unbalanced forces

The world's biggest ships are oil tankers, up to 500 m long. They are very difficult to control.

The engines can provide a force to drive the ship forwards, backwards or sideways. The force of drag (friction with the water) tends to slow it down.

The crew must control these forces carefully. A giant supertanker takes a very long time to slow down, and a small mistake in the timing can result in a disastrous collision.

a A tanker does not have brakes like a car. How can the captain slow it down?

This oil tanker has hit the rocks.

Steady as she goes

The ferry captain can control the ship's speed by changing the force of the engine. To change the ferry's speed, the forces on it must be unbalanced. An unbalanced force can also change the ferry's direction.

For most of its journey, the ferry maintains a steady speed. The engines give a forward push to balance the drag of the water.

If the captain wants to go faster, the force of the engines must be increased so that it is greater than the drag of the water.

To go slower, the force of the engines must be reduced. It's the drag of the water that slows the ferry down.

A SeaCat ferry rises out of the water. This reduces the drag force on it.

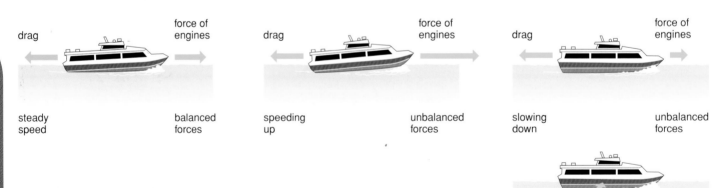

To change direction, the engines provide a sideways force.

b You are rowing a boat across a lake. You stop rowing and quickly come to a halt. Use the idea of unbalanced forces to explain why this happens.

Masses large and small

A large ferry has a large mass – millions of kilograms – so it needs a big unbalanced force to make it accelerate. A speedboat has a much smaller mass. It needs a much smaller unbalanced force to give it the same acceleration. The larger an object's mass, the greater the force needed to give it a particular acceleration.

A force of 1 N will give a mass of 1 kg an acceleration of $1\,\text{m/s}^2$. A force of 2 N will give the same mass (1 kg) an acceleration of $2\,\text{m/s}^2$. You can see that force, mass and acceleration are related by:

Force = mass × acceleration

Worked examples

1 What force is needed to give a speedboat of mass 200 kg an acceleration of $5\,\text{m/s}^2$?

Using the equation, force = mass × acceleration, gives:

Force = $200\,\text{kg} \times 5\,\text{m/s}^2 = 1000\,\text{N}$

2 What acceleration will the speedboat have if the unbalanced force on it is 600 N?

Rearranging the equation, force = mass × acceleration, gives

Acceleration $= \dfrac{\text{force}}{\text{mass}} = \dfrac{600\,\text{N}}{200\,\text{kg}} = 3\,\text{m/s}^2$

c What force is needed to give a mass of 5 kg an acceleration of $10\,\text{m/s}^2$?

Questions

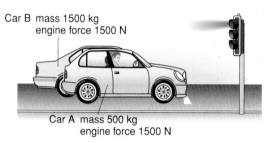

Car B mass 1500 kg
engine force 1500 N

Car A mass 500 kg
engine force 1500 N

1 These two cars are waiting at the traffic lights. When the lights change, they will accelerate away. Calculate the acceleration of each car. Why does the smaller car have the greater acceleration?

2 This car is travelling fast along the road. The diagram shows the forces on the car.

air resistance
500 N

force of engine
700 N

a What is the unbalanced force acting on the car?

b If the car's mass is 800 kg, what is its acceleration?

3 A car is approaching traffic lights. Three forces act on it:

the forward force of its engine: 500 N

the backward force of its brakes: 1000 N

air resistance: 400 N

a Draw a diagram to show the forces on the car.

b What is the unbalanced force acting on the car?

c If the car's mass is 600 kg, what is its acceleration?

Summary

- An unbalanced force may start an object moving, speed it up, or slow it down.

- The greater the unbalanced force, the greater the acceleration it produces: force = mass × acceleration

- A force of 1 N will give a mass of 1 kg an acceleration of $1\,\text{m/s}^2$.

Racing drivers need to be sure that their cars are in good condition before they go out on the track. A single misjudgement can lead to a nasty accident. Fortunately, racing cars are now designed to withstand strong impacts, so serious casualties are rare.

Avoiding skidding

Stewart is driving along the road. Just in time, he notices the STOP sign ahead. He applies the brakes and comes to a halt at the junction.

It takes a short time – about two-thirds of a second – for Stewart to react when he sees the sign. During that time, the car travels a short distance along the road. This is the **thinking distance**.

This driver was unlucky – and crashed into the finishing post!

The brakes provide a backward force to slow the car. The brakes increase the friction between the tyres and the road. The distance travelled by the car while the brakes are on is called the **braking distance**.

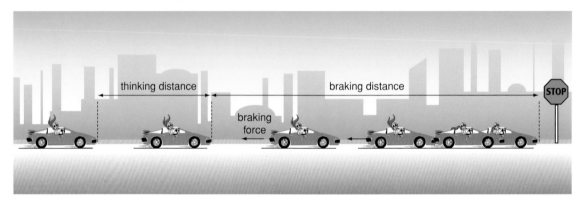

So the **stopping distance** is made up of these two distances.

a **Write an equation relating the three distances highlighted above.**

If Stewart had noticed the STOP sign a little later, he would have had to press harder on the brakes. Then the frictional force might not have been great enough to stop the car in time; the car would have gone into a skid. You may have done this yourself, while riding a bike.

If visibility is poor (because of rain or snow, or because you are on a winding road) it is important to drive more slowly. You get less warning of the need to stop.

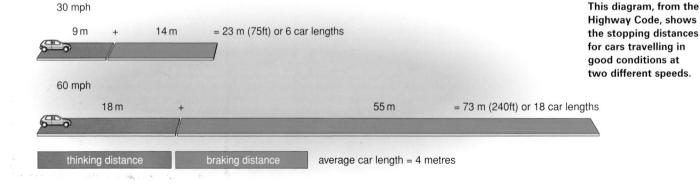

This diagram, from the Highway Code, shows the stopping distances for cars travelling in good conditions at two different speeds.

b Imagine that Stewart had been travelling at a greater speed when he saw the STOP sign. Explain why his thinking distance would have been greater.

c Explain why he would have needed to a bigger braking force to stop the car before he reached the sign.

Dangerous driving

Drivers need to think ahead, to make sure they are ready to stop safely if necessary. Several factors affect how quickly they can stop:

◆ How fast the car is moving

The faster the car is moving, the further it will travel before the force of the brakes can bring it to a halt.

◆ How quickly the driver can react

The driver may be tired, or under the influence of alcohol or drugs. A tired or drugged driver is slow to react, so the thinking distance is greater.

◆ The state of the road

◆ The condition of the car

If the road is wet or icy, the driver has to apply the brakes gently, to avoid skidding. A smaller braking force takes longer to stop the car. If the car's brakes or tyres are worn, the braking force will again be reduced. The MOT test helps to ensure that most cars are roadworthy.

d Oil on a race track can make it slippy. How should racing drivers drive if they notice an oily patch on the track? Explain your answer.

Questions

1 Look at the diagram from the Highway Code. It shows stopping distances when road conditions are good.

  a What road conditions might increase the stopping distance of a car?

  b Explain why the thinking distance is twice as much at 60 mph as at 30 mph.

  c Explain why the stopping distance is more than twice as much at 60 mph as at 30 mph.

  d A child steps out into the road, 80 m ahead of a car. The car is travelling at 60 mph. Can the driver be sure of stopping in time? (Think carefully about your answer.)

2 A large lorry and a small car are travelling at the same speed along a main road. The traffic lights ahead turn red, and both drivers apply the brakes. Explain why the lorry needs a greater braking force than the car, if they are to stop in the same distance.

This man's driving has attracted the attention of the police.

DIGGING DEEPER
Some European roads have markings which indicate how far apart cars should travel. If drivers ignore these markings, they are more likely to run into the back of the car in front if it stops suddenly.

Summary

- A faster-moving vehicle needs a bigger force to stop it quickly.

- The stopping distance of a car depends on its speed, the speed of the driver's reactions, the road conditions and the condition of the car

When the space shuttle comes in to land, it is travelling very fast. Because it is moving so fast, there is a lot of friction with the air, which helps to slow it down. The outside of the shuttle gets very hot. It is covered with special heat-resistant tiles to prevent the astronauts inside from being cooked.

Friction in fluids

The picture shows how you can see the effect of the air's friction. Drop a ball and a crumpled piece of paper. The ball reaches the ground first. The paper is slowed down by the force of **air resistance** (friction with the air).

◆ Gravity pulls the ball and the paper downwards.

◆ Air resistance opposes gravity.

Friction acts on any object moving through a gas (such as the air) or a liquid (such as water). Gases and liquids are known as **fluids**, because they can flow. The faster the object moves, the greater the friction.

This skydiver is moving at terminal velocity. She can feel the air rushing past, making the force of air resistance.

a Draw a diagram to show the forces on the paper as it falls at a steady speed. The ball accelerates all the way to the floor. Draw a diagram to show the forces on the ball. In each case, state how the forces explain the object's motion.

Falling step-by-step

How do the forces change as the parachutist falls? Before she opens her parachute:

◆ At first, only gravity acts. This makes her accelerate.

◆ Friction increases as she moves faster.

◆ Soon friction balances gravity.

Now she has reached a steady speed, known as **terminal velocity**. She opens her parachute.

◆ The parachute pulls upwards with a large force, because there is much more air resistance.

◆ The parachutist slows down until friction again balances gravity.

Now she moves at a slow, steady speed, ready for a safe landing.

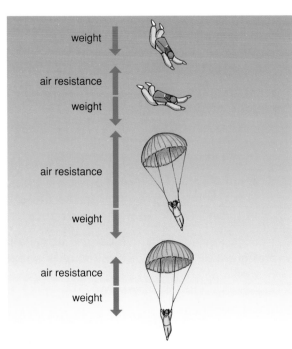

b Explain why the force of air resistance decreases after the parachute has been opened.

Top speed

Cars have to push their way through the air, too. When the driver presses hard on the accelerator pedal, the engine provides a big force to push the car forward. This forward force is greater than the backward force of air resistance. We say that there is a **resultant** force on the car, making it accelerate forwards.

At top speed, air resistance pushes back with an equal force. There is no resultant force on the car. The car can't go any faster than this.

Racing cars have big engines and a streamlined shape, so that they can go faster than an ordinary car.

c Explain why a car can go faster if it has a streamlined shape.

Questions

1 a Draw a diagram of a car moving at top speed. Show the forces acting on it: the driving force of the engine, and the force of air resistance.

b What can you say about the sizes of these forces?

c Suggest **two** things that could be changed so that the car could go even faster.

2 Look at these graphs. They represent the way in which different quantities might vary when a shuttlecock is dropped towards the ground. Choose the graph for which the quantity on the vertical (y) axis might represent:

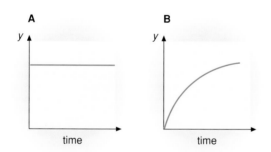
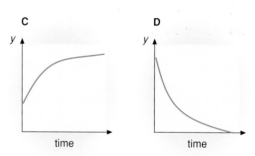

a the force of air resistance on the shuttlecock;

b the resultant force on the shuttlecock;

c the weight of the shuttlecock;

d the speed of the shuttlecock.

3 Look at the drawings of the falling parachutist opposite.

a During which part of her fall is there a *downward* resultant force on her?

b During which part of her fall is there an *upward* resultant force on her?

c In which part of her fall is there *no* resultant force on her?

Summary

• Friction increases as an object moves faster through a fluid.

• A falling object reaches top speed (terminal velocity) when friction balances the pull of gravity.

Any object which is moving has **kinetic energy**. The car and the lorry in the picture both have kinetic energy. The faster they go, the more kinetic energy they have.

When the photo was taken, the car and the lorry were travelling at the same speed. The lorry has much more kinetic energy than the car, because it has much more mass.

Kinetic energy depends on two quantities: mass and speed.

◆ Greater mass means more kinetic energy.

◆ Greater speed means more kinetic energy.

a **A car is moving along the road. An unbalanced force is pushing it forward. Is its kinetic energy increasing, decreasing or staying the same? Explain your answer.**

Calculating kinetic energy

Here is how to calculate the kinetic energy of a moving object:

Kinetic energy = $\frac{1}{2}$ × mass × (speed)^2

Like all forms of energy, kinetic energy is measured in joules (J).

Worked example

Calculate the kinetic energy of a runner of mass 60 kg, running at 10 m/s.

First, write down the equation for kinetic energy:

Kinetic energy = $\frac{1}{2}$ × mass × (speed)^2

Now substitute in the values from the question.

Kinetic energy = $\frac{1}{2}$ × 60 kg × (10 m/s)^2

Take care with the calculation! It is only the speed which is squared – the brackets are there to remind you of this.

Kinetic energy = $\frac{1}{2}$ × 60 × (10)^2 J = $\frac{1}{2}$ × 60 × 100 J = 3000 J

(With practice, you will be able to do this calculation in one step.)

The table shows some calculated values of kinetic energy for different objects, moving at their top speeds.

Object	Mass (kg)	Top speed (m/s)	Kinetic energy (J)
hummingbird	0.003	8	0.096
peregrine falcon	0.8	12.7	64.5
sprinter	60	10	3 000
family car	800	30	360 000
jumbo jet	400 000	250	12 500 000 000

b Calculate the kinetic energy of a stone of mass 4 kg falling at 20 m/s. (If your answer is 1600 J, try again!)

Changing kinetic energy

This aircraft is getting up speed as it races down the runway, ready for take-off. Its kinetic energy increases as it goes faster.

To increase its kinetic energy, the aircraft burns fuel. You can see the dirty exhaust fumes coming from its engines. The energy stored in the fuel is being transferred to the aircraft as kinetic energy.

The aircraft has a lot of mass – hundreds of tonnes. It takes a lot of energy to get such a large mass moving at high speed.

When a driver applies the brakes, the car slows down. Friction in the brakes transfers energy; the car's kinetic energy decreases, and the brakes get hot. The force of friction transfers energy mostly as heat.

c Use these ideas to explain why a lot more fuel is used in getting a lorry up to top speed, compared with a car.

Rally drivers make good use of their brakes, which can get very hot.

Questions

1 Look at the table which shows values of kinetic energy for various objects. The peregrine falcon moves faster than a sprinter, but its kinetic energy is much less than the sprinter's. Explain why this is.

2 Calculate the kinetic energy of a car of mass 600 kg moving at 20 m/s.

3 Which has more kinetic energy, a runner of mass 60 kg moving at 10 m/s or a runner of mass 100 kg moving at 6 m/s?

4 It is much harder for a lorry than a car to stop in a short distance. Explain why a lorry's brakes must provide a much bigger braking force than a car's, if it is to stop in the same distance as the car.

DIGGING DEEPER
Although Isaac Newton discovered a lot of what we now know about forces, he knew nothing about energy. The scientific idea of energy was not invented until long after he died.

Summary
- The greater its mass and the greater its speed, the greater an object's kinetic energy.

- Kinetic energy = $\frac{1}{2} \times \text{mass} \times (\text{speed})^2$

Here are some things that you might think of as 'hard work': chopping wood, washing the dishes, writing an essay for your English homework, watching a video of a Shakespeare play. But this isn't what scientists mean by **work**.

In science, you do work if you use a **force** to do something: pushing or pulling something along, or lifting something up, or changing the shape of something.

a In the picture, who is doing work (in the scientific sense), the boy or the girl? Explain your answer.

Forces transferring energy

You need energy to do work – pulling, pushing, lifting, stretching. If you carry on doing work, you will eventually run out of energy. The force you use is transferring energy from you to the object you are moving.

Here are some examples of forces doing work (transferring energy):

A The log will not slide easily along the ground, because of friction. You need to pull it with a force to make it move along.

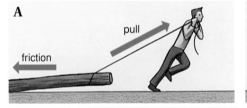

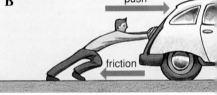

The log and the ground then get warm, because of the rubbing of friction. Your energy has been transferred as **heat**.

B The car is stationary. You need to push it with a force to start it moving.

The car then starts to move. Your energy has been transferred to it as **kinetic energy**.

C The shopping bag is heavy. You need to use a force to lift it onto the table.

The shopping bag is then higher than before. Its **gravitational potential energy (GPE)** has increased.

D The spring is stiff. You need to use a force to stretch it.

The spring is ready to snap back when you release it. It is a store of **elastic potential energy**.

b What form of energy appears when a force does work against friction?

c What form of energy is stored when an elastic (springy) object is stretched?

DIGGING DEEPER
The unit of energy is the joule, named after James Prescott Joule, an English scientist who made a study of energy transfers. On his honeymoon in the Alps, he measured the temperature of water at the top and bottom of a waterfall. It was warmer at the foot because some of the gravitational potential energy (GPE) it had at the top had been transferred as heat energy.

How much work?

The amount of energy transferred by a force tells you the amount of work the force has done. The amount of work is measured in joules (J), just like the amount of energy.

> Work done = energy transferred

A bigger force transfers more energy, and the further it moves, the more energy it transfers. So the amount of work done is the force multiplied by the distance moved:

> Work done = force × distance moved in the direction of the force

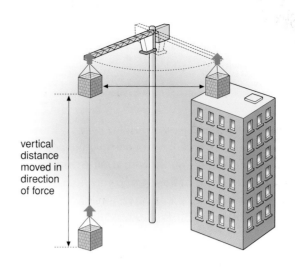

vertical distance moved in direction of force

The picture shows why we have to say *in the direction of the force*. The lifting force of the crane does work when it is raising the load vertically upwards, because the load is getting higher and its GPE is increasing. We say that the crane is doing work against gravity. The lifting force does no work when the load is moving sideways, because the load isn't getting any higher.

It is important to measure the distance moved by a force correctly. Gravity is pulling downwards on this car as it moves horizontally, but gravity is doing no work. The car is not moving in the direction of the force.

d The road is pushing up on the car as it moves along, balancing the force of gravity. Explain why the upward push of the road is doing no work.

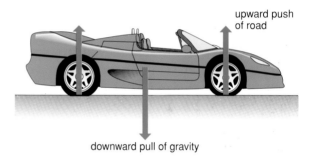

upward push of road

downward pull of gravity

Worked example

The crane lifts a load of 10 000 N to the top of a building, 25 m high. How much work is done by the lifting force?

> Work done = force × distance moved in the direction of the force

Substitute in the values from the question:

> Work done = 10 000 N × 25 m = 250 000 J

Remember that the answer will come out in joules (J).

e How much work would be done by the crane in lifting a load of 8000 N to the top of the same building?

Questions

1 Are these people doing work (in the scientific sense)? Explain your answers.

   a A man pushing a shopping trolley.

   b A child stretching a rubber band.

   c A boy sitting watching a science programme on TV.

2 How much work is done when someone pushes a car for 50 m with a force of 400 N?

Summary

- Doing work is a way of transferring energy using a force:
- Work done = energy transferred
- To calculate work done:
  Work done = force × distance moved in the direction of the force

No-one has ever seen the solar system looking like this. You would have to travel far out into space to be able to look down and see the planets in their orbits. It is hard to tell, but the orbits of the planets are not quite circular. Their shape is called an **ellipse**, a squashed circle, with the Sun close to the centre. Pluto's orbit is the most elliptical.

Planets closest to the Sun travel fastest, and take the least time to complete one orbit. Pluto takes the longest time for one orbit – almost 250 Earth years!

a Which planet is closest to the Sun? Is Pluto always furthest from the Sun?

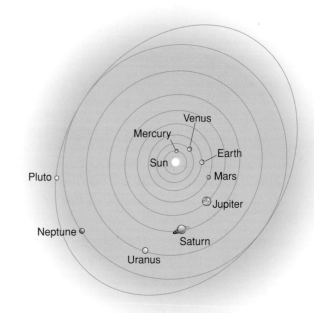

Held by gravity

The Earth moves around the Sun at an average distance of 150 000 000 km (150 million kilometres). It travels at almost 30 km/s – that's about 1000 times the motorway speed limit.

Moving objects tend to keep moving in straight lines. It takes an unbalanced force to make them follow a curved path. There needs to be a large force to keep the Earth in its orbit around the Sun.

The Sun is a massive object – its mass is about 2×10^{30} kg (2 million million million million million kilograms). This gives it a strong gravitational pull. It is the force of gravity, between the Sun and the Earth, which holds the Earth in its orbit.

Each planet feels the pull of the Sun's gravity. The furthest planets feel only a weak pull, because the force of gravity decreases quickly as you move away from the Sun.

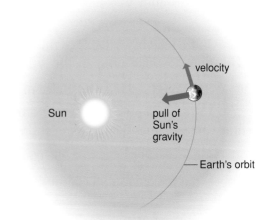

The Earth has a gravitational pull, too. The Earth's gravity pulls on the Moon and holds it in its orbit around the Earth.

The Moon is held in its orbit by the Earth's gravity.

Falling into the Sun

The pictures show what would happen if the Sun's gravity changed.

The speed of the Earth and the pull of the Sun's gravity combine to keep the Earth in its orbit. The Earth must move fast, otherwise it would fall in towards the Sun.

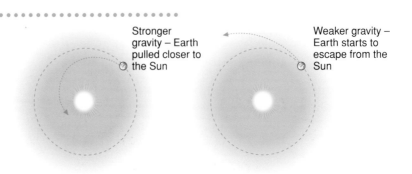

Stronger gravity – Earth pulled closer to the Sun

Weaker gravity – Earth starts to escape from the Sun

b What would happen if an extra force made the Earth move faster along its orbit? Draw a diagram to show how its path would change.

Icy messengers

Comets also orbit the Sun. A comet is a frozen ball of ice and dust, much smaller than a planet. They spend most of their time far out in space, beyond the most distant planets. Occasionally, a comet will move in towards the Sun.

As the comet warms up, dust and gas evaporate from it. This starts to glow, forming the comet's tail. That's when we may be able to see the comet.

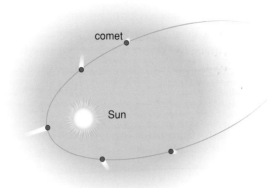

c Is the orbit of a comet circular or elliptical?

Questions

1 a Draw a diagram to show a comet in its orbit around the Sun.

b Where in its orbit is a comet when we can see it? Explain your answer.

c As a comet approaches the Sun, it speeds up. What force causes it to accelerate?

d How does the kinetic energy of a comet change as it approaches the Sun? How does its gravitational potential energy change?

e What energy change occurs as a comet travels away from the Sun?

2 Astronomers have found planets orbiting around distant stars. The drawing shows three such planets.

a Which planet is pulled on most strongly by the star's gravity? How can you tell?

b Explain why planet X must move most quickly.

c Explain why planet Z takes longest to orbit the star.

3 Imagine that the Earth suddenly stopped dead in its orbit.

a What force would be pulling on the Earth?

b Would the forces on the Earth be balanced or unbalanced?

c In which direction would the Earth start to move?

> ### DIGGING DEEPER
> If you draw an accurate diagram of the Earth's elliptical orbit, you will not be able to tell that it is not perfectly circular. Our distance from the Sun varies by about 1% during the year, and our eyes cannot see such a small variation in the size of a circle.

Summary
- Planets and comets travel along elliptical orbits around the Sun.
- They are held in their orbits by the force of gravity.
- They must travel at just the right speed if they are to stay in their orbit.

Do you ever watch satellite television? The signals relayed from a satellite out in space are picked up by a dish on the outside of the house. Weather forecasters also make use of satellites, to photograph cloud patterns and to make other measurements.

Over the poles

Some **satellites** are used to monitor the Earth. They travel along orbits quite close to the Earth's surface – perhaps 500 km up. They take about 90 minutes to make one complete orbit.

As they orbit, the Earth is turning beneath them. This means that they get a different view during each orbit.

The pull of the Earth's gravity keeps these satellites in their orbits, just as the planets are kept in orbit round the Sun by the pull of its gravity. Without the Earth's gravity, satellites would fly off into space.

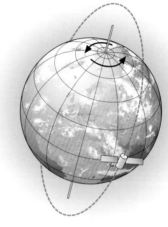

a Estimate how many times in a day a monitoring satellite will orbit the Earth. Why is it impossible to give a precise answer to this question?

A monitoring satellite in a polar orbit.

Monitoring satellites can make detailed images of the Earth's surface, such as this view of Glasgow and central Scotland.

Far out in space

The satellites that relay television programmes are known as **communications satellites**. They are much farther out in space than monitoring satellites – about 40 000 km away. The Earth's gravity is much weaker out there, so the satellites need only travel quite slowly to stay in their orbits. They take much longer to orbit the Earth – 24 hours in fact.

Their orbit has been chosen specially. They are directly above the equator, and they travel around at the same rate that the Earth is spinning. This means that they appear to stay at the same point in the sky all the time. A television satellite dish points directly at the satellite which is sending it signals.

This special orbit is described as **geostationary**, which means 'Earth-stationary'. If you could look down on the Earth from the satellite, you would see that you were directly above a fixed point on the equator all the time. If the satellite was in an orbit closer to the Earth, or farther away, it would move gradually

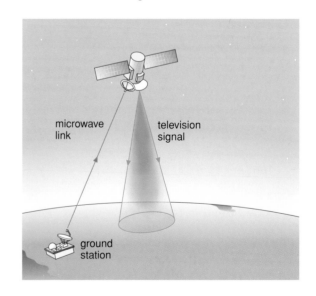

microwave link

television signal

ground station

across the sky, and your dish would have to move round to keep track of it.

There is only room for about 400 satellites spaced out around the orbit. If there were more, they would be too close together and your dish would pick up signals from two or more at the same time, and this would cause interference.

b How many orbits of the Earth are completed by a geostationary satellite in one day? Explain why you can give a precise answer to this question.

International calls

If you have relatives or friends living in a distant part of the world, it is likely that your phonecalls to them are transmitted via communications satellites. The signal is beamed up to the satellite, and then sent down to a distant receiving station.

c Draw a diagram to show how a phonecall could be transmitted from the UK to India via a communications satellite.

This mobile telephone can be used in remote parts of the world. Its aerial sends signals up to a communications satellite.

Questions

1 How might these people benefit from satellites?

   a A meteorologist (weather forecaster).

   b A sports fan.

   c Someone from Australia working in the UK.

2 Many satellites orbit the Earth:

   • monitoring satellites orbit close to the Earth;

   • communications satellites orbit about 40 000 km away;

   • the Moon is the Earth's natural satellite, about 400 000 km away.

   a What force keeps these satellites in their orbits?

   b Explain why a monitoring satellite must travel faster than a communications satellite.

3 a Draw a scale diagram to show the orbit of a geostationary satellite around the Earth. (Radius of Earth = 6400 km; radius of orbit = 40 000 km.)

   b Add arrows to show the direction of movement of a geostationary satellite, and the rotation of the Earth.

   c Add the orbit of a satellite in low-earth orbit, 500 km above the Earth's surface.

   d There are about 400 geostationary satellites in orbit. Estimate the average distance between them.

DIGGING DEEPER

If you have a telephone conversation with someone on the other side of the world, you may notice a short delay before you hear their reply to your questions. This is partly because the signal has to travel out into space and back again; it is also partly due to delays introduced by the electronic switching systems used.

Summary

• Satellites orbit the Earth; they are held in their orbits by the Earth's gravity.

• Monitoring satellites provide useful information about the Earth's surface, e.g. for weather forecasting.

• Communications satellites are further out, in geostationary orbits, taking 24 hours to complete one orbit. They transmit television and telephone signals.

11:13 Stars and galaxies

The Sun is a star – a fairly average star. Beyond the Solar System, there are billions more.

The Sun belongs to a vast group of stars called the **Milky Way**. It is impossible to count all the stars in the Milky Way. There are probably about 100 000 million of them, making up our **galaxy**.

If you could look at our galaxy from far off, you would see that it is like a flat disc with a spiral shape. There is a huge cluster of stars at the centre, and two spiral arms trailing out into space. Our Sun is halfway out along one of the arms.

The stars in a galaxy are far apart. It takes a spacecraft several years to reach the furthest planets, but it would take many centuries to reach the next star. The distances between stars are millions of times greater than the distances between planets in the Solar System.

a Why don't we see our galaxy as a spiral or as a disc?

More stars, more galaxies

With binoculars or a telescope, you can see many more stars in the night sky. These are all part of our own galaxy. But far beyond our galaxy there are other galaxies, and you may be able to see some of them if you know where to look.

Astronomers have seen and photographed many more galaxies. Some are spirals, like the Milky Way; others have more irregular shapes. They believe there may be as many as 100 000 000 000 galaxies in the **Universe**. With as many as 100 000 000 000 stars in each galaxy, that means there may be as many as 10 000 000 000 000 000 000 000 stars in the Universe!

The Universe is the whole of space that we can possibly see. It contains all the matter and energy we can know about.

b Check the calculation (above) which estimates the number of stars in the Universe.

Sticking together

Stars group together to form a galaxy, attracted to each other by gravity. Astronomers have found that galaxies are grouped together as well. A galaxy is a very big object with lots of mass, so its gravity is strong. Galaxies attract each other, and so they cluster together. Because galaxies cluster together, there is lots of empty space in between them.

Spreading out

When astronomers looked at the light from distant galaxies, they found something surprising: it was redder than the light

The Milky Way is a spiral galaxy.

Powerful telescopes can show up other galaxies like these, far beyond the Milky Way.

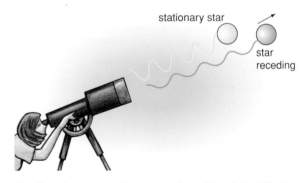

The light from a receding star looks redder; it is shifted towards the red end of the spectrum.

from nearby stars. This is called a '**red-shift**'. The farthest galaxies showed the biggest red-shifts.

How could they explain this? They realised that the Universe itself must be expanding. We can picture this with the help of a toy balloon. On the surface of the balloon, we draw the Earth, a star, and a light wave coming from the star. As the balloon is blown up, the light wave is stretched out by the expanding material of the balloon.

In the same way, the light from distant galaxies becomes stretched as the space it is travelling through expands. This is why we see that all galaxies are moving away from us, and moving apart from each other. The expansion of space is carrying them farther and farther apart.

c The farthest galaxies show the biggest red-shifts. What does this tell you about their speeds?

The 'big bang'

Now we can picture the history of the Universe. If the galaxies today are moving apart, at one time they must have been much closer together. Most astronomers believe that they must have begun with everything squashed into a tiny space. Between 10 and 15 billion years ago, there was a giant explosion, the '**big bang**', so that today the whole Universe is expanding.

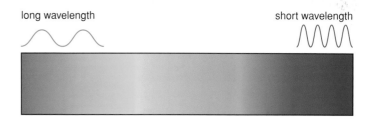

long wavelength   short wavelength

At the blue end of the spectrum, light waves have short wavelengths. At the red end they have longer wavelengths.

The balloon represents the Universe. As it expands, it stretches out the light waves which are passing through it, so that they appear redder.

early days   billions of years later

As time goes by, the Universe expands, so that the galaxies move farther and farther apart.

Questions

1 Define each of the following terms:

   the Universe   a galaxy   gravity   red-shift

2 Imagine that you had an ultra-fast spaceship. Describe what you would see if you set off into space, travelling right across the Universe.

3 **a** What evidence is there that galaxies are moving apart?

   b What link is there between the speed of a galaxy and its distance from the Earth?

   c What does this evidence suggest about the origin of the Universe?

Summary

- The stars in a galaxy, and clusters of galaxies, are held together by the force of gravity.

- The stars in a galaxy are far apart, compared with the distances between planets. Galaxies are far apart, compared with the distances between stars.

- The farthest galaxies show the biggest red-shifts, suggesting that they are moving away fastest.

- Scientists have deduced that the Universe started with a big bang, when all matter exploded from a single point.

Astronomers believe that our Sun is a fairly ordinary star, roughly halfway through its life. But how did it begin? And why will it end?

Birth of a star

When astronomers use powerful telescopes to look at distant galaxies, they can see giant dust clouds where new stars are forming. This gives them an idea about how the solar system formed.

Most scientists think that the solar system formed from a giant, swirling cloud of dust and gas. The gravity of each particle in the cloud pulled on all the others, so that they got closer and closer together.

◆ Gravity pulled together a lot of gas (mostly hydrogen) to form the Sun. As it got more and more squashed together, it got hotter and hotter as the molecules bounced off each other.

◆ Dust collected together to form the inner rocky planets. Further out, gases collected together to form the outer planets.

a Suggest why rocky planets formed close to the Sun, while the gassy planets formed further out.

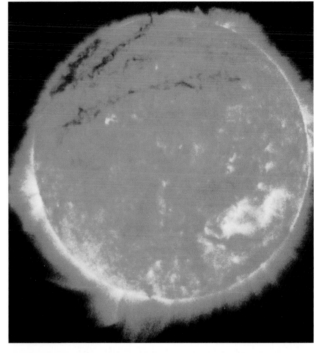

Space telescopes show that the surface of the Sun is patterned with hotter and cooler regions.

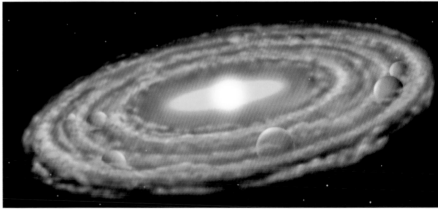

A scientific idea of how the solar system formed.

Billions of years

The Sun has lasted for about 5 billion years, and will probably last for another 7.5 billion years. It is very stable, because the inward pull of gravity is balanced by the outward force of the hot particles pushing against each other.

During this time, vast amounts of energy are released as heat and light. Inside the Sun, where the temperature is millions of degrees, nuclei of lighter elements (hydrogen and helium) join together to form nuclei of heavier elements. This is how carbon, oxygen, nitrogen etc are formed. The process is called **nuclear fusion**, and it is the source of a star's energy.

b Is it correct to say that the Sun 'burns' hydrogen?

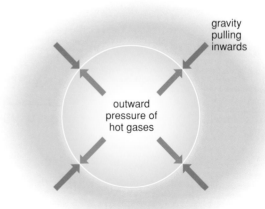

gravity pulling inwards

outward pressure of hot gases

Death of a star

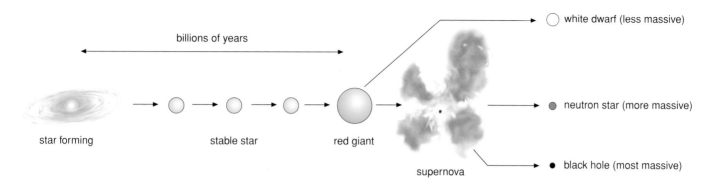

The life of stars; how they end up depends on their mass.

Towards the end of its life, the Sun will expand and become cooler – a **red giant**. It is likely to swallow up the inner planets, including the Earth. Later, its gravity will pull it back in so that it becomes a small, bright star – a **white dwarf**. The matter in such a star is highly compressed, with a density millions of times denser than any matter on Earth.

A star which is heavier than the Sun has a different history. After becoming a red giant, it collapses inwards and then explodes outwards – a **supernova**. Gas and dust fly out into space. The small remnant becomes a very dense **neutron star**.

The matter which spreads out into space contains important elements such as carbon, oxygen and iron. The early universe probably only contained hydrogen. Because we find these heavier elements in the Earth, this suggests that the matter from which the solar system formed probably came from earlier exploding stars.

The very heaviest of stars may leave a small and exceedingly dense object called a **black hole**. This is so dense that its gravitational field is so strong that nothing can escape from it. Not even light can escape which is why it is called black. We can observe the *effects* of black holes. For example, they may suck in gases from neighbouring stars. We can detect X-rays emitted by these gases as they spiral into the black hole.

c Put these objects in order, starting with the least dense:

Sun   red giant   black hole   neutron star   white dwarf

Questions

1 a What substance did the Sun mostly form from?

b Why does the Sun have a strong gravitational pull?

2 Draw a diagram to show the different stages in the life of the Sun.

3 Draw a diagram to show the sequence of events by which hydrogen gas in space eventually becomes carbon, oxygen and other elements on a planet such as Earth.

DIGGING DEEPER
The Sun is a ball of gas. Because of this, it rotates in a different way from the Earth. By watching sunspots as they travelled around, astronomers noticed that the Sun spins faster at its equator than at its poles. (Time for one rotation = 25 days at equator, 35 days at poles.)

Summary

- The force of gravity causes stars, and the planets which orbit them, to form from clouds of dust and gas in space.

- Energy is released in a star by the process of nuclear fusion, in which nuclei of light elements join together to form nuclei of heavier elements.

- Eventually, the Sun will expand to become a red giant, and then contract to become a white dwarf.

- A heavier star may explode as a supernova, leaving a neutron star behind. The heaviest stars leave black holes.

Astronomers have discovered dozens of planets in orbit around other stars. But is there any evidence that any of them are inhabited by living creatures? And is there life elsewhere in the solar system?

A century ago, an American called Percival Lowell made a detailed study of Mars. He expected to see evidence of life there. His telescope gave him a rather blurred view, and he thought he could see signs of a network of canals, constructed by martian engineers.

Now we know that there are no seas or canals on Mars, although there may have been water there at one time.

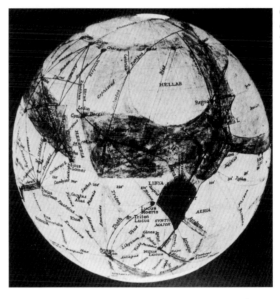

One of Percival Lowell's drawings of 'seas' and 'canals' on Mars.

Looking for life

One way to look for life in the solar system is to send a spacecraft. We can receive pictures back on Earth, or a robot machine might collect samples and return them to Earth. Spacecraft have visited some likely places, including Mars and one of Jupiter's moons called Europa. Images and samples can be examined to see if they contain anything living, or any fossils. So far, nothing has been found.

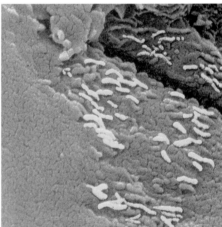

This lump of rock is a meteorite which came from Mars. Some scientists claim to have found fossilised bacteria in it, but many others disagree with their findings.

Checking the atmosphere

When a spacecraft was sent to Jupiter, it looked back towards Earth. It could detect the oxygen in our atmosphere. Oxygen is a good indicator of life; on a dead planet, the oxygen has all been used up and is trapped in rocks.

Scientists look for such signs of life in the atmospheres of other planets. They might also place a sample of material from another planet in a sealed container to see if the air around it changes because of the presence of living organisms.

a Why is there oxygen in our atmosphere?

This spacecraft has landed on Mars. A small rover vehicle has moved over to the rock on the right. By checking soil and atmospheric gases, such a craft could look for signs of life.

Listening for life

Because we broadcast radio and television signals around the world, we are sending messages out into space all the time. Observers on a different planet might detect these and wonder whether there was intelligent life on Earth.

Radio telescopes provide lots of useful information about stars and other galaxies, but so far they have not detected signals from intelligent creatures elsewhere in space.

Scientists have been listening out for radio signals coming from space for over 40 years. (This is known as the Search for Extra-Terrestrial Intelligence, SETI.) They hope to find meaningful, regular signals which would indicate that another civilisation was trying to get in touch; so far, they have detected nothing but random 'noise'.

◆ Some scientists argue that there are billions of planets in the Universe. Many are similar to Earth, and so are likely to support life.

◆ Other scientists argue that, if there is intelligent life elsewhere, it would have made contact with us by now.

b What do you think?

Questions

1 When the Earth formed, its atmosphere was mostly nitrogen, carbon dioxide and sulphur dioxide. Now the atmosphere contains 20% oxygen. Why has its composition changed?

2 Saturn has a rocky moon called Titan. List some ways in which we could look for evidence of life on Titan.

3 If oxygen is detected in the atmosphere of another planet or Moon, would that mean that there was animal life on the planet?

4 We could try to make contact with an alien civilisation by sending signals out into space. Do you think we should try this? What signals should we send?

DIGGING DEEPER
In the nineteenth century, scientists took very seriously the idea that there were people similar to us on Mars. They debated the ways in which they might differ from us, and how we should behave when we eventually met them.

Summary

• Scientists have used various methods to look for life elsewhere in the Solar System and beyond. So far, they have been unsuccessful.

Astronomers have discovered planets orbiting around distant stars.
Could one of these planets be home to intelligent life?

Here is a discussion from an imaginary chat-room for astronomy students.

Starmaster: *We've notched up over 70 extra-solar planets now. What do you think the chances are of finding life out there?*

OllieG: *Pretty low, I reckon. They're mostly giant planets and close to their stars. Would you want to live on a hot Jupiter? I don't think there could be much more than a bunch of bacteria out there, at most.*

Smith@Oxford: *Perhaps you're thinking too much about life on Earth. It could be completely different out there – evolution has turned up some pretty strange creatures. Think of those worms living in red-hot water in the ocean depths. And there are bacteria living in cracks in the rocks hundreds of metres below the Earth's surface.*

OllieG: *Did you ever meet an intelligent worm or bacteria?*

Starmaster: *What should we be looking for if we want to find life on a distant planet?*

Smith@Oxford: *There's a chance we might be able to see the planet's atmosphere. At least, we might pick up light from the planet and be able to analyse it, find out what it's made of. Look for methane and oxygen.*

Astropat: *Can I join in? What's methane got to do with it?*

Smith@Oxford: *Animals produce methane. Plants produce oxygen. Methane gets oxidised quickly, so if there's any there, there must be animals or rotting plants producing it.*

OllieG: *Sounds a smelly old planet. I'm not going if there's no oxygen.*

Starmaster: *Who said anything about going there?*

OllieG: *It's one of the options.*

Astropat: *It would take several lifetimes. These planets are light-years away. Better to send a signal. We might get a reply before we die.*

Starmaster: *Isn't that dangerous? Drawing attention to ourselves, inviting attention from aliens?*

OllieG: *You won't get a Nobel prize if you don't take chances. And what's the alternative?*

Starmaster: *Just sit quiet and listen. Perhaps there's someone out there trying to make contact.*

Astropat: *But that still leaves you with the same problem. Are you going to reply if you pick up their signals?*

Smith@Oxford: *We've got a radio telescope here. We could put in a bid to use it when it's not in service, either to send signals or to search for them.*

You can't have intelligent life with just one head

OllieG: *Any chance of using it on the quiet? We don't want too many people asking awkward questions.*

Astropat: *Don't you think a lot of people would want to have a say in this?*

OllieG: *There's always people ready to get in the way of scientific progress.*

Smith@Oxford: *Yes, it's the next logical step really, making contact with other intelligent civilisations.*

Questions

Science is a mixture of facts, theories and debates. Here are some questions about factual information in the chat-room discussion.

1 The newly discovered planets are described as *extra-solar planets*. What does *extra-solar* mean?

2 The new planets are described as *hot Jupiters*. They are as big as Jupiter, or bigger. Why are they hot? Why might they be difficult for life to exist on?

3 The gas we use for cooking is methane, CH_4. When it burns, it combines with oxygen from the air. What two substances are produced? Why is methane in a planet's atmosphere a sign of life?

Here are some questions about scientific theories.

4 Do the people in the discussion appear to believe in the theory of evolution?

5 Many people do not accept the theory of evolution. What alternative ideas do they have?

6 If living creatures were found on another planet, would it change their ideas?

Here are some questions about debates in science.

7 In the chat-room discussion, who seems to be most prepared to take risks and ignore other people's ideas? Give an example to support your answer.

8 Who seems to think that science moves ahead with its own momentum, rather than being under human control? Give an example to support your answer.

9 The students are suggesting a project to contact alien civilisations. What are the dangers of this?

10 How could the students' project be debated more widely? Who should be involved in the debate? Who should decide whether the project should go ahead?

11 Give an example of a scientific idea or problem which has been in the public eye recently. Who has been involved in the debate? Where could you find out about the debate? Is there any way you could contribute to the debate?

End of module questions

1 A truck is moving along a straight road. The table shows how its position changes with time.

Distance travelled (m)	0	250	500	750	1000
Time taken (s)	0	10	20	30	40

a Draw a distance–time graph to represent the truck's motion.

b Explain how you can tell from the graph that the truck is moving at a steady speed.

c From the gradient of the graph, calculate the truck's speed.

d What other piece of information would you need in order to know the truck's *velocity*?

2

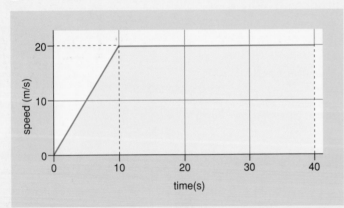

The graph represents the motion of a car.

a Use the graph to calculate the car's acceleration during the first 10 s of its journey.

b How far did the car travel during the first 40 s of its journey?

3 A cyclist is travelling along a straight road. She reaches the top of a steep slope, and speeds up as she runs downhill.

At the top of the hill, her speed is 5 m/s. 4 s later, she is moving at 13 m/s.

a By how much has her speed increased during the 4 s?

b Calculate her acceleration, giving the correct units.

4 The car in the picture is moving along a straight road at a steady speed. The arrows show the forces acting on the car.

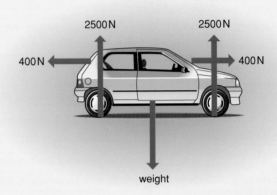

a Are the forces acting on the car balanced or unbalanced? Give a reason to support your answer.

b How big is the force of air resistance on the car?

c How big is the weight of the car?

5 The drawings show a parachutist at different points in his free fall. The arrows indicate the forces acting on him.

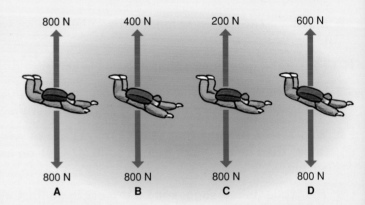

a At point A, he is moving at a steady speed. Explain how you can tell this from the diagram.

b At the other three points, the parachutist is accelerating (speeding up). At which point does he have the greatest acceleration? Explain your answer.

6 The stopping distance of a car as it travels along a road is made up of the thinking distance and the braking distance:

$$\text{Stopping distance} = \text{thinking distance} + \text{braking distance.}$$

a Explain as fully as you can why the braking distance may be greater if the road is wet or icy.

b Explain as fully as you can why the stopping distance may be greater if the driver has been drinking alcohol.

7 The Highway Code talks about 'the two second rule'. This is a way of checking that you are a safe distance behind the vehicle in front. You should pass a fixed object, such as a lamppost, at least 2 s after the car in front.

The driver of a green car sees an accident ahead and brakes as hard as she can. Her car stops in 1.5 s, during which time it travels 30 m.

The driver of a red car also brakes when he sees the green car's brake lights come on. During the interval between when he sees the light and when he applies his brakes, the car moves 25 m. Once the brakes are on, the car stops in a distance of 65 m.

a How far does the red car travel from the moment the brake lights come on in the green car?

b How far behind the green car must the red car be to avoid crashing into it?

c If the red car is travelling at 30 m/s (just under 70 mph), how many seconds must it be behind the green car?

8 When a car driver brakes suddenly, her car slows down at a rate of 5 m/s². If the mass of the car is 600 kg, calculate the force of the brakes which causes it to slow down.

9 The boy in the picture pushes a heavy box for a distance of 10 m along the ground. If the boy's pushing force is 150 N, calculate the work he does in pushing the box.

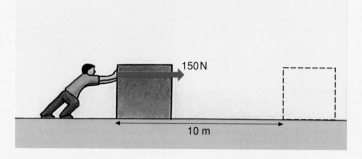

10 Four forces are acting on the lorry shown in the illustration.

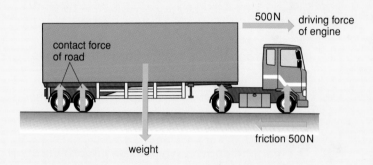

a Which two forces do no work as the lorry moves along? Explain why they do no work.

b Which two forces are doing work?

c Calculate the work done by each of these forces as the lorry moves 100 m horizontally.

11 Jupiter is a planet with several moons in orbit around it. The diagram shows the orbits of four of these moons.

a What force holds the moons in their orbits?

b Which moon takes longest to make a complete orbit around Jupiter? Give a reason for your answer.

12 The diagram shows two satellites in orbit around the Earth.

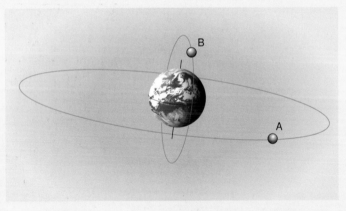

a Satellite A is in a geostationary orbit. How long does it take to orbit the Earth?

b Suggest a use for satellite A.

c Satellite B is a monitoring satellite. Explain how its orbit allows it to monitor the whole of the Earth's surface.

13 The Sun is a star in the Milky Way galaxy.

a What is a galaxy?

b The Sun formed from a cloud of dust and gas in space. Explain how this happened.

c Eventually, the Sun will swell up so that it engulfs the Earth. What type of star will it have become?

14 The atmosphere of the Earth contains a lot of oxygen. So far, no other planets or moons in the solar system have been found with as much oxygen in their atmospheres.

Explain what this suggests about the existence of life on these other planets and moons.

15 When astronomers look at the light coming from stars in distant galaxies, they notice two things:

- the light is shifted towards the red end of the spectrum;
- the more distant the galaxy, the bigger the red-shift.

a State as fully as you can what this suggests about how these galaxies are moving.

b How do these observations support the 'big bang' theory of the origin of the Universe?

16 The nuclei of heavy elements are formed in stars. When the stars die, they explode and these nuclei spread out into space.

a What name is given to the process by which nuclei of heavier elements are formed inside stars from nuclei of lighter elements?

b Nuclei of heavier elements are found in the Sun and planets of the solar system. What does this suggest about the material from which the solar system formed?

Recap material – paper 2

Module 06: Earth materials

Material included in paper 2

How can so many useful products be made from crude oil?

Crude oil is mostly made from a mixture of molecules made from carbon and hydrogen only (hydrocarbons). This mixture may be separated into fractions containing hydrocarbons of similar chain length by boiling the oil and letting it condense at different temperatures. This is called fractional distillation. Hydrocarbon properties vary with the molecules size (number of carbon atoms). The bigger the molecule, the higher the boiling point, which makes the hydrocarbon less volatile.

Large hydrocarbons can be heated and 'cracked' (broken down) to make smaller and more useful molecules, some of which are used as fuels. A hot catalyst is used to speed up this thermal decomposition. Other products of cracking are have double C=C covalent bonds. These are called alkenes and are said to be unsaturated. They are more reactive and are used to make plastics (polymers) such as poly(ethene) and poly(propene).

Fuels containing carbon and hydrogen release carbon dioxide and water into the atmosphere when burnt. They may also contain some sulphur, which forms sulphur dioxide.

How was the Earth's atmosphere formed?

Burning fossil fuels releases carbon that has been locked up in the rocks for hundreds of millions of years. This causes the level of carbon dioxide in the atmosphere to increase. Some, but not all, of this is re-absorbed as it reacts with sea water, mostly forming insoluble calcium carbonate.

Why have all mountains on Earth not worn away by now?

At the surface of the Earth younger sedimentary rocks are found on top of older ones. They can show evidence about how they formed, such as ripple marks caused by current or wave action, or horizontal bedding caused by discontinuous deposition.

Older sedimentary rock layers can sometimes be found tilted, folded, fractured (faulted) and even overturned. This shows evidence of enormous forces and that the Earth's crust is unstable in places.

Recap questions

 1 A chemical engineer was analysing a new oil to see if it contained a fraction suitable for use as petrol. From a book of data she obtained the following boiling points for hydrocarbons.

Number of carbon atoms	Boiling point°C
6	69
7	99
8	
9	151
10	174

a Use the information from the table to draw a scattergraph, adding a line of best fit.

b At what temperature do you think a hydrocarbon with 8 carbon atoms would boil?

c She read that petrol contains 8 carbon-chain atoms. When she distilled her oil she got three fractions.

Fraction	Temperature collected °C	Amount collected cm³
1st	99	40
2nd	126	30
3rd	151	30

Which fraction would be best to use for petrol? Explain your answer.

d If this oil was processed commercially, what volume of 'petrol' would you get from every 100 litres of oil? Show your working

e Some of the longer chain fractions have no direct use. Instead they are vaporised and passed over a hot catalyst. What is this process called and what does it do?

f Some of the new short molecules are used as fuels. What important use are the rest put to?

g Ethene is one of these short molecules. What polymer (plastic) is made from this?

h Draw a structural diagram of ethene and use it to explain how this polymer is formed.

2 Fuels are chemicals we burn to get energy.

a Most fuels contain carbon and hydrogen atoms. Which two new compounds are formed when these fuels burn?

b Write this as a word equation:

fuel + _____ → _____ + _____

c Is this reaction endothermic or exothermic?

d Write a balanced chemical equation for the combustion of methane (CH_4).

e Fossil fuels often contain sulphur. What gas is formed from these atoms when the fuel burns?

f Why is this a problem?

3 The diagram shows a simplified example of the carbon cycle.

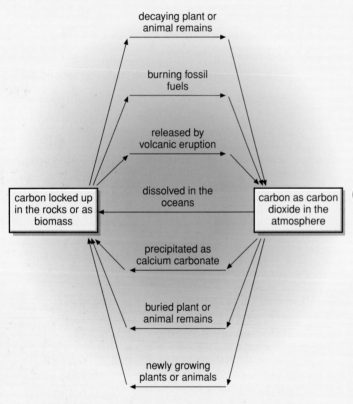

a For the hundred years up to 1700 AD few fossil fuels were burnt and the percentage of carbon dioxide in the atmosphere remained fairly constant. What does this tell us about the natural processes that control the amount of carbon dioxide in the atmosphere.?

b Over the last 100 years, vast amounts of fossil fuel have been burnt, pumping enormous quantities of carbon dioxide into the atmosphere. Suggest two reasons why the increase in carbon dioxide in the atmosphere over this period is not as great as might have been expected.

c The fossil fuels, which may have taken 300 million years to form, are likely to have been used up within 300 years from the start of the industrial revolution. Yet new fossil fuels are still forming today in swamps and oceans. So why is the fact we are burning fossil fuels causing problems for the atmosphere?

4 Weathering and erosion produce debris that is carried down to the sea.

a Why is this sediment usually laid down in horizontal layers in the sea? (What force is at work...?)

b Over time, the layers of sediment harden to sedimentary rock. Horizontal layers of sedimentary rock can sometimes be seen in cliffs around the coast – often tens of metres above sea level. Suggest **two** possible reasons for this.

c Fossils of sea creatures are found in rocks 5km above sea level in the Alps. Which of your two possible explanations is more likely in the light of this evidence?

d Often the rocks in the Alps are faulted, folded and even at times overturned. What global processes could possibly lead to such large-scale deformation of he rocks of the Earth's crust?

5 Some igneous rocks found in the mountains of Scotland formed during a period of mountain building 400 million years ago, some 40km down in the Earth's crust.

a How is it that these rocks can be seen at the surface today?

b Copy and use the table below to work out just how fast (or slow!) this process has been.

time taken	amount of erosion
400 million years	40km that's...
400 000 000 years	40 000 metres or...
	40 000 000 millimetres
divide both by 4 ...	
100 000 000 years	_____millimetres
now divide by 1000 000	
100 years	_____millimetres
divide by 10...	
10 years	___ millimetre
1 year	_____ millimetre

Material included in paper 2

Heat energy is transferred out of buildings by conduction, convection and radiation. By understanding these mechanisms, we can show how to reduce the rate of heat loss from buildings.

Electrical devices can perform many useful energy transfers. However, some of the energy transferred is wasted; the devices are not 100% efficient. All of the energy transferred eventually ends up in the environment, making it warmer.

Electricity is generated in a variety of ways; each has an impact on the environment.

- Burning fossil fuels produces waste gases, including carbon dioxide (which increases the greenhouse effect) and sulphur dioxide (which produces acid rain).

- Nuclear power stations produce radioactive waste.

- Wind farms can be ugly and noisy.

- Hydroelectric and tidal schemes flood land which might have other uses.

Each method of generating electricity has other advantages and disadvantages. For example:

- Nuclear power stations are slow to start up.

- Solar cells are expensive, but useful in remote locations.

- Wind and solar power are dependent on the climate; tidal power depends on the state of the tide.

You should be able to compare their merits, including the various costs involved, and the need to match supply and demand.

Recap questions

1 The diagram shows a generator in two positions. On the right, it has been rotated through 180° relative to its position on the left.

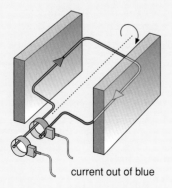 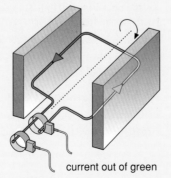

current out of blue   current out of green

Indicate whether each of the following statements is true or false.

a The generator produces alternating current. True/False

b Electric current is supplied to the generator through the slip rings. True/False

c The coil must be turned back and forth to produce alternating current. True/False

d The magnets have opposite poles facing one another. True/False

e A coil with more turns would generate a greater induced voltage. True/False

2 In the UK, most of our electricity comes from power stations where fossil fuels are burned. In order to use less fossil fuels, an increasing amount of electricity is generated in power stations which use alternatives to fossil fuels.

a Give one reason why it is desirable to find alternatives to fossil fuels.

b The table shows three ways of generating electricity. Unfortunately, none of these can be relied on to provide a steady supply of electricity. Copy the table, and in the second column explain why the supply from each varies considerably.

Method of supply	Reason why supply varies
Tidal power station	
Wind generators	
Solar cells	

c Explain why this makes it difficult to match supply to demand.

d New nuclear power stations may be built in the UK. Older ones must be de-commissioned. Explain why this is difficult to do. Why does this add to the cost of the electricity produced by a nuclear power station?

e Solar cells are expensive to make, so the electricity they produce is costly. State one situation in which they would be a good choice for producing electricity, and give a reason to support your choice.

3 Ayan wants to save some money on her heating bills. She also wants to help to protect the environment.

The local council recently sent her a leaflet about saving energy around the home. Here is a table from the leaflet that shows you how insulating your house can save you money:

Type of insulation	Cost to install	Saving each year on your fuel bill
Loft insulation	£200	£100
Double glazing	£1500	£50
Hot water cylinder jacket	£10	£60
Aluminium foil behind radiators	£2	£10
Cavity wall insulation	£500	£100
Draught excluders	£60	£15

Ayan can't afford to make all the changes this year.

a Which two types of insulation will save more money from her bill in one year than they cost to install?

b How many years will it take for Ayan to save back the installation cost of:

Loft insulation?

Draught excluders?

Double glazing?

c Ayan decides that she can afford to spend up to £500 on insulation this year. What forms of insulation would you advise her to spend her money on? Explain your answer.

d Ayan's house is heated using oil. Is oil a renewable or non-renewable energy resource?

e Oil is burnt to heat the water in Ayan's boiler. Which greenhouse gas does burning oil produce?

f Explain why installing insulation will help to protect the environment.

Module 10: Electricity

Material included in paper 2

Potential difference, current and resistance are related by:

p.d. (V) = current (A) × resistance Ω

The graphs show how p.d. and current are related for three devices.

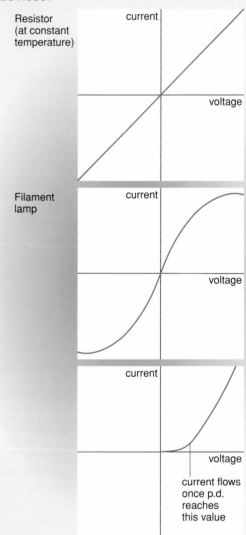

A light dependent resistor has less resistance when light falls on it; a thermistor has less resistance when it is hotter.

When a wire carrying a current is placed in a magnetic field, a force acts on it. The greater the current and the stronger the field, the greater the force. This is made use of in electric motors and circuit breakers.

A voltage can be induced by moving a magnet into and out of a coil of wire, or by rotating a coil in a magnetic field. To increase the induced voltage:

- use a stronger magnetic field;
- increase the speed of movement;
- use a coil with more turns, or a greater area.

An a.c. generator has slip rings and brushes to lead the current away. You should be able to explain how such a generator works.

Recap questions

 1 The diagram shows an experiment to investigate a thermistor. The thermistor is connected in series with a lamp, an ammeter and a battery. As the water is heated, the thermistor gets hotter.

The graph shows how the current flowing through the thermistor depends on its temperature.

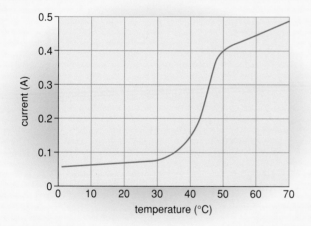

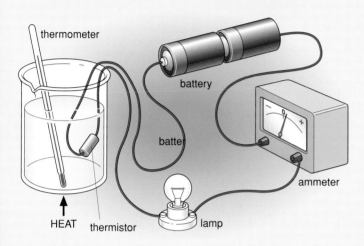

a Describe what the graph shows about how the resistance of the thermistor changes as it is heated.

b At a temperature of 40°C, the potential difference across the thermistor is 3.0 V. What is its resistance at this temperature?

c The lamp will light up if the current flowing through it is greater than 0.4 A. Describe how the brightness of the lamp will change as the water is heated, starting at 20°C.

 2 The diagram shows an experiment to investigate the factors which affect an induced voltage. The coil of wire is connected to a voltmeter. The magnet can be moved in and out of the coil.

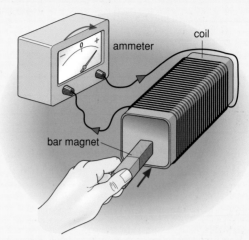

In the table below, the first column shows how the magnet can be moved in different ways. Copy the table and in the second column, write down how you would expect the reading on the voltmeter to change as a result. (The first row has been completed.)

Choose from:

Voltage increases

Voltage decreases

Voltage reverses

Voltage becomes zero

Movement of magnet	Reading on voltmeter
North pole moved in quickly	Large voltage
South pole moved in quickly	
North pole moved in slowly	
Magnet held still inside coil	

 3 Alex was writing up her lab work at home. Unfortunately she had rushed her work in class and had forgotten to write down some important information about her results.

During the class she had tested a lamp and a diode. For each she measured the current flowing through the component and the voltage across it. She then reversed the connections to each component and tried again.

Here is Alex's results table:

Voltage (V)	Current in component A (amps)		Current in component B (amps)	
	Normal	Reversed	Normal	Reversed
0	0	0	0	0
2	0.4	-0.4	0.2	0
4	0.7	-0.7	0.4	0
6	0.87	-0.87	0.6	0
8	0.95	-0.95	0.8	0
10	1.0	-1.0	1.0	0

a Draw two sets of axes to show Alex's results. (You will need to put current on the y-axis and voltage on the x-axis).

b Plot the results for each component onto your axes.

c Is component A a lamp or a diode? Give reasons for your decision.

4 Ali measured the current through and the voltage across a resistor and recorded his results.

Voltage (V)	Current (A)
2.50	0.04
4.10	0.07
5.90	0.10
9.70	0.16
11.50	0.19

a Plot a graph of his results, with current on the x-axis.

b Draw a best fit straight line through his points.

c Comment on the accuracy of his readings.

d Use the graph to estimate the current at 8V.

e Extrapolate the graph to estimate the current at 15V.

5 In a simple electric motor, a coil spins in a magnetic field what would happen to the spinning motor if each of the following changes was made:

a The current was increased.

b The current were reversed.

c The number of turns in the coil was reduced.

Glossary of terms

acceleration The rate of change of velocity; acceleration = change of velocity/time taken.

activation energy The energy needed to start a reaction: used to break bonds.

adapt To become more suitable for.

adaptation/s A feature or features that make a structure more suitable for its function.

air resistance The drag force on an object moving through the air; a form of friction.

albino Lack of a pigment in the skin, fur or feathers causing an animal become white.

alkali metal A reactive metal, such as sodium from group 1 of the periodic table, that reacts with water to form an alkaline solution.

allele Some genes have two different forms called alleles.

amino acids Protein molecules are made from chains of amino acids.

amplitude The height of a wave; its maximum disturbance.

anaemia A disorder affecting red blood cells. Because of this, blood cannot carry enough oxygen.

analogue An analogue signal has a shape that corresponds to the shape of the signal being carried; the opposite of a digital signal.

anhydrous Without water of crystallisation.

antibiotics Chemicals used to destroy bacteria in the body.

asexual reproduction Reproduction that does not involve the formation of gametes. New organisms formed by asexual reproduction are genetically identical to the parent organism.

atomic number The number of protons in an atom; same as the proton number.

atom The smallest part of an element that still has the properties of that element.

background radiation We are exposed to background radiation all the time, from radioactive substances around us, and from cosmic rays.

balanced equation A way of describing a chemical reaction using formulae for reactants and products; the number of each type of atom must be the same on both sides of the equation.

batch process A process such as fermentation where a fixed amount of reagents are reacted in discrete units.

'big bang' The explosion in which the Universe is thought to have been created.

biomass The mass of living organisms in an area.

black hole An object in space that is so massive and dense that its gravity prevents light from escaping.

boiling point The temperature at which all of a liquid turns to a gas.

braking distance The distance travelled by a car while the brakes are applied.

brine A solution of sodium chloride in water, such as sea water.

camouflage A feature that makes it more difficult to spot an organism.

carbohydrase An enzyme that breaks down carbohydrates.

carbon cycle The flow of carbon compounds through plants, animals and decomposers.

carrier An individual with a recessive allele that does not show as a characteristic because of the presence of a dominant allele.

catalyst Something that speeds up a chemical reaction without itself being used up.

cellulose The carbohydrate that forms plant cell walls.

chain reaction Neutrons released when one nucleus splits then cause more nuclei to split, releasing further neutrons, and so on.

chemical formula A description of a chemical compound using symbols and numbers to show how many of each type of atom is found in that compound.

chromosomes Long threads containing many genes, found in the nucleus of a cell.

clone Group of genetically identical organisms.

closed system A reacting system is closed if none of the products can escape.

communications satellite A spacecraft orbiting the Earth used to transmit telephone and TV signals.

compete Try to gain an advantage over another organism.

competition What happens when there are not enough resources for all the organisms in a habitat.

compost Decaying remains of plants.

compound A new substance formed when atoms from two or more elements become chemically joined together.

concentration The amount of a chemical in a fixed volume of solution.

condense To turn from a gas to a liquid.

continuous process A process such as oil refining where reagents are continually fed into the reacting vessel and the products continually removed.

contraceptive pill   A pill containing hormones that prevent an egg becoming fertilised.

count rate   The reading on a Geiger counter showing the rate at which radiation has been detected.

covalent bonds   Chemical bonds formed when non-metals share electrons; molecules have covalent bonds.

covalent compound   A compound formed when atoms from two or more elements are joined by covalent bonds.

critical angle   If a light ray strikes an internal surface at a greater angle than this, it will be reflected; none is refracted.

cuttings   Small pieces of plant stem, root or leaf that grow into new plants.

cycle   A series of processes that always occur in the same order.

cystic fibrosis   An inherited disorder affecting the breathing and digestive systems. It is caused by a faulty recessive allele.

daughter atom   An atom produced when a radioactive atom, the parent atom, decays.

decay   The breakdown of dead and waste material. When a radioactive atom decays, it emits radiation and becomes a different type of atom.

decomposers   Organisms that break down waste material and dead material.

diffraction   The spreading out of waves when they pass through a gap or around an obstacle.

digital   A digital signal carries information in the form of a string of on and off pulses; the opposite of an analogue signal.

distance–time graph   A graph showing how the distance travelled by an object depends on the time.

DNA   A complex molecule that contains coded information to control inherited characteristics. Each gene is a section of a DNA molecule.

dominant   An allele that produces a characteristic when it is present on only one of a pair of chromosomes.

egg cell   The female sex cell (gamete).

elastic potential energy   Energy stored by an elastic object when it is stretched or squashed.

electrolysis   The tearing apart of a molten (or dissolved) ionic compounds using electricity.

electromagnetic radiation   Energy travelling in the form of waves.

electromagnetic spectrum   All types of electromagnetic radiation, arranged in order according to their wavelengths and frequencies.

electron   A small particle with tiny mass and a single negative charge.

electron shells   The positions that electrons can occupy around an atom – same as energy levels.

electronic structure   The way electrons are arranged around an atom.

element   Something made of one type of atom only.

ellipse   A squashed circle; objects orbiting under gravity have orbits shaped like ellipses.

empirical formula   The formula found by experiment given in terms of the simplest ratio of the elements.

endothermic   A reaction that takes in energy.

energy levels   The positions that electrons can occupy around an atom – same as electron shells.

enzyme   An organic catalyst.

equilibrium   The balance point in a reversible reaction reached when the rates of the forward and back reactions are equal.

eutrophication   Oxygen depletion in water caused by excess growth of plants.

evaporation   When a liquid turns to a gas below its boiling point.

evolution   The process of gradual change taking place in organisms over many generations. Organisms become better adapted to their environment.

exothermic   A reaction that gives out energy.

extinct   Extinct species used to live on the Earth but no longer exist.

fermentation   The conversion of sugar to ethanol and carbon dioxide.

fertilisation   The fusion of egg and sperm cells to form the first cell of a new individual.

fertilisers   Chemicals that are used to make plants grow better and to increase the yield of crops.

fertility drug   A drug used to increase the chances of a woman becoming pregnant.

fluids   Liquids and gases are fluids; they are substances that can flow.

food chain   A series of organisms, each dependent on the previous one for food.

food web   A series of interconnected food chains.

force   A push or a pull; measured in newtons (N).

formula mass (M_r)   The sum of the relative atomic masses of all the atoms in a compound (e.g. for water H_2O: $2 \times 1 + 16 = 18$).

fossils   The 'remains' of plants and animals from many years ago, found in rocks.

freezing   When a liquid cools and turns to a solid.

frequency   The number of waves per second; measured in hertz (Hz).

fructose   A sweet sugar found in fruit.

galaxy   A cluster of billions of stars, held together by gravity.

galena   Lead sulphide, the ore of lead (PbS).

gametes   Specialised sex cells involved in sexual reproduction in plants and animals.

gas syringe   A graduated syringe used to measure the volume of a gas.

gene Part of a chromosome, which controls an inherited characteristic.

genetic engineering Changing the genes of an organism. For example, genes from humans can be added to bacteria.

geostationary A satellite in a geostationary orbit takes 24 hours to complete one orbit.

giant ionic structure A giant structure formed from positive and negative ions and held together by strong electrostatic forces.

glucose The simple sugar produced by photosynthesis.

GM crops Genetically modified crops. These are crop plants that have had new genes added from another species.

gravitational potential energy (GPE) The energy stored by an object that has been raised up against the force of gravity.

group Name given to the vertical columns of the periodic table; elements in the same group have similar properties.

Haber process The industrial process used to make ammonia from nitrogen and hydrogen.

haematite An oxide ore of iron (Fe_2O_3).

half-life The average time taken for half the atoms in a sample of a radioactive substance to decay.

halide An ionic compound of one of the halogens, such as chlorine.

halogen A member of group 7 of the periodic table, such as chlorine.

heat Energy moving from a hotter place to a colder place, because of the temperature difference.

herbicides Chemicals used to kill weeds.

heterozygous An individual is heterozygous when the alleles in a pair are different – for example, Aa.

homozygous An individual is homozygous when both alleles in a pair are the same – for example, AA or aa.

hormones Chemicals that are transported around the body in the blood. These chemicals control body processes.

immobilised enzyme An enzyme that has been fixed in some way for use in an industrial process.

inherited disorders Disorders that are caused by dominant or recessive alleles, which are passed from parents to their children.

insulation A way of reducing heat loss.

intercropping Growing one type of crop in between another type of crop.

ion A charged particle.

ionic bond A bond formed by the electrostatic attraction between oppositely charged ions.

ionic compound A compound formed by the electrostatic attraction between oppositely charged ions.

ionic lattice A giant structure formed from positive and negative ions and held together by strong electrostatic forces.

ionised An ionised atom or molecule is electrically charged because it has lost or gained electrons.

isomerase An enzyme that converts glucose to fructose.

isotopes Atoms of an element come in different forms, depending on the numbers of neutrons they have in their nuclei.

kinetic energy The energy of a moving object.

lactic acid The acid that makes milk turn sour.

lactose The sugar in milk.

light wave A form of electromagnetic radiation which we can see.

limewater A solution of calcium hydroxide; used as the test for carbon dioxide.

lipase An enzyme that breaks down fats and oils.

longitudinal wave Any wave in which particles move back and forth, along the direction in which the wave is travelling.

meiosis The type of cell division that produces gametes. During this type of cell division the number of chromosomes is reduced – the gametes contain half the number of chromosomes that the parent cell contains.

melting point The temperature at which a solid turns to a liquid.

menstrual cycle The monthly cycle of changes in a woman's reproductive system, controlled by hormones.

microbe Another word for a microorganism.

microorganism An organism so small that it can only be seen through a microscope.

Milky Way Our galaxy.

mitosis The type of cell division forming two cells that are identical to the parent cell.

model In science we use models to help us explain ideas.

mole The amount of a substance containing 6.02×10^{23} particles (e.g. the relative atomic mass or formula mass in grams).

molecules Particles made from atoms joined by covalent bonds.

monatomic gases Gases that exists as single atoms, such as helium or the other noble gases.

mutation Change in a gene that produces new forms of the gene.

natural selection   Factors such as predation and competition for food affect the survival of organisms. Because of these factors, the best adapted organisms are selected for survival.

negative ion   An atom or cluster of atoms with a net negative charge.

neutron   A sub-atomic particle with no electric charge and a relative mass of 1.

neutron star   One way in which a star may end its life, as a giant ball of neutrons.

newton   The unit of force; symbol N.

nitrifying bacteria   Bacteria that convert ammonium compounds into nitrates.

nitrogen cycle   The flow of nitrogen compounds through plants, animals and decomposers.

noble gas   A member of group 0 (or 8) of the periodic table, such as neon.

non-renewable   Once used it cannot be replaced.

nuclear fission   When the nucleus of a massive atom splits into two large fragments. Radiation of various kinds is released.

nuclear fusion   When the nuclei of two small atoms join together to form a more massive nucleus; energy is released.

nuclear model   The picture of an atom with a tiny nucleus at its centre, and electrons orbiting it.

nucleon number   The number of nucleons (protons and neutrons) in a nucleus.

nucleus   The central part of the atom containing the proton(s) and, for all except hydrogen, the neutrons; has most of the mass of the atom.

open system   A reacting system is open if some of the products can escape (or are removed).

optical fibre   A fine glass fibre; a ray of light bounces along inside the fibre by total internal reflection, following its curves.

organic farming   Farming without using pesticides or manufactured fertilisers.

ovary   Female sex organ where eggs are produced.

parent atom   A radioactive atom that decays to become a daughter atom.

period   Horizontal row of the periodic table.

periodic table   A way of arranging all the different elements in a table to link up those with similar properties.

pesticides   Chemicals that kill pests such as insects.

photosynthesis   A series of reactions in which plants use light energy to make food.

pituitary gland   A gland in the brain that produces hormones, including hormones that control reproduction.

plum pudding model   The picture of an atom as a sphere of positive charge with negatively-charged electrons embedded in it.

pollen grains   Grains containing male gametes produced by the male parts of flowers.

positive ion   An atom or cluster of atoms with a net positive charge.

precipitate   An insoluble solid that sometimes forms when two reacting solutions are mixed.

pressure   The force a gas exerts over unit area.

prey   Animals that are eaten by other animals.

producers   Green plants that use light energy to make food.

products   The chemicals that form as a result of a chemical reaction.

protease   An enzyme that breaks down proteins.

proton   A sub-atomic particle with a positive charge and a relative mass of 1.

proton number   The number of protons in an atom.

putrefying bacteria   Bacteria that break down dead material into ammonium compounds.

pyramid of biomass   A diagram that shows the mass of living organisms at each stage in a food chain.

pyramid of numbers   A diagram that shows the number of organisms at each stage in a food chain.

pyrite   Fool's gold – the sulphide ore of iron (FeS_2).

radioactive isotopes   Atoms of an element may come in several forms or isotopes; some are radioactive.

reactants   The chemicals that react together in a chemical reaction.

reaction rate   The rate at which products are formed (or reactants are lost) in a chemical reaction.

recessive allele   An allele that produces a characteristic only when the dominant allele is not present.

recycle   Convert back into a useful material.

red giant   A stage in the life of a star; it swells up and becomes dimmer.

red-shift   The change in wavelength of light from a distant star; it looks redder because it is receding.

reflection   When waves bounce off a surface.

refraction   When waves change direction because they move into a different material where their speed changes.

relative atomic mass (A_r)   The number of protons added to the number of neutrons in an atom.

renewable   Can be replaced after being used up.

resistant   Antibiotic-resistant bacteria are not destroyed by the action of antibiotics.

respiration   A series of reactions in which living organisms release energy from food.

resultant   The resultant force is the unbalanced force when two or more forces act on an object.

reversible reaction   A reaction that can occur in either direction.

rock salt   The natural mineral form of sodium chloride.

satellite   A spacecraft or other object in orbit around (for example) the Earth.

seismic wave   A shock wave travelling through the Earth; usually set off by an earthquake.

seismograph   An instrument for detecting seismic waves.

selective breeding   Selection of plants and animals for breeding because they have useful and desired characteristics.

sex chromosomes   The chromosomes that control the sex of a person. In humans, XY is male and XX female.

sickle cell disease   An inherited disease affecting red blood cells. People with the disease suffer from severe anaemia.

skin cancer   Cancer of skin cells, which can be caused by over-exposure to sunlight.

spectrum   A series of waves, arranged in order according to their wavelengths and frequencies.

speed   How far an object travels in a given time; speed = distance travelled/time taken.

sperm   The male sex cell (gamete).

stabilised enzyme   An enzyme that has been treated so that it will last for a long time in an industrial process.

starch   A carbohydrate made from glucose molecules joined together.

stomata   Tiny holes on the surfaces of plant leaves, which are used for exchanging gases with the atmosphere (singular: stoma).

stopping distance   The distance travelled by a vehicle between the time when the driver notices the need to stop and when the vehicle stops.

sublimation   When a solid turns straight into a gas (or vice versa).

sucrose   The sweet sugar used at home.

supernova   When a star explodes towards the end of its life.

surface area   The area of surface available for a chemical reaction to take place.

surface area to volume ratio   A ratio calculated by dividing the total surface area of an organism by its volume.

sustainable development   Development that conserves natural resources.

terminal velocity   The top speed of an object falling through the air.

testis   Male sex organ where sperm cells are produced (plural: testes).

thinking distance   The distance travelled by a vehicle between the time when the driver notices the need to stop and when the brakes are applied.

tissue culture   A cloning technique involving growing groups of cells into new plants.

total internal reflection (TIR)   When a ray is entirely reflected within a transparent material because its angle of incidence is greater than the critical angle.

transverse wave   A wave in which particles move from side to side, at right angles to the direction in which the wave is moving.

ultrasound   Sound that is too high-pitched to hear; its frequency is above 20 kHz.

Universe   All the matter and energy that exists.

vapour   A gas formed by evaporation from a liquid.

velocity   The speed of an object in a particular direction.

wavelength   The length of a single wave, measured from one wave crest to the next.

weight   The force on an object caused by the pull of the Earth's gravity.

white dwarf   A stage in the life of a star when it is relatively small, dense and bright.

womb   Part of the female reproductive system. The lining of the womb provides food and oxygen for a growing embryo.

word equation   A way of describing a chemical reaction by naming the reactants and products.

work   Energy transferred by a force. Work done = force × distance moved in the direction of the force.

yeast   A single-celled organism that ferments sugar to alcohol and carbon dioxide.

yield   The amount of product you get; often expressed as a percentage of what is theoretically possible.

Data sheets

Reactivity Series of Metals

Potassium	most reactive
Sodium	
Calcium	
Magnesium	
Aluminium	
Carbon	
Zinc	
Iron	
Tin	
Lead	
Hydrogen	
Copper	
Silver	
Gold	
Platinum	least reactive

(elements in italics, though non-metals, have been included for comparison).

Formulae of Some Common Ions

Positive ions		Negative ions	
Name	**Formula**	**Name**	**Formula**
Hydrogen	H^+	Chloride	Cl^-
Sodium	Na^+	Bromide	Br^-
Silver	Ag^+	Fluoride	F^-
Potassium	K^+	Iodide	I^-
Lithium	Li^+	Hydoxide	OH^-
Ammonium	NH_4^+	Nitrate	NO_3^-
Barium	Ba^{2+}	Oxide	O^{2-}
Calcium	Ca^{2+}	Sulphide	S^{2-}
Copper(II)	Cu^{2+}	Sulphate	SO_4^{2-}
Magnesium	Mg^{2+}	Carbonate	CO_3^{2-}
Zinc	Zn^{2+}		
Lead	$Pb2^+$		
Iron(II)	Fe^{2+}		
Iron(III)	Fe^{3+}		
Aluminium	Al^{3+}		

The periodic table of elements

KEY

Mass number A		
	1	
	H	
	Hydrogen	
	1	

Atomic number (Proton number) Z

Periodic table (each cell shows mass number, symbol, name, atomic number):

1	2											3	4	5	6	7	0
																	4 **He** Helium 2
7 **Li** Lithium 3	9 **Be** Beryllium 4											11 **B** Boron 5	12 **C** Carbon 6	14 **N** Nitrogen 7	16 **O** Oxygen 8	19 **F** Fluorine 9	20 **Ne** Neon 10
23 **Na** Sodium 11	24 **Mg** Magnesium 12											27 **Al** Aluminium 13	28 **Si** Silicon 14	31 **P** Phosphorous 15	32 **S** Sulphur 16	35 **Cl** Chlorine 17	40 **Ar** Argon 18
39 **K** Potassium 19	40 **Ca** Calcium 20	45 **Sc** Scandium 21	48 **Ti** Titanium 22	51 **V** Vanadium 23	52 **Cr** Chromium 24	55 **Mn** Manganese 25	56 **Fe** Iron 26	59 **Co** Cobalt 27	59 **Ni** Nickel 28	63 **Cu** Copper 29	64 **Zn** Zinc 30	70 **Ga** Gallium 31	73 **Ge** Germanium 32	75 **As** Arsenic 33	79 **Se** Selenium 34	80 **Br** Bromine 35	84 **Kr** Krypton 36
85 **Rb** Rubidium 37	88 **Sr** Strontium 38	89 **Y** Yttrium 39	91 **Zr** Zirconium 40	93 **Nb** Niobium 41	96 **Mo** Molybdenum 42	99 **Tc** Technetium 43	101 **Ru** Ruthenium 44	103 **Rh** Rhodium 45	106 **Pd** Palladium 46	108 **Ag** Silver 47	112 **Cd** Cadmium 48	115 **In** Indium 49	119 **Sn** Tin 50	122 **Sb** Antimony 51	128 **Te** Tellurium 52	127 **I** Iodine 53	131 **Xe** Xenon 54
133 **Cs** Caesium 55	137 **Ba** Barium 56	139 **La** Lanthanum 57	178 **Hf** Hafnium 72	181 **Ta** Tantalum 73	184 **W** Tungsten 74	186 **Re** Rhenium 75	190 **Os** Osmium 76	192 **Ir** Iridium 77	195 **Pt** Platinum 78	197 **Au** Gold 79	202 **Hg** Mercury 80	204 **Tl** Thallium 81	207 **Pb** Lead 82	209 **Bi** Bismuth 83	210 **Po** Polonium 84	210 **At** Astatine 85	222 **Rn** Radon 86
223 **Fr** Francium 87	226 **Ra** Radium 88	227 **Ac** Actinium 89															

Elements 58–71 and 90–103 have been omitted.

The value for mass number is normally that of the commonest isotope, e.g. ^{35}Cl not ^{37}Cl.

Bromine is approximately equal proportions of ^{79}Br and ^{81}Br.

Formulae List

This list shows the formulae for quantitative relationships in the Physical Processes section of the specification which candidates will be expected to recall (N.B. for convenience, formulae are also given here in symbolic form even though this form is not required by the specification).

$$\text{potential difference (volt, V)} = \text{current (ampere, A)} \times \text{resistance (ohm, } \Omega) \qquad V = IR$$

$$\text{power (watt, W)} = \text{potential difference (volt, V)} \times \text{current (ampere, A)} \qquad P = VI$$

$$\text{energy transferred (kilowatt hour, kWh)} = \text{power (kilowatt, W)} \times \text{time (hour, h)} \qquad E = Pt$$

$$\text{total cost} = \text{number of Units} \times \text{cost per Unit}$$

$$\text{energy transferred (joule, J)} = \text{power (watt, W)} \times \text{time (second, s)} \qquad E = Pt$$

$$\text{acceleration (metre/second squared, m/s}^2) = \frac{\text{change in velocity (metre/second m/s)}}{\text{time taken for change (second, s)}} \qquad a = \frac{v - u}{t}$$

$$\text{wave speed (metre/second, m/s)} = \text{frequency (hertz, Hz)} \times \text{wavelength (metre, m)} \qquad v = f\lambda$$

$$\text{efficiency} = \frac{\text{useful energy transferred by device}}{\text{total energy supplied to device}}$$

$$\text{work done} = \text{energy transferred}$$

$$\text{work done (joule, J)} = \text{force applied (newton, N)} \times \text{distance moved in direction of force (metre, m)} \qquad W = Fs$$

$$\text{power (watt, W)} = \frac{\text{work done (joule, J)}}{\text{time taken (second, s)}} \qquad p = \frac{W}{t}$$

$$\text{weight (newton, N)} = \text{mass (kilogram, kg)} \times \text{gravitational field strength (newton/kilogram, N/kg)} \qquad w = mg$$

$$\text{change in gravitational potential energy (joule, J)} = \text{weight (newton, N)} \times \text{change in vertical height (metre, m)} \qquad gpe = mg\Delta h$$

$$\text{kinetic energy (joule, J)} = \frac{1}{2} \times \text{mass (kilogram, kg)} \times \text{speed}^2 \, [(\text{metre/second})^2, (\text{m/s})^2] \qquad ke = \frac{1}{2}mv^2$$

$$\text{energy transferred (joule, J)} = \text{potential difference (volt, V)} \times \text{charge (coulomb, C)} \qquad E = VQ$$

$$\text{charge (coulomb, C)} = \text{current (ampere, A)} \times \text{time (second, s)} \qquad Q = It$$

$$\text{force (newton, N)} = \text{mass (kilogram, kg)} \times \text{acceleration (metre/second square, m/s}^2) \qquad F = ma$$

$$\frac{\text{voltage across primary (volt, V)}}{\text{voltage across secondary (volt, V)}} = \frac{\text{number of turns on primary}}{\text{number of turns on secondary}} \qquad \frac{V_p}{V_5} = \frac{N_p}{N_5}$$

Hazard symbols

You will need to be able to recognise, and explain the significance of, the following hazard symbols.

Oxidising
These substances provide oxygen which allows other materials to burn more fiercely.

Harmful
These substances are similar to toxic substances but less dangerous.

Highly flammable
These substances easily catch fire.

Corrosive
These substances attack and destroy living tissues, including eyes and skin.

Toxic
These substances can cause death. They may have their effects when swallowed or breathed in or absorbed through the skin.

Irritant
These substances are not corrosive but can cause reddening or blistering of the skin.

Index